PHILIP
PENDLETON
COOKE

Poet ❧ Critic ❧ Novelist

PHILIP PENDLETON COOKE

POET ~ CRITIC ~ NOVELIST

Selections edited with an introduction by

John D. Allen

Publications of
The East Tennessee State University
Research Advisory Council
Johnson City, Tennessee

for John, Jr.

CONTENTS

PREFACE ix

ACKNOWLEDGMENTS xiii

INTRODUCTION xv

I   VERSE 1
II   FICTION 115
III   ESSAYS AND LETTERS 265
Bibliography 328
Appendix (*Unsigned Items, Perhaps by Cooke*) 339
Notes 341

PREFACE

The achievement of Philip Pendleton Cooke during the four-year period ending with his death in 1850 at the age of thirty-three, should rank him high among the minor creative writers in the pre-Civil War South, perhaps in the nation.

Already well known for a few lyric poems, he published a collection of narrative and lyric verse which by several critics, including Poe, was highly praised. He composed four meritorious novels, several lively fictional sketches, and twenty chapters of an unfinished historical romance. To the *Southern Literary Messenger*, where most of his writing, early and late, first appeared, he contributed at least five critical essays, one of them— *Living Novelists*—in three installments and running to book length.

Evidently his creative talents had greatly matured during the years when Cooke was struggling to earn a meager income from a despised profession, the law; and had he lived he might well have attained a place in literature beside his cousin John Pendleton Kennedy, or the prolific William Gilmore Simms, or that later poet-critic Sidney Lanier. The view expressed by the anthologist Rufus W. Griswold at the news of Cooke's death—"the finest poet that ever lived in Virginia—one of the finest that have written in our day"—* would seem to have been no exaggeration. But praised though he was by Poe and other contemporaries, no collection of the works of Cooke has hitherto appeared; and today he is scarcely remembered, even by students of Southern literature.

Two or three of Cooke's poems, reproduced not from the revised versions in his book but from periodicals, have been variously anthologized. Scholarly interest in the facts of his life and the kinds and qualities of his work can to some extent be satisfied by scholarly studies. A master's thesis, "Philip Pendleton Cooke," presented by May Alcott Thompson in 1923 to Columbia University, apparently was the first such project. In a doctoral dissertation, "Philip Pendleton Cooke, a Biographical and Critical Study," prepared during 1937–38 and presented to Vanderbilt University early in 1939, the present writer preserved information gleaned from a variety of

* Letter dated Feb. 19, 1850, to John R. Thompson, editor of the *Messenger*.

sources, including descendants—all, it seemed, which at that date could be gleaned.

A paper entitled "Philip Pendleton Cooke: Virginia Gentleman, Lawyer, Hunter, and Poet," by David K. Jackson, was included in the collection *American Studies in Honor of William Kenneth Boyd*, published by the Duke University Press in 1940. Two years later, under the title *Philip Pendleton Cooke*, an abridgement of the Vanderbilt dissertation was published with the original bibliography by the University of North Carolina Press. Finally, in his *The South in American Literature*, published by the Duke press in 1954, Jay B. Hubbell included an excellent brief estimate of Cooke.

Such have been the sources for factual information regarding the author. But useful as they may be as information, they do not provide means for the first-hand study which the scholar might want to make. This collection is intended to meet the need, a need which, in view of the growing interest during recent years in nineteenth century Southern literature, would seem to be adequate justification.

In accordance with the overall plan—to provide as much as possible of the superior writing by Cooke—most of his juvenile compositions have been omitted. Biography has been pruned and critical discussion limited to generalizations. From the essays and letters most of the quotations and other secondary matter have been excised. In a few places where economy of space might result, advantage has been taken of permission graciously granted by the University of North Carolina Press to reproduce phrasing employed in *Philip Pendleton Cooke*. This, however, has been confined to the Introduction, which condenses the biographical portions of the earlier volume.

Selections are grouped under the headings I—*Verse*, II—*Fiction*, and III—*Essays and Letters*, each preceded by a brief factual-critical statement. For its possible value to students and others, the original bibliography is again presented.

Cooke complained more than once to editors about mistakes in spelling produced by careless or ignorant printers. Unfortunately, his own manuscripts exibit such blemishes, or what at any rate would be judged so by present-day lexicographers. Moreover, in orthographic performance he was not himself dependable; for example, the name of Cooper's hero might to-day contain one "p", tomorrow two. It is not always possible, however, to determine what was in fact the preferred spelling of a word in Cooke's day; and it has seemed perhaps best to tolerate variants except the more obvious errors.

Larger liberty has been taken with Cooke's punctuation and paragraphing. The former was much too generously employed as judged by present-day practice. Numerous long stretches barren of the latter suggested that the author, in great haste to catch the Richmond mail coach, had left the task to the *Messenger* editor, who had left it to the printer, who had drowsed. Alterations, however, are minimal; and no verbal changes have been made in the text.

To Dr. Robert J. Higgs and Dean Arthur H. DeRosier, Jr., of the East Tennessee State University staff, thanks are due for helpful suggestions. In conclusion, it should be said that in this as in other projects related to Cooke, my wife has given invaluable aid.

J. D. A.

Acknowledgments

The following paragraphs formed a portion of the Foreword to *Philip Pendleton Cooke:*

Materials for a life of Cooke were widely scattered, and I am indebted to a variety of sources for the information I have employed. For use of special collections in the Duke University Library, the library of Peabody Institute, the Library of Congress, the New York Public Library, the Boston Public Library, the library of Harvard University, and the library of Princeton University, I am greatly indebted. Other libraries whose manuscript collections and periodical files have also been helpful include those of the University of North Carolina, the University of Virginia, the Virginia Historical Society, the Maryland Historical Society, the University of Pennsylvania, the Pennsylvania Historical Society, Columbia University, the American Antiquarian Society, Yale University, and the Hendley Library, Winchester, Virginia. Records in the Martinsburg, Virginia, Court House provided data for the genealogy of Cooke.

Mrs. Archibald B. Bevan of Millwood, Va., and Miss Anne Meade of Baltimore, granddaughters of Cooke, gave invaluable aid by granting free use of manuscript materials, as did Cooke's niece, Miss Mariah P. Duval of Charlottesville, Va., and his nephew, Dr. R. P. Cooke of Lexington. Other relatives who aided are Mrs. Charles Lee of Sea Island, Ga., Mrs. Jennie Winston Hunter of Doswell, Va., and the late Mr. Edward D. Quarles, secretary of the Valentine Museum, Richmond, Va.

I gratefully acknowledge the information given me by Dr. William H. Whiting, Jr., of Hampden-Sydney College, Virginia, and the late J. H. Whitty of Richmond. I am especially indebted to P. W. Turrentine of the University of Arkansas for copies of three letters from Cooke to Nathaniel Beverley Tucker, and to Dr. Edd Winfield Parks of the University of Georgia for having interested me in Cooke. . . .

The almost three decades since the foregoing was written have produced many changes. They have not lessened my sense of the obligation then expressed.

J. D. A.

February, 1969

Introduction

Mindful of the reserve appropriate for a Virginia gentleman-poet, Philip Pendleton Cooke composed in the autumn of 1845 such account of his life as seemed not improper to offer the reading public. Rufus W. Griswold was preparing another of his popular anthologies; Cooke was to be included; and there had been correspondence, mainly through and with his cousin in Baltimore, John Pendleton Kennedy, twenty years Philip's elder and chief of the Kennedy-Cooke literary clan. Would Cooke send some of his verses to Griswold? And a biography?

Cooke would, and did, though not before Kennedy had warned him that certain poems must be forwarded at once or lose a place in the new edition of the *Poets and Poetry of America.* Cooke had found himself very much interrupted, he informed Griswold, and that must make his excuse for the shortcomings of the pieces he enclosed. He was sending "Emily—Proem to the Froissart Ballads," which Griswold would perceive had been thoroughly elaborated; he supposed it was too long for Griswold's purpose. Of the smaller pieces "Young Rosalie Lee" was published ten years ago, "and *took* in the South singularly well, considering the flippancies of phraseology and false rhymes &c. that disfigure it—but which I have never ventured to change. I send it to you because it did take." The other enclosures had never been published. He had many other pieces which he had intended to retouch and send, so that Griswold might have a full budget to select from; "but I 'put it off,' was interrupted, and now must send you what I have without delay."

As for his biography, he might say with Canning's knife-grinder, "I have none." He was born on October 26, 1816, in the town of Martinsburg, Berkeley County, Virginia. His father, John R. Cooke, was and had long been a man of honorable distinction in the bar of the state. His mother, Maria Pendleton, was sister to John Pendleton Kennedy's mother. As for himself, he had spent several years at Princeton and, he believed, graduated, although he never distinguished himself or took an honor.

While at Princeton he had contributed several pieces of verse to the *Knickerbocker;* and on his return to Winchester, where his father then resided, "I began (then 18) to write prose and verse for the Messenger, then just started. Before 21 I was a lawyer and married; my wife was Willianne Burwell; I am happy by my fireside at this place on the banks of the Shenandoah, in view, and within a mile, of the Blue Ridge. I go to county towns, at the sessions of courts, and hunt and fish, and make myself as happy with my companions as I can." He had lately spurred himself again into continuous composition and meant "to *finish* books." He had already projected several. "And this is the 'sum and story' of this 'human life' of mine." [1]

This much about himself Cooke thought proper to relate; and if Griswold could make anything out of such material, Cooke would wonder at his skill.

Griswold made the usual sketch for his *Poets and Poetry of America*, to which he added apparently sincere praise of Cooke's talent. Many of Cooke's pieces were very beautiful, he believed. "Florence Vane" was one of the most poetical songs that had been written in this country. The longer poems were elaborate, "full of striking thoughts and delicate fancies"; and nearly all of them contained touches of tenderness which showed to what issues his spirit was attuned. [2]

From various sources a longer biography can be pieced out than Cooke had submitted to Griswold.

His ancestors, maternal and paternal, were unarguably gentry. Since 1674, Pendletons had lived in Tidewater Virginia, a branch moving westward with the frontier to the Valley; and Pendleton men had been Revolutionary patriots, judges, statesmen. Pendleton women had married Claytons, Barbours, Dandridges, Strothers, Kennedys, Gaineses, Cookes, often with excellent results. For example, in addition to the novelist John Esten Cooke, the younger and less gifted brother of Philip, three of his first cousins variously distinguished themselves: David H. Strother, the artist and travel writer better known as "Porte Crayon"; John Pendleton Kennedy, statesman and novelist; and the latter's brother, Philip Pendleton Kennedy, one of several hunting companions and author of *The Blackwater Chronicle*.

From an early migrant from County Hereford to New England descended Nathaniel Cooke, wealthy Philadelphia merchant and patriot, whose physician son Stephen, while a prisoner of war in the Bermudas, fell in love with Catherine, daughter of the governor of the island, John Esten. After the Revolution they married and settled in Alexandria, later in Leesburg, in Virginia, where he died in 1816, the year of his poet-grandson's birth.

Two of Stephen Cooke's sons—John Esten, the eldest, and Philip St. George, the youngest—were widely known in their day, the former in medicine and in the ministry and the latter as author of military works and as a Union brigadier general during the War Between the States. A third, John Rogers Cooke, born in Bermuda in 1788, settled as a young lawyer in the back-country village of Martinsburg about 1810. There, three years later, through marriage with Maria Pendleton, he allied himself with leading families of Martinsburg and Berkeley County. He moved to Winchester in 1828, and then to nearby Glengary, the dowry of his wife, always the prosperous barrister and generous, perhaps spendthrift, gentleman.

But with the panic of 1837 and the subsequent depression, he was beset by a series of financial cares, arising in part from an unfortunate venture in coal-mining with relatives and in part from a readiness to endorse notes. Then Glengary burned. Forced into bankruptcy, he moved in 1839 to nearby Charlestown and, in 1840, to Richmond, where until his death in December, 1854, he struggled to free himself from debt.

Family records and traditions reveal little of the first fifteen years in the life of Philip Pendleton Cooke. He played with his cousin Philip Kennedy, who, however, when he came to write Cooke's biography, knew and had learned little that might not be said of most boys. That he played with and was a schoolmate of another cousin, David H. Strother, the Kennedy cousin recorded. But of those years Strother, too, remembered little "except that Philip was a handsome boy, with large brown eyes, and dark curling hair, sprightly and amiable.—For the rest he was like other boys—and I never heard that he gave any peculiar promise for the future." [3]

Possibly the environment of Martinsburg was hardly one to elicit from a youth of Philip's temperament public evidence of aesthetic promise. True, since 1812 there had been a Martinsburg Academy, where among other other subjects one might study Latin and Greek; and doubtless in Philip's time the curriculum offered all that a healthy boy would care to absorb.[4] Encouragement to versify, however, would have come not from the village but from the country around, and from his reading.

The town of Martinsburg, itself, although the center and county seat of prosperous Berkeley, remained a semi-frontier settlement. Less than a century earlier all had been wilderness, part of the hardly known region separated by the barrier of the Blue Ridge from populated Virginia. Then, in 1732, had come "the restless Johannes Joosten Hite with his twenty families, and they with horses and wagons, with milch cattle and flocks, and above all with a determination to remain all their days in this Valley of the Shenando."

Scotch-Irish and German settlers followed the Dutch; and after Lord Fairfax had built his hunting lodge, Greenway Court, at White Post in 1748, began the wave of immigration from middle and Tidewater Virginia— "sons of the landed Gentry—true Cavalier stock." Now "The Valley was rapidly filling with eager settlers." And soon "the Red Men vanished into the west, forever, as the pioneers thronged down from Packhorse Ford on the north, from the Blue Ridge on the east." [5]

These two distinct streams of migrants doubtless determined the atmosphere of the two towns where was spent Cooke's youth: Martinsburg, settled mainly by Dutch, Scotch-Irish, and Germans; and Winchester, dominated by Tidewater scions who, before and after the Revolution, had acquired large grants of land in the surrounding countryside. This influence may be observed in Cooke's mature work. For example, his first short novel, *John Carper, the Hunter of Lost River*, reflects both in its characters and in its setting the homespun society of the Martinsburg area during the

Revolution; it may well have grown out of such a tale as a smart youngster might still have heard from some ancient veteran in the Martinsburg of 1825. Three novels, however, obviously reflect, though perhaps with a romantic mirror, Winchester and the gentry of Frederick County.

The extent to which Cooke was later attracted by the Frederick gentry and its diversions is suggested by a letter written some years before his death to Griswold. It had occurred to him to turn his passion for hunting, and his " 'crowding experiences' (gathered in fifteen or sixteen years of life in the merriest Virginia Society) of hunting, fishing, country races, character and want of character, woods, mountains, fields and water," into a rambling book.[6] The design was never carried out, although the posthumously published essay-anecdote "The Turkey-hunter in the Closet" may well have been intended as a chapter for such a book.

During the three years before his admission to Princeton University in 1831, Cooke attended the Winchester Academy. He began, or continued, to write verse, most of it destroyed in the burning of Glengary if not earlier by himself. And like all of her other male cousins of appropriate age, it would appear, he fell romantically in love with Mary Evelina Hunter Dandridge, the not displeased inspiration of many a poetic outburst and, later, the wife of the statesman R. M. T. Hunter.

Of Cooke's activities at Princeton, which both his father and his grandfather had attended, surviving records tell little. The very sketchy manuscript volume, Minutes of the Faculty, records that on May 17, 1832, Cooke was examined and admitted to the sophomore class. Some weeks later he addressed to his father the only letter that remains from his youth and early manhood, one of the few letters, in fact, that have survived from the years prior to 1840.

This was the fourth time, he complained, that he had written home, and not one word had he received in return. He could not account for it except by supposing that "your letters may have miscarried. Phil P—— has received 2 letters and Stephen & Ed P—— each one (from home)." From the boys he had learned that his family were all well.[7]

They were all very comfortably situated there at Princeton. His fellow students were, most of them, fine, open-hearted fellows. He knew of but one or two among the number who were really dissipated. Now that he had become acquainted with all around him, his situation had lost most of that irksomeness which he had felt upon leaving a land where nearly all were his acquaintances and friends for a land of strangers. It was now about half after six (morning). He had been up ever since five and had attended both prayers and recitations.

He had written thus far when the breakfast horn blew, after which, on going to the post office, he had found "a letter from Ma." It had been sixteen days, it seemed, in coming. He was certain some one had written. The tutor would be around in a moment or two and he must necessarily close. His love was to be given "to Ma and all. Tell Sister A—— that she must answer my letters—as soon as she can do so conveniently. I hope you will be here this summer but for the present—adieu—." A postscript requested, "Write to me, and let me know particularly how the house comes on." [8]

The few brief references to Cooke in the Minutes of the Faculty suggest a sensitive, high-spirited youth who, however, in the judgment of the Princeton faculty, was hardly a luminary of the first magnitude in formal scholarship. For the winter session of his senior year he averaged, with two others, seventy-four, attaining thereby the rank of eighteenth in a class of thirty-four. And less than a month before he was to receive his degree, he and a fellow-student were suspended from the college "for a mutual personal assault upon each other," Cooke indefinitely, his fellow for a period of two weeks.[9]

No inkling of the origin of the altercation eluded the restraints of academic decorum, which was satisfied with the baldest statement of fact. At any rate, Cooke did not long remain suspended. Three days after the regular senior examinations this entry appeared in the Minutes for August 13, 1834: "Mr. Philip P. Cooke, who was suspended from the College on the 17th utl., was admitted to examination:—and the Faculty, having examined him, resolved to recommend him, with the other members of the class, to the Board of Trustees for the first Degree in the Arts."

A quick temper is said to have had a part in another incident of Cooke's undergraduate days, described half a century later from Shepherdstown by a roving correspondent. "I had a night and part of a day with Hon. Alexander R. Boteler. . . . He drew for me a rough sketch of his room-mate, Philip Pendleton Cooke. . . . 'Florence Vane' was written in his room. Whenever he wanted to write, Cooke dashed everything off the table; and one day he dashed on the floor a new suit of Boteler's clothes. In return, Boteler threw out of the window a book which 'Florence Vane' (Mrs. R. M. T. Hunter) had given to the young poet. Instantly there was a fight, but that served to make them better friends than before." [10]

Such stories as the foregoing suggest that despite his reserve and his romantic temperament, Cooke was a sufficiently normal youth, on pleasant enough terms with some, if not all, of his associates. By his fellows in the American Whig Society, composed of students whose families, like his, were foes to Andrew Jackson, he apparently was held in high regard. A resolution of the society, passed some weeks after Cooke's death, referred to his "numerous friends and admirers" and spoke of his "brilliant poetical genius" which had reflected high honor on the institution.[11] Yet he seems to have had few close friends and to have been influenced in his attitudes and his career no more by them than by his instructors. Benjamin H. Brewster, a classmate, remembered him as "remarkable for his pride"; he impressed one as a "stately and dignified youth, who kept himself apart from his fellow-collegians." [12] And John S. Hart, a young instructor in ancient languages during Cooke's years at Princeton, also had "a very vivid recollection" of his character: "proud, resolute, but very sweet-tempered, and remarkable for his dignity and personal beauty. His head was really noble, his eyes dark, his hair curling chestnut, and his person erect and vigorous." The adjectives are not, it is true, original with the instructor. John Esten Cooke supplied them many years later in a sketch of "my brother, of whom you so kindly inquire," published by Hart in a manual of American literature. But fraternal affection, Hart believed, had in its choice of descriptives "barely done justice to one of nature's noblest gentlemen." [13]

Of the academic values offered by the Princeton of his youth, Cooke acquired more than his academic standing would suggest. The prose essays of his mature years, though not burdened with classical allusions, grew out of a mind well grounded in the classics of Greco-Roman culture; and their style exhibits classic qualities of precision and restraint. That in addition to Latin he had at least a reading knowledge of French, German, and Italian is clear from examination of his personal letters and his poetry and prose. The chief values Cooke obtained from Princeton, however, and those most observable in his later work were found not in the classroom but in the library—"in studies," Philip Pendleton Kennedy remembered, "out of the line of the usual college learning—history, romance, poetry—general literature." [14] He paid more attention to "Belles Lettres, poetry and the departments of elegant learning generally," agreed John Esten Cooke, "than to the dryer, but more important, studies of the Collegiate course." His knowledge of mathematics, philosophy, and languages was appreciative and respectable, "but by no means profound or critical. His attainments were, nearly all, in the direction of polite literature—and were striking and unusual. Wandering at large in the libraries of the College, he seems to have emulated the habits of the bee—to have sought for the sweets of letters, in the 'flowery parterres' of Spenser, Chaucer (always favourites with him) and the elder poets of the language, to whom his devotion continued earnest and unchanging throughout life." [15]

It would be an error, however, to suppose that Cooke was indifferent to the literature produced in his own day. To his father's home came The Edinburgh Review and most of the other leading British periodicals. These would have given him, from boyhood, some acquaintance with contemporary literary figures. One of his critical essays, Living Novelists, shows intimate knowledge of the works of Bulwer, Dumas, G. P. R. James, D'Israeli, Scott, and Cooper; and other essays and letters, extending the list of prose authors, evidence familiarity with contemporary poetry of England and America.

The letters also evidence Cooke's respect for science. "The exact sciences," he believed, "and history (read with an intelligence that groups facts and puts them away in the Mind) and the best poetry of the best Poets, afford matter enough for any youth no matter how he may devour books, and should constitute the great bulk of his study until he enters upon professional reading."[16]

Such, in his maturity, was Cooke's advice for his younger brothers. It suggests that, despite his fondness at Princeton for the remote in time and space, he had laid there the foundations of a well-rounded education.

When, having completed the Princeton curriculum in two years, Cooke returned to Winchester in the summer of 1834, he evidently felt little enthusiasm for the course which his father urged upon him, the study of law. Dutifully, however, he read and remembered enough law for admission to the bar. Until the burning of Glengary and the breakup of his father's family, he may have been of some assistance to the father in a practice which then extended over the counties of Frederick, Berkeley, Jefferson, and Clarke. In his later years he repeatedly turned to the law as a possible means of assuring comfort for his own family. But he knew in those later years that he detested the law;[17] and from the beginning his heart rejected it.

For some months after Cooke's homecoming, literature seems to have had little competition from Blackstone. During the Princeton years Cooke had continued to write poems, three of which—"Song of the Sioux Lovers," "The Consumptive," and "Dhu Nowas"—appeared in the *Knickerbocker Magazine*. John Esten Cooke mentions, in addition to these three, "Count Herman" and "The Moss Troopers," "these all appearing in the Knickerbocker and Winchester papers, where also were published Goluon, Isabel, Kemp, the Glider."[18] Elsewhere he names, as composed during the same period, "The Season of Youth," "The Dream," and "Napoleon in Egypt"[19] —a total of twelve published poems, if the memory of the younger brother is to be trusted. Doubtless there were other efforts which Cooke did not consider worthy to submit to publishers.

The freedom of peaceful, happy Glengary encouraged for a time the literary experimentation that had begun at Princeton. Two of Cooke's new poems appeared in the *Southern Literary Messenger* for January, 1835; another in the March number, one in the April. Also in the April number was published the first installment of the essay "English Poetry," continued in the number for June. The volume of this published work is not great, but it is probably only a small part of all Cooke wrote. Ten years later he spoke in a letter to his father of "six months of continuous composition, such as that at Glengary in my nineteenth year."[20] Since his pen was a fluent one, and since little else from the period survives, many of his compositions, still in manuscript form, evidently perished in the burning of Glengary in 1839, when everything of value was destroyed.

If the quality of the manuscripts destroyed averaged no higher than the published work, the loss to literature was not great. Cooke's poetic talent matured slowly, notwithstanding his fluency in versifying. Only in "Rosalie Lee" and in a rare line in other poems is there promise of the future poet. Cooke's own estimate of the value of his juvenilia is expressed in two letters

to Nathaniel Beverley Tucker, late in 1835. Tucker, who recently had been
made professor of law at William and Mary College, had formed connections with the *Messenger;* and in its infancy he was able to render much
assistance to the publisher and nominal editor, T. W. White, through the
reading of manuscripts and in the offering of critical advice. For some motive, perhaps because he recognized the genuine talent beneath the artifici-
alities and crudities of youth, he wrote to Cooke during the summer of 1835.
Unfortunately, neither this nor any other of his letters to the younger man
seems to have been preserved. Cooke's reply, however, makes it obvious that
at least in part Tucker's object was to encourage the younger man:

> The stuff that you criticised to White and, through him, to me, cer-
> tainly deserved harsh treatment. I had however some excuse for think-
> ing it worth publishing:—my father (only a tolerable judge of Poetry)
> praised it highly—so did other friends, at the time in the house, at the
> request of one of whom the verses were written—*hurriedly.* I say
> 'hurriedly' for they and some half dozen more rejected stanzas were
> written at a single sitting—perhaps in two hours.
>
> My standard of poetic excellence is very high, and I rarely fail to see,
> after the excitement of composition has passed way, the want of merit
> in my pieces. None of them have *any* merit, me judice, except a short
> piece which you may have seen—'Rosalie Lee.' This I haven't seen since
> it was published, and only remember as a rather pretty extravaganza.
> However, if I thought them all as they should be, I would *now* care
> nothing for criticism, as I have given up Poetry and verse making. Par-
> nassus—so far as crops of worldly produce—dollars—are concerned is
> as barren as a worn-out tobacco field. Besides a Poet's reputation, even
> if he succeeds to the top of his wishes, is of little or no avail—as it comes
> too late. We can warm to no poetry that hasn't a mistress coupled with
> our thought of the Poet:—while he lives there is too much flesh and
> blood reality about our thought of him—too little mistiness. Byron was
> popular as a Poet because the humbug mystery of his bearing, and the
> eccentricity of his fortunes, were not discovered to be the one a hum-
> bug and the other a most *unromantic* eccentricity. Other writers have
> gained present reputation by their poetical works from the peculiarity
> of the works themselves; they have been such as to enable one to form
> no idea whatever of the author—to keep him in a mysterious darkness—
> the mysterious invisibility of the nightingale whose song we listen to.
>
> But this is all nonsense I fear, or at any rate useless—perspicua vera
> non probanda sunt. Pardon the Latin—I am just now fresh from Lord
> Coke, and 'smell of the shop.'
>
> I haven't your letter by me, but I remember that you speak of the
> deep interest you take in the Messenger. I sincerely trust that your in-
> terest will be active. The only monthly magazine of the South ought
> hardly to depend for support upon the feeble efforts of boys. *I* am just

nineteen and have reason to believe myself older than a majority of Mr. White's contributors.—[21]

Tucker's answer to the foregoing evidently counseled against Cooke's decision to give up poetry for Lord Coke. But the advice was for the moment unavailing. Tucker's letter had been mislaid, Cooke replied in December, 1935, but he had read it more than once and recalled its contents. He had noted the main point in Tucker's counsel, that it would be worth while for him—"author of some few tame verses and of 'a compilation which any one might compile' " [22]—to come before the public a candidate for a reputation and pay as an author. He had noted, too, the ways and means by which Tucker had suggested success would be attained. They were certainly well pointed out, and the advice was wise and sound. If ever he became a candidate for reputation and pay as an author, he would certainly follow it:

But, my dear Sir, all things have a hindrance. The 'student of 19' may not be 'clogged by the habits which fit the man of fifty for the pursuit of an intricate profession and unfit him for every thing else';—he may not have 'mouths to feed—a family to chain him down to the one path,' but he may have, and oftenest *has*, other and serious hindrances. . . .

The profession (Law) for which I am preparing myself with some little enthusiasm, and which I have been taught by my Father to look upon as a road to distinction and wealth, is so far removed from 'pleasant poesies' that it is impossible to reconcile them. One or the other must be given up. You think, and say, that at 19 so much life is before one that the pursuit of 'light letters' may be begun and failed in, and still allow a sufficiency of after time for more arduous and *certain* pursuits. (I have made a bungling sentence of that—I am too unwell to write clearly. It conveys my meaning.) I have to answer that, altho 'there may be *time* enough after failure,' yet the mind is little fitted, depressed as it must be by failure, frittered away as it must be by frivolous pursuit, cowed, diseased, dreamy, and timid, as it can't help being— for beginning *de novo* a dull and difficult profession. This is a general objection. I have objections arising from my own peculiar situation. A large mass of business awaits me. The sooner I am prepared to receive it the better. . . .

As a lawyer reputation and fortune await me. I say this from no idle vanity. I have power of study—close study—and fluency of speech. These with very *little* brain would ensure success. Besides, my Father's business is so extensive that I will be launched by means of it into practice *at once*. He has promised me much of it.

As an author (*of poetry*) a painful fear of the world's censure—a restless ache of mind—a morbid yearning after the high place among men—(painful, all painful, during their unquiet life, and terrible when failure follows them) await me. I would not live that shrinking and sensitive and cowering existence for—*success*. And what chance would there be of this? Even Wn. Irving was 'wretchedly poor for years'—a type of temporary failure *in prose.* But look at our Poets. Bryant (the master of them all) has sheltered himself from starvation behind the columns of a political newspaper. [Illegible] have no room for eminence, but one and all have found no means of support in 'printing their inspiration.'

If in the course of time I find it possible to loosen some of the strings binding me to my profession I will imitate my cousin J. P. Kennedy and become a novelist. I will dress what Poetry of thought I may possess, in prose—the dress will make it sell—and *the sale of a book and the reputation of its author certainly go together.* It is for this reason that in speaking of 'failure' I have spoken of 'want of pay.' One is the sign of the other. But authorship will be a matter of secondary consideration. . . .[23]

Cooke doubtless was sincere in expressing an intention to give up the making of verses. But the *Messenger* for January, 1836, contained the rather long poem "Lady Leonore and Her Lover," in addition to the third chapter of "English Poetry"; and other contributions were published in the April, May, and August numbers. Then, indeed, his literary activity apparently ebbed. Between August, 1836, and September, 1840, nothing that can be confidently attributed to Cooke appeared in the pages of the *Messenger,* and only two or three items appeared elsewhere.

Cook's romantic affection for his cousin evidently also declined; at any rate, suffered a sea-change with her marriage in October, 1836. Moreover, there were other diversions, one of which another cousin, Pendleton Kennedy, celebrates in his memoir:

Like the valiant Sir Thomas Erpingham in France, he was

"Very fatal in the field."

Almost innumerable wild turkeys and pheasants, ducks, hares, partridges—to say nothing of the deer—has he slain in his time,—and a very hearty trencherman was he, too, in helping to consume them. Before yet the faintest dull grey streak had appeared in the dawn, he has breasted the steep hill-sides of the forest—no dainty huntsman; but a bold and couragous one, that would meet the hoar-frost with rapture, and feel an unusual thrill at his heart when the snows were deepest, and the streams most glassed in ice:—and let him but once get upon the tracks of his game, and the oldest, most trained and regularly bred hunter of the hills, was not keener in the pursuit—and he was durable, too, as a hound:—I have known him cross the streams waist-deep when the waters were almost frozen, and shake himself dripping on the opposite bank with a wild delight, that was almost savage.

In the Fall and Winter the forests were as familiar to him as his own parlour. He loved their wild recesses, and knew all their points of beauty—where the sun broke the grandest upon them in the morning, and where the dying rays fell saddest and sweetest upon their hidden vales. . . . His imagination was all alive in the dim and shadowy forests, and bold mountains around where he dwelt; and the poetry of his nature was all astir in him, when he frequented their untrodden wilds. And hence came some of the best inspiration of his poetry—the most thoughtfully dwelt upon—the truest to nature, and with more too of his real soul in them."

To John Esten Cooke, though more sedate in temper and far less the sportsman than his poet-brother, the social aspects of the latter's life at Glengary seemed worthy of a canvas not entirely deficient, he believed, in interest. On it, he remembered in his "Recollections," would figure "very many gay festivals and country frolics"—fishing parties of young men and maidens, wandering at ease along the banks of the beautiful streams, or sailing in the boat which gently rocked today upon the current, under the great willow shadowing the Opequon, as in other years—gay riding parties, too, galloping through the spring or autumn woods—the time enlivened by the smiles of ladies fair—by many a jest, and by joyous laughter long since hushed, but ringing still in the memories and hearts of those who remained to read those lines—night-hunting with hounds, or with the spear used in transfixing fish seen by the light of the blazing torch—horse races—country weddings where, to the merry violin, the joyous reel went on its way in triumph, and the festival was kept up, without flagging, day after day and night after night. These, and "a hundred other scenes" of his brother's youth and his own, might he describe.

Cooke's marriage to Willianne Corbin Tayloe Burwell [24] on May 1, 1837, promised no cessation to the cavalier life so glowingly pictured by the memory of John Esten Cooke. A daughter of William Nelson Burwell of Glenowen, and a descendant of Robert "King" Carter of Corotoman, she had lived at nearby Saratoga with an uncle, Nathaniel Burwell, who had adopted her after her father's death. She is described as having great personal beauty and charm of manner—the descriptive lines in Cooke's poem, "Emily," undoubtedly refer to her—and attendance at the academy for young ladies conducted by Miss Margaret Mercer at Bellemonte had assured the cultural graces considered appropriate to an heiress and maiden of nineteen. After marriage, she went to live at Glengary as "Sister Willie," the "rare being come from fairy land," of John Esten Cooke's recollections. Her quiet cheerfulness and strength of character were to serve her husband in good stead during the troubled years to come.

Until the loss of Glengary, where after marriage he had continued to live, Cooke apparently had no serious cares. The bankruptcy of the father, however, and his ultimate removal to Richmond gravely changed the picture, which for some years remained dark. He had a growing family with no means of support, at first, other than occasional small fees from practice of a despised profession in Martinsburg, where he resided, and neighboring towns. Fees promised him, the widespread and severe economic depression of the early 1840s made difficult to collect. Debts accumulated; and extant letters to his father for the years 1842–45 frequently contained requests for small sums for one or another pressing need. In the meantime he had himself been declared bankrupt, probably as a consequence in part of having endorsed his father's notes; and family tradition says that Nathaniel Burwell, angered by possible jeopardy of his ward's dowry, carried Willianne away to live at Saratoga.

As early as 1840, Cooke had hoped to improve the outlook by emigration to Missouri. "I propose going to the west early in April *if possible,*" he wrote to his father in March. "Anne will house herself during my absence at Saratoga whither we have been invited. . . . *Anne loves you all* with an affection greatly matured by our recent and long sojourn together. She says she 'will not' go to Missouri without first visiting you in Richmond. I do not know, however, that *she* will make the visit (money is too scarce with us all for such jaunts) but *I* will most certainly visit you before my final removal. I *rely* upon your success and prosperity and look with confidence to bright and famous new days for both of us." [25]

The exploratory trip was not to occur, however, until the following year. In August he informed his father:

I have returned from my journey with my plans matured—and everything fair before me. . . . I have fixed on Palmyra in Marion Co., Mo. as my place of residence. It is healthy, full of business, and a *Whig* town in a Whig county. I became acquainted with every body worth knowing in the town, and made an *impression.* They urged me to 'come out'—promised me business—and to send me to the Legislature as soon as I made a good speech. . . . I can get a nice cottage establishment for $100 per annum; and, if I choose, the finest residence (a really elegant establishment) in the place, for $150 per annum. I will take out servants. My funds will be abundant *next Spring* for my removal, etc. . . . I left Anne in Clarke yesterday. She had just got a letter from Ma, and was much gratified. I have been back 9 days.[26]

Cooke was never, in fact, to represent Palmyra in the legislature nor to make a speech to its Whig citizens, although the thought of emigration occasionally entered his mind, even after a change in prospects made emigration seem less attractive as a solution to his problems. The journey, however, was not wholly without gain. Scenes and characters in one of the novelettes [27] reflect impressions gathered during the journey from Virginia to Missouri and return.

Two years later Cooke did make a speech, probably political in purpose though not overtly so and addressed not just to Whigs but to all citizens of Martinsburg and its environs. In some five thousand words, he delivered on July 4, 1843, an oration that for dignity, learning, and good sense doubtless compared favorably with the hundreds delivered on that day throughout the land. By the local newspaper it was described as "beautifully chaste in language, forcible and eloquent in style, and in every way adapted to give, as it did, universal satisfaction." Cooke's "volunteer" toast at the "sumptuous barbecue" which followed was discreet enough for an occasion which may have been intended by friends and relatives as a first step in a political career at home:

> The good old town of Martinsburg—Receiving all
> the benefits of modern improvements, but not affected
> in her old fashioned propriety by their innovations.[28]

But like the trip to Palmyra, Cooke's oratory was to bear no edible economic fruit.

In the meantime the hope for a literary career had slowly revived, perhaps aroused at first by a request from Poe who since July, 1839, had been an editor of the *Gentleman's Magazine* in Philadelphia. Poe's letter is not extant, but its purport can be inferred from Cooke's answer, which with other epistolary material is presented in a subsequent section under the caption "Essays and Letters." The correspondence elicited two poems, "Florence Vane" and "Earl March," published early in 1840. But with the June number Poe's connection with the periodical ended; and nothing more by Cooke appeared. Two superior poems, "Life in the Autumn Woods" and "The Power of the Bards," graced the *Southern Literary Messenger* for December, 1843. Not until the removal to The Vineyard early in 1845, however, was Cooke free and comfortable in the practice of authorship, as at Glengary ten years earlier he had been.

Built by Nathaniel Burwell, the dwelling with its surrounding area meant a new stage in the career and a brighter vista in the fortunes of Philip Pendleton Cooke. The economic security of his family was now assured. The attitude of Mr. Burwell had softened. Cooke, it would appear, settled down to enjoyment of The Vineyard, occasional gentlemanly practice in the neighboring courts of law, hunting jaunts now and then with friends, and the serious pursuit of literature in several of its branches.

The house itself, the surroundings, and the location of the estate with reference to the scenes of Cooke's youth, all were such as to give pleasure to one of his temperament. A two-story brick structure, with sunny exposure looking eastward to the Blue Ridge and westward across the Valley to the Alleghanies, it stood on the summit of a spacious knoll two miles from the village of Millwood. Ample grounds for lawns, gardens, and orchard surrounded it. Behind, sloping down to the Shenandoah, distant only a short mile, grew a virgin forest where on any morning before sunrise Cooke might confidently expect to bag a turkey or, along the river bank, a brace of ducks. Far down in the foreground, and off to the left and right, a keen eye could make out the roofs of other country houses, and, farther away,

Carter Hall in Millwood, and Old Chapel (where gentry families worshiped and, in time, were buried) and, on winter mornings, blue smoke from the chimneys of Winchester. Winchester was twelve miles away. Charlestown was only nineteen, and from there to Martinsburg was only fourteen. Within the quadrilateral formed by Millwood and these three, lived most of Cooke's relatives and friends.

Cooke's qualified satisfaction with his present status was expressed in the first letter to his father after removal to The Vineyard. Father and son, it reveals, had become involved with relatives in a speculation in Texas land; payment for their respective shares was shortly to fall due; funds were not available. "By the way, the passage of the Texas Bill must have already rendered your whole interest more valuable than it was before; and if so, can you not sell a portion of it for the price you agreed to give for all, and so save the rest?"

He was, the letter continued, "as happy a man in my mere 'circumstances' —that is my 'surroundings' " as could be found anywhere. His house was good; his wife the most devoted, affectionate, and true creature in the world; his children sweet, obedient, healthy, good-looking, and intelligent. He had all the comforts of life in sufficient abundance, and beyond them, habits of economy which would make one or two hundred dollars a year—a sum he could hope to earn—enough for all his extra indulgences. He had just begun gardening, and trimming up trees, and "you know how delightful such work is. Did we not enjoy it, in 'fates despite' at Glengary?—in old times?

With the birds singing around my eaves, and my children, making merry out of doors and in, (I have grown very tolerant of noisy children) I am of course cheery and fresh at heart; but still even now I cannot wholly, nor can I ever, rid myself of the two troublesome griefs (if I may call them by so strong a name) which dash my cup. In the first place, you are struggling with the daily cares of life, and cannot be entirely happy. And, then, I am becalmed out of the current which the great world of men is moving onward upon; am sunk into inglorious quiet, whilst my temper is for action; am pruning trees, riding to a village to bring a plain action, or set aside an office judgment, reading books I have already read; and all this, and only this, whilst I incessantly hear internal voices that say 'Up—Up—the world is winning.' Your present cares, which thank God, you have a manly and heroic nature to encounter, give me most trouble. You *know*, my beloved Father, that I would leap into a gulph to rid you of them; and if you do not know, then let me tell you here once for all that I could *not consent to live* an hour after my conscience charged me with having preferred myself to you—my happiness to yours, You, from whom I draw my life, have bequeathed me much of your own high nature—if you had not done so, I might have looked without pain or grief, I might have looked in all the untroubled comfort of 'the wretch concentrated all in self,' on your cares which I cannot remove. I sometimes leap like a horse to the spur, when stung by this thought of your daily cares, and my own inaction, and then I take refuge in the dream that one day we may yet, God willing, stand shoulder to shoulder in some fair region of the South, and cheer each other and be happy together—we and ours.[29]

For the present, Cooke contented himself with the real satisfactions to be derived from employment with the affairs of The Vineyard. Actual management of the estate, more than a thousand acres in extent, apparently remained in the hands of Nathaniel Burwell until his death in November, 1849, two months before the death of Cooke. But to minister to a poet's taste for gardening there was ample space about the house. A memorandum in Cooke's own hand suggests the variety and strength of that taste. It records the planting of sixty-six fruit trees—peaches, pears, apples, and many others—no two of the same variety and each numbered and named in a neat column. Later entries note the progress of the trees and the planting of eighteen grape-vines, with location of the vines indicated in a carefully drawn sketch.[30]

So circumstanced, Cooke naturally entertained thoughts of authorship, as a letter to his father informed. This, and his legal study, he would resume as soon as he got things tidy about him. A postscript added:

"Some of my long ago published pieces have lately taken a fresh start and I hear of them in different places republished with puffing flourishes." [31]

One of the pieces to which he referred doubtless was "Florence Vane," strongly praised by Poe in a lecture in New York and then republished in the *Broadway Journal* for March 15, 1845. Poe's encouragement elicited a poem scarcely known today but deservedly ranked as one of Cooke's best. Printed in the *Broadway Journal* for December 20, Poe referred to it a week later in the editorial miscellany:

"The truly beautiful poem entitled 'The Mountains,' and published in our last Journal," would put every reader in mind of "the terseness and severe beauty of Macaulay's best ballads—while it surpasses any of them in grace and imagination. Not for years has so fine a poem been given to the American public." It was the composition of Mr. P. P. Cooke of Virginia, "author of 'Florence Vane,' 'Young Rosalie Lee,' and other exquisitely graceful and delicate things. Mr. Cooke's prose, too, is nearly as meritorious as his poetry." [32]

Poe's glowing praise, seconded it would seem by John Pendleton Kennedy, evidently prompted Rufus Griswold to request, through Kennedy, material for a new edition of *The Poets and Poetry of America*. To a letter from Kennedy, Cooke responded:

I got your letter this morning and as the 8th of October is very near at hand I write at once to say that I will endeavour to do all you advise and ask—but I fear I shall not be able to do it. I have no 'port folio.' My verses are scattered about on *scraps* of paper of all colours, shades, and degrees of antiquity. Uncle Phil has the only 'Book' I ever put them into, and that contains only my crudities—and only a few of *them.* More than what I have said, my papers generally in coming from Martinsburg to 'The Vineyard, near Millwood Clarke Co.' (Remember that as my directive) caught on fire, not from their impetuosity of nature, but from the miserable Winchester and Potomac Engine, and were some quite, and most in part, *burnt.* Caleb Balderstone's fire and that of the Treasury Building will give you an idea of the benefit this gives me in excusing myself to my friends for the procrastinations and non performances of the last (how many!) years of my useless, but considerably happy life.

He had been engaged for some months in writing a book of long poems called "Froissart Ballads." "I have finished the 'Bridge of Lusac,' (the story of the Death of Sir John Chandos) and 'The Master of Bolton' and have opened a treaty (indirectly) with the Harpers [33] for the publication of it, a novel, a history of Virgin[ia] or a School Book or anything that will give me a few hundred per annum in addition to my present sufficient, but not super-abundant, means of living. I want a little 'Springs' and 'travel' money." These long poems, of course, would not suit Mr. Griswold. Of short ones "it will take me a day or two to select and arrange such as I would not be ashamed to see printed. This requisite day or two, with the country delays of mail, will put it past the 8th before they could get to you—probably. I will however do my best to have them ready with the 'Biography'! . . . .

You say "Give the Turkeys a holiday." I got your letter in the midst of a party of my friends who were met here to eat a young gobler that I killed yesterday. I will however let his companions alone until I get rid of this task of 'fame and honour' that your cajolery of Griswold has put upon me. Write if you please at once.[34]

As early as April, 1843, Cooke had planned a book of narrative verse based on *Froissart's Chronicles.* But like emigration to the West and a political career, the project had not matured, although several stories had been composed. Taken up again in 1845, as the foregoing letter to Kennedy implies, the plan was not in fact completed before Cooke's inclusion in Griswold's anthology. After much correspondence with his sponsors and various delays, *Froissart Ballads, and Other Poems* was published in 1847. A modification of the original project, it was favorably noticed in various periodicals; but the returns were meagre, and thereafter Cooke's literary labors were confined almost entirely to prose.

That these labors were respectable in volume, if not particularly remunerative, the publishing record and extant letters reveal. What is probably the last letter from Cooke to his father contains a passage which suggests with what earnestness he practiced authorship. Mainly concerned with advice to John Esten and with affairs of the Burwell estate, it closes: "I am positively sick with writing and chewing before a hot fire. I have done a morning's work at my novel before writing this." [35]

The novel was never completed. During the post-Christmas holidays Cooke went hunting; and to retrieve a wounded duck (turkey, one tradition says) that had fallen into the Shenandoah, he waded into the icy river. Cold developed from the exposure. Pneumonia swiftly followed. Cooke died at The Vineyard on Sunday, January 20, 1850, at the age of thirty-three.[36]

The body was buried in the churchyard cemetery of Old Chapel, near Millwood, where Cooke had worshiped with the Episcopal gentry of the neighborhood. The branches of a willow tree spread over the grave; and carved in the marble monument is the form of a lyre like that over the grave of Keats.

From the records of his life, much abridged in the foregoing, and from his writing the character and temperament of Philip Pendleton Cooke may be inferred. The juvenilia suggest a proud, sensitive, reserved, romantic youth luxuriating in a sentimentalized past and touched by Byronesque world-weariness and Shelleyan melancholy. Fond of the remote in time, he remained. But never a recluse or an ascetic, he in fact liked and was liked by people; and in nature, experienced through outdoor sports appropriate to the vigorous physique of a gregarious Virginia aristocrat, he early discovered values no less attractive than the enchantments of the age of chivalry. That he was ever in fact much of a sentimentalist, his fondness for the poetry of Chaucer makes doubtful.

Tempered by adversity, and his old-world values threatened by those of the new, to which his Baltimore cousin had profitably adjusted, Cooke learned in maturity to look at the world with a somewhat realistic and, on occasion, an ironically satirical eye. What he saw did not embitter him. To the end he remained the cheerful, affectionate husband and father, the open-hearted and generous friend.

I VERSE

&&&&&&&&&&&&&&&&&&&&&&&

A Foreword   *3*

B Poems

 Young Rosalie Lee 6
 The Ballad of Count Herman 7
 Earl March and His Daughter 8
 Florence Vane 10
 Life in the Autumn Woods 11
 The Power of the Bards 14
 The Mountains 16
 Emily 21
 The Murder of Cornstalk 29
 Love and Be Kind 36
 To My Daughter Lily 37
 To Edith 39
 The Story of Ugolino 40
 Geoffrey Tetenoire 43
 The Master of Bolton 50
 Orthone 94
 Sir Peter of Bearn 99
 Our Lady's Dog 108
 Imaginary Ills 110
 Pan and Echo 111

Foreword

Thirty-eight poems are credited to Cooke in the bibliography of his writings, some of them unsigned or signed with initial or pseudonym but identified as his by mention in memoirs, letters, editorial commentary, and the like. Twelve of the thirty-eight had appeared in periodicals before his twentieth birthday; and from them he selected one for inclusion in *Froissart Ballads and Other Poems*, published early in 1847. Of the sixteen others in the volume, ten had also received prior publication. Four of the five ballads and one short lyric were new.

To the seventeen selected by Cooke, three others (the second, third, and last) have been added, the first two composed probably before 1841 and the last published in 1848. The twenty are presented in the chronological order of first publication (in one instance, probable composition), rather than in the order of the volume, which grouped the "Other Poems" after the ballads. For the volume, Cooke importantly revised the wording in several of the lyrics; and the final versions are followed, including spelling.

Cooke's juvenile poems can for the most part be dismissed as the respectable compositions of a talented and precocious youth, somewhat given to sentimental posturing. They reflect much reading in classical and English authors, a fondness for the remote in time and space, discriminating use of an extensive vocabulary, energy and grace in expression of conventional attitude or theme. Like the early verses of Keats, however, they savor of the derivative.

Although not of equally superior quality, the twenty selected poems appreciably surpass most of the early period. The good features of the juvenilia remain, with little or no suggestion of mere imitation, though it would be foolish to deny that Cooke's fondness for Chaucer and Scott exerted no general influence on a poet who, like them, was by endowment a bard with an urge to tell entertaining stories. Nor would there be point in forgetting that Cooke the lyricist wrote during a period labelled in the histories as the "Age of Romanticism." It would be difficult, however, to discover in the mature poetry of Cooke evidence of specific influence by any one of his contemporaries, British or American, extensive though his reading was in both fields. In fact, both as man and as poet the mature Cooke might with as much reason be labelled "Classical" as "Romantic." That without being self-consciously so he was as much "native American" as any of his contemporaries, "The Mountains" and "Life in the Autumn Woods" will suggest.

In addition to the qualities observable in the early verse of Cooke, a few others more evident in the later poems require mention. His ear for rhythm and for other means of producing verbal music was admirable. For example, the charm of "Florence Vane," his most widely popular lyric and one often set to music during the Eighteen-Forties, is explained much more by reference to the skillful arrangement of sounds than to content or mood.

In both the narratives and the lyrics, the style is brisk, limpid, robust, distinctively personal in quality. The feelings and emotions expressed in the lyrics evidently derived not from pages of old books but from the poet's personal experience with nature and with humankind. Not least important, his best poems have an air of unstudied informality, as if the poet were speaking his piece as post-prandial diversion for boon companions—as, according to tradition, he frequently did speak. But despite this impression, Cooke usually tailored his verse; and the thirty-nine identified poems reflect an exceptional degree of interest in prosodic experimentation, many of the traditional shorter varieties and verse-forms being represented. For narratives, however, he favored the four- or six-line common ballad stanza and loose tetrameter couplets with frequent variations.

In a Preface to his volume, from which the following passages are taken, Cooke explained the original plan of the collection:

> The motto of my title-page—the opening lines of the Ricciardetto of the Roman poet and prelate, Forteguerri—gives an accurate idea of the plan of the Froissart Ballads, as I originally conceived it:
>
> > "A certain freak has got into my head,
> >   Which I can't conquer for the life of me,
> > Of taking up some history, little read,
> >   Or known, and writing it in poetry."

The Proem was written whilst my "freak" or purpose was still of this limited character; and it represents the ballads—not then begun, but spoken of as finished—as versified transcripts from Froissart. Perhaps, if I had carried out this purpose of fidelity to the noble old chronicler, my poetry would have been all the better for it. I have, however, not done so. The Master of Bolton, and Geoffrey Tetenoire are no where in Froissart, but stories of my own invention. . . . The remaining poems, Orthone, Sir Peter of Bearn, and Our Lady's Dog, are written upon the original plan, and as faithful to the text of Froissart as the necessities of verse permitted me to make them.

The reader may be disposed to undervalue poems professing to be versifications of old stories, on the ground of a want of originality. I ask only, in anticipation of this, that he will recollect the fact that, from Chaucer to Dryden, such appropriations of old story were customary with the noblest poets of our English language. . . . I shall hope to be justified in that plan of my work to which, in three poems out of five, I have adhered, and to which it is my purpose to adhere in some future poems.

In this connexion I may as well inform the reader that the ballads now published, which he may find already too numerous considering their quality, are only a few of my projected, and, in some cases, roughly-executed Froissart Ballads. The Bridge of Lusac, Mont d'Or, The Death of Young Gaston of Foix, Belleperche, and several others, are still behind. If my verse lives at all beyond the present day, I may hereafter add these stories to the present list, and make the collection answer, in bulk, at least, to the somewhat over-loud note of preparation sounded in the Proem.

Notwithstanding favorable reception by critics, *Froissart Ballads* was not a financial success; and no additional ballads appeared. In fact, the only other extant poem composed by Cooke after 1847 would appear to be the last among the twenty below.

Cooke dedicated the volume to John Pendleton Kennedy.

YOUNG ROSALIE LEE

I love to forget ambition,
  And hope, in the mingled thought
Of valley, and wood, and meadow,
  Where, whilome, my spirit caught
Affection's holiest breathings—
  Where under the skies, with me
Young Rosalie roved, aye drinking
  From joy's bright Castaly.

I think of the valley, and river,
  Of the old wood bright with blossoms;
Of the pure and chastened gladness
  Upspringing in our bosoms.
I think of the lonely turtle
  So tongued with melancholy;
Of the hue of the drooping moonlight
  And the starlight pure and holy.

Of the beat of a heart most tender,
  The sigh of a shell-tinct lip
As soft as the land-tones wandering
  Far leagues over ocean deep;
Of a step as light in its falling
  On the breast of the beaded lea
As the fall of the faery moonlight
  On the leaf of yon tulip tree.

I think of these—and the murmur
  Of bird, and katydid,
Whose home is the graveyard cypress,
  Whose goblet the honey-reed.
And then I weep! for Rosalie
  Has gone to her early rest;
And the green-lipped reed and the daisy
  Suck sweets from her maiden breast.

(SLM, March, 1835)

THE BALLAD OF COUNT HERMAN

Count Herman, Count Herman,
  Take charger and ride;
For Revé the Robber,
  Hath stolen thy bride.
I saw him but now,
  On a colt of Ukrain,
And the false-hearted lady,
  Rode fast at his rein.

Count Herman hath mounted
  His trusty black steed;
And called on the Virgin
  His errand to speed.
And with neigh to the wind
  And with hoof to the hill
The charger hath answered
  His master's stern will.

Through the paths of a forest,
  By burg and by shore,—
Over rock, over sod,
  Over brake, over moor;—
The haughty Count Herman
  Rode fast and alone,
'Til his weary ear gathered
  The rush of the Rhone.

In a vale by the Rhone,
  When the vine and wild rose
Had sunk with the sun
  Into charmed repose,
The robber knelt low
  To the bride of the Lord,
And soothed her fierce sorrow
  With wile and with word.

Oh, sweet were thy whispers
  Thou robber Revé,
Young King of the Viol
  And Lord of the Lay!

The grief of the Lady
  Is turned into joy,
And she stoops her soft cheek
  To the beautiful boy.

One hour—another,
  The lovers saw pass,—
Their roof the wild vine
  And their couch the soft grass.
But the shadowy wings
  Of the third fleeting hour,
Bore the tramp of a steed,
  To their love-haunted bower.

A struggle of anguish,
  A cry and a moan;
A plunge that scarce troubled
  The breast of the Rhone!
May solve the dark riddle
  Why never again,
Met the robber and lady,
  In peace or in pain!

Ye may hear the truth sung
  In the old madrigals,
How the moody Count Herman
  Pass'd back to his halls.
And how the false lady
  Pined dreary and lone,
In a convent high perched
  On a crag by the Rhone.
[Quoted in Kennedy Memoir—Editor.]

EARL MARCH AND HIS DAUGHTER

Earl March had a winsome daughter,
  A maiden fair to see;
Her cheeks they were tinged with coral,
  Her neck was of ivory.
This child of a haughty noble
  Loved one of low degree;

But the high ne'er wed the lowly,
  And her lover crossed the sea.

It was an eve in April
  Earl March looked on his child,
Her cheeks were wan and sunken,
  Her eyes were dim and wild.
The old Earl bowed:—over his forehead
  His right hand idly went,
And he played with his silken girdle
  As in moodiness he leant.

*   *   *   *   *

'Twas an eve toward June's sweet ending,
  The shades of the sun were long;
To her terrace paced lady Ellen,
  In the midst of her damsel throng.
Her sire had sent in April
  To her lover, beyond the main,
A letter of courteous kindness
  Much urging him back again.

"Now cheer thee—cheer thee, daughter,"
  Quoth the knight, "the hour is nigh."
And then, up spoke a damsel,
  "His coming I descry."
Right gleesome were the damsels,
  The love-lorn lady smiled,
'Twas the first for many a summer,
  And the old Earl kissed his child.

Along the tasselled forest,
  Over the heath away,
A cavalier came bravely
  In the light of the setting day.
His plumes were rich and lofty,
  His cap was of golden sheen,
And he came on his bounding courser
  Like a lover true, I ween.

"Now cheer thee— Ellen—Ellen—
  Cheer thee, my daughter pale;

Yon youth, on the fleet-foot courser,
  Will cure thy weary ail."
He came—his tall plumes rustled
  At the sick girl's very feet,
But he passed her by unheeding,
  And spurred his courser fleet.

Then a change came o'er the lady—
  A change most sad to see—
The big veins swole like serpents
  On her neck of ivory.
"He knows me not," she muttered,
  And meekly bowed her head,
"Could he—could he—forget me?"—
  Word never more she said.

Toll—toll the bell, Earl March!
  Thy kindness came too late;
Young Ellen, thy winsome daughter,
  Is a cold and pulseless weight.
Oh little hath the myrtle
  With human hearts to do,
And who so plucks love's flower,
  Will pluck but bitter rue.
          (*Burton's Gentleman's Magazine*, Feb., 1840)

FLORENCE VANE

I loved thee long and dearly,
  Florence Vane;
My life's bright dream, and early,
  Hath come again;
I renew, in my fond vision,
  My heart's dear pain,
My hope, and thy derision,
  Florence Vane.

The ruin lone and hoary,
  The ruin old,
Where thou didst hark my story,
  At even told,—

That spot—the hues Elysian
  Of sky and plain—
I treasure in my vision,
  Florence Vane.

Thou wast lovelier than the roses
  In their prime;
Thy voice excelled the closes
  Of sweetest rhyme;
Thy heart was as a river
  Without a main.
Would I had loved thee never,
  Florence Vane.

But, fairest, coldest wonder!
  Thy glorious clay
Lieth the green sod under—
  Alas the day!
And it boots not to remember
  Thy disdain—
To quicken love's pale ember,
  Florence Vane.

The lilies of the valley
  By young graves weep,
The pansies love to dally
  Where maidens sleep;
May their bloom, in beauty vying,
  Never wane
Where thine earthly part is lying,
  Florence Vane!

(*Burton's Gentleman's Magazine*, March, 1840)

LIFE IN THE AUTUMN WOODS

Summer has gone!
And fruitful autumn has advanced so far,
That there is warmth not heat in the broad sun,
And you may look with steadfast gaze upon
  The ardours of his car;
The stealthy frosts, whom his spent looks embolden,
  Are making the green leaves golden.

What a brave splendour
Is in the October air! How rich and clear—
How life-full, and all joyous! We must render
Love to the Spring-time, with its sproutings tender,
          As to a child quite dear—
But autumn is a noon, prolonged, of glory—
          A manhood not yet hoary.

          I love the woods
In this best season of the liberal year;
I love to haunt their whispering solitudes,
And give myself to melancholy moods,
          With no intruder near;
And find strange lessons, as I sit and ponder,
          In every natural wonder.

          But not alone
As Shakspeare's melancholy courtier loved Ardennes,
Love I the autumn forest; and I own
I would not oft have mused as he, but flown
          To hunt with Amiens—
And little recked, as up the bold deer bounded,
          Of the sad creature wounded.

          That gentle knight,
Sir William Wortley, weary of his part,
In painted pomps, which he could read aright,
Built Warncliffe lodge—for that he did delight
          To hear the belling hart.
It was a gentle taste, but its sweet sadness
          Yields to the hunter's madness.

          What passionate
And wild delight is in the proud swift chase!
Go out what time the lark, at heaven's red gate,
Soars joyously singing—quite infuriate
          With the high pride of his place;
What time the unrisen sun arrays the morning
          In its first bright adorning.

          Hark the shrill horn—
As sweet to hear as any clarion—

Piercing with silver call the ear of morn;
And mark the steeds, stout Curtal, and Topthorn,
  And Greysteil, and the Don—
Each one of them his fiery mood displaying
  With pawing and with neighing.

  Urge your swift horse
After the crying hounds in this fresh hour—
Vanquish high hills—stem perilous streams perforce—
Where the glades ope give free wings to your course—
  And you will know the power
Of the brave chase—and how of griefs, the sorest,
  A cure is in the forest.

  Or stalk the deer:
The same red fires of dawn illume the hills,
The gladdest sounds are crowding on your ear,
There is a life in all the atmosphere;—
  Your very nature fills
With the fresh hour, as up the hills aspiring,
  You climb with limbs untiring.

  It is a fair
And pleasant sight, to see the mountain stag,
With the long sweep of his swift walk, repair
To join his brothers; or the plethoric bear
  Lying on some high crag,
With pinky eyes half closed, but broad head shaking,
  As gad-flies keep him waking.

  And these you see,
And, seeing them, you travel to their death,
With a slow stealthy step from tree to tree—
Noting the wind, however faint it be;
  The hunter draws a breath
In times like these, which he will say repays him
  For all care that waylays him.

  A strong joy fills—
A rapture far beyond the tongue's cold power—
My heart in golden autumn: fills and thrills!
And I would rather stalk the breezy hills—
  Descending to my bower

Nightly by the bold spirit of health attended—
    Than pine where life is splendid.
(SLM, December, 1843)

THE POWER OF THE BARDS

Wisdom, and pomp, and valour,
    And love, and martial glory—
These gleam up from the shadows
    Of England's elder story.

If thou wouldst pierce those shadows
    Dark on her life of old,
Follow where march her minstrels,
    With music sweet and bold.

Right faithfully they guide us
    The darksome way along,
Driving the ghosts of ruin
    With joyous harp and song.

They raise up clearest visions,
    To greet us every where—
They bring the brave old voices
    To stir the sunny air.

We see the ships of conquest
    White on the narrow sea;
We mark from Battle Abbey,
    The plumes of Normandy.

We see the royal Rufus
    Go out the chase to lead—
Wat Tyrrel's flying arrow—
    The dead king's flying steed.

We go with gallant Henry,
    Stealing to Woodstock bower,
To meet his gentle mistress,
    In twilight's starry hour.

We see Blondel and Richard,
    We hear the lays they sing;
We mark the dames adjudging
    Betwixt the bard and King.

We join the iron Barons,
  Doing that famous deed—
Wringing the great old charter
  From John at Runnymede.

We ride with Harry Monmouth
  On Shrewsbury's bloody bounds;
We hear the fat knight's moral,
  On Percy Hotspur's wounds.

We mark the bannered Roses—
  The red rose, and the white,
And Crookback's barded charger
  Foaming in Barnet fight.

We see bluff Harry Tudor,
  To royal Windsor ride,
With fair-necked Bullen reining
  A palfrey at his side.

We join Queen Bess, the virgin,
  And prancingly go forth,
To hold that stately revel
  At stately Kenilworth.

We join the ruder revels,
  Under the greenwood tree,
Where outlaw songs are chaunted,
  And cans clink merrily.

We join the curtal friar,
  And doughty Robin Hood,
And Scathelock, and the miller,
  At feast in green Sherwood.

We greet Maid Marian bringing
  The collops of the deer,
And pitchers of metheglin
  To crown the woodland cheer.

We lie down with the robbers
  At coming of the dark,
We rise, with their uprising,
  At singing of the lark.

And, blending with his matins,
　　We hear the abbey chimes—
The chimes of the stately abbeys
　　Of the proud priestly times.

*　*　*　*　*

And owe we not these visions
　　Fresh to the natural eye—
This presence in old story—
　　To the good art and high?—

The high art of the poet,
　　The maker of the lays?
Doth not his magic lead us
　　Back to the ancient days?

For evermore be honoured
　　The voices sweet, and bold,
That thus can charm the shadows
　　From the true life of old.
　　　　　(*SLM*, December, 1843)

THE MOUNTAINS *

"Lowland, your sports are low as is your seat;
The Highland games and minds are high and great."
　　　　　　　Taylor's Braes of Mar

I

The axle of the Lowland wain
Goes groaning from the fields of grain:
The Lowlands suit with craft, and gain.

Good Ceres, with her plump brown hands,
And wheaten sheaves that burst their bands,
Is scornful of the mountain lands.

But mountain lands, so bare of corn,
Have that which puts, in turn, to scorn
The Goddess of the brimming horn.

* [The poem "The Death of Arnold Winkelried," published in the *Messenger* for October, 1847, consists of nine slightly modified stanzas from Part III of "The Mountains" and four new stanzas.—Editor.]

Go mark them, when, with tramp and jar,
Of furious steeds, and flashing car,
The Thunderer sweeps them from afar.

Go mark them when their beauty lies
Drooping and veiled with violet dyes,
Beneath the light of breathless skies.

No lands of fat increase may vie
With their brave wealth—for heart and eye—
Of loveliness and majesty.

II

I stand upon an upland lawn;
The river mists are quite withdrawn—
It is three hours beyond the dawn.

Autumn works well! but yesterday
The mountain hues were green and gray:
The elves have surely passed this way.

With crimping hand, and frosty lip,
That merry elfin fellowship,
Robin and Puck and Numbernip,

Through the clear night have swiftly plied
Their tricksy arts of change, and dyed
Of all bright hues, the mountain side.

In an old tale Arabian,
Sharp hammer-strokes, not dealt by man,
Startle a slumbering caravan.

At dawn, the wondering merchants see
A city, built up gloriously,
Of jasper, and gold, and porphyry.

That night-built city of the sands
Showed not as show our mountain lands,
Changed in a night by elfin hands.

We may not find, in all the scene,
An unchanged bough or leaf, I ween,
Save of the constant evergreen.

The maple, on his slope so cool,
Wears his new motley, like the fool
Prankt out to lead the games of Yule.

Or rather say, that tree of pride
Stands, in his mantle many-dyed,
Bold monarch of the mountain side.

The ash—a fiery chief is he,
High in the highland heraldry:
He wears his proud robes gallantly.

Torch-bearers are the grim black pines—
Their torches are the flaming vines
Bright on the mountain's skyward lines.

The blushing dogwood, thicketed,
Marks everywhere the torrent's bed,
With winding lines of perfect red.

The oak, so haughty in his green,
Looks craven in an altered mien,
And whimples in the air so keen.

The hickories, tough although they be,
The chestnut, and the tulip-tree,
These too have felt the witchery.

The tree of life, and dusky pine,
And hemlock, swart and saturnine—
Staunch like a demon by his mine—

These still retain a solemn dress;
But sombre as they be, no less
Make portion of the loveliness.

III

Just now no whisper of the air
Awoke, or wandered, any where
In all that scene so wild and fair.

But hark! upborne by swift degrees,
Come forth the mountain melodies—
The music of the wind-tost trees.

And, startled by these utterings,
The parted leaves, like living things,
Skirl up, and flock on shining wings.

And, rising from the rainbow rout,
A hawk goes swooping round about—
And hark! a rifle-shot, and shout.

The rifle of the mountaineer—
I know its tongue, so quick and clear—
Is out, to-day, against the deer.

Right hardy are the men, I trow,
Who build upon the mountain's brow,
And love the gun, and scorn the plough.

Not such soft pleasures pamper these
As lull the subtil Bengalese,
Or islanders of Indian seas.

A rugged hand to cast their seed—
A rifle for the red deer's speed—
With these their swarming huts they feed.

Such men are freedom's body guard;
On their high rocks, so cold and hard,
They keep her surest watch and ward.

Of such was William Tell, whose bow
Hurtled its shafts so long ago,
At red Morgarten's overthrow.

Of such was Arnold Winkelreid,
Who saved his fatherland at need,
And won in death heroic meed.

That deed will live a thousand years!
Young Arnold, with his Switzer peers,
Stood hemmed and hedged with Austrian spears.

No mountain sword might pierce that hedge,
But Arnold formed the Bernese wedge—
Himself, unarmed, its trusty edge.

His naked arms he opened wide,
"Make way for liberty," he cried,
And clasped the hungry spears—and died.

He *made* a gap for Liberty,
His comrades filled it desperately—
And Switzerland again was free.

IV

But mark! on yonder summit clear,
Stands the bold hunter of the deer,
The rifle-bearing mountaineer.

From this far hill, we may not now
Mark the free courage of his brow,
Or the clear eyes, which well avow

The manly virtues of a heart,
Untrained to any baser art,
And bold to dare its lot and part.

But a strong vision may define,
His gaunt form's every giant line,
Motionless in the broad sunshine.

And his long gun we note and know—
That weapon dire of overthrow,
More terrible than Tell's true bow.

But mark again—his step descends;
And now his stately stature blends
With the vague path whereon he wends.

Bare is the gray peak where he stood—
Again the blue sky seems to brood
Over a lovely solitude.

V

Our life on earth is full of cares,
And the worn spirit oft despairs
Under the groaning load it bears.

When such dark moods will force their way,
When the soul cowers beneath their sway,
Go forth as I have done to-day.

Boon nature is a foe severe
To pallid brow, and shadowy fear,
And lifts the fallen to valiant cheer.

Heed her good promptings—muse and learn—
And, haply, to thy toils return
With a clear heart, and courage stern.
          (*The Broadway Journal*, Dec. 20, 1845)

EMILY

A Proem To The Froissart Ballads

"Uprose the sun, and uprose Emily."
                    Chaucer

Young Emily has temples fair,
Caressed by locks of dark brown hair.
A thousand sweet humanities
Speak wisely from her hazel eyes.
Her speech is ignorant of command,
But it can lead you like a hand.
Her white teeth sparkle when the eclipse,
Is laughter-moved, of her red lips.
She moves—all grace—with gliding limbs,
As a white-breasted cygnet swims.

In her sweet childhood, Emily,
Was wild with natural gayety,
A little creature, full of laughter,
Who cast no thought before or after,
And knew not custom or its chains.
The dappled fawns upon the plains,
The birds that filled the morning skies
Above her, with their ecstacies—
Of love and music prodigal—
Were not more gladly natural.

But with this childish merriment,
Mind, and the ripening years, have blent
A thoughtfulness—not melancholy—
Which wins her life away from folly;

Checking somewhat the natural gladness,
But saved, by that it checks, from sadness—
Like clouds, across a May-morn sailing,
Which take the golden light they are veiling.
She loves her kind, and shuns no duty,
Her virtues sanctify her beauty,
And all who know her say that she
Was born for man's felicity.
I know that she was born for mine;
Dearer than any joy of wine,
Of pomp, or gold, or man's loud praise,
Or purple power, art thou to me—
Kind cheerer of my clouded ways—
Young vine upon a rugged tree!

Maidens who love are full of hope,
And crowds hedge in its golden scope;
Therefore they love green solitudes
And silence for their better moods.
I know some wilds where tulip trees,
Full of the singing toil of bees,
Depend their loving branches over
Great rocks, which honeysuckles cover
In rich and liberal overflow.
In the dear time of long ago,
When I had wooed young Emily,
And she had told her love to me,
I often found her in these bowers
Quite rapt away in meditation,
Or giving earnest contemplation
To leaf, or bird, or wild-wood flowers;
And once I heard the maiden singing,
Until the very woods were ringing—
Singing an old song to the hours!
I well remember that rare song,
It charged the hours with cruel wrong—
Wrong to the verdure of the boughs—
Wrong to the lustre of fair brows.
Its music had a wondrous sound,
And made the greenwood haunted ground.

But I delay: one jocund morn—
A morn of that blithe time of spring,
When milky blossoms load the thorn,
And birds so prate, and soar, and sing,
That melody is every where,
On the glad earth and in the air—
On such a morn I went to seek,
Through our wild haunts, for Emily.
I found her where a flowering tree
Gave odours and cool shade. Her cheek
A little rested on her hand;
Her rustic skill had made a band,
Of fair device, which garlanded
The beauty of her bending head;
Some maiden thoughts, most kind and wise,
Were dimly burning in her eyes.
When I beheld her—form and face
So lithe, so fair—the spirit race,
Of whom the better poets dreamed,
Came to my thought, and I half deemed
My earth-born mistress, pure and good,
Was some such lady of the wood
As she who worked at spell and snare,
With Huon of the dusky hair,
And fled, in likeness of a doe,
Before the fleet youth Angelo.
But these infirm imaginings
Flew quite away on instant wings.
I called her name. A swift surprise
Came whitely to her face, but soon
It fled before some daintier dyes,
And, laughing like a brook in June,
With sweet accost she welcomed me;
And I sate there with Emily.
The gods were very good to bless
My life with so much happiness,
The maiden on that lowly seat—
I sitting at her little feet!
Two happier lovers never met
In dear and talk-charmed privacy.

It was a golden day to me,
And its great bliss is with me yet,
Warming, like wine, my inmost heart—
For memories of happy hours
Are like the cordials pressed from flowers,
And madden sweetly.

                         I impart
Naught of the love-talk I remember,
For May's young pleasures are best hid
From the cold prudence of December,
Which clips, and chills, all vernal wings;
And love's own sanctities forbid,
Now, as of old, such gossipings
In hall, of what befalls in bower.
But other matters of the hour,
Of which it breaks no faith to tell,
My homely rhyme shall chronicle.
As silently we sate alone—
Our love-talk spent—two mated birds
Began to prate in loving tone;
Quoth Emily, "They sure have words!
Didst hear them say '*My sweet*,' '*My dear*'?"
And as they chirped, we laughed to hear.

Soon after this a southern wind
Came sobbing, like a hunted hind,
Into the quiet of the glen.
The maiden mused awhile, and then
Worded her thought right playfully.
"These winds," she said, "of land and sea,
My friend, are surely living things
That come and go on unseen wings.
The teeming air, and prodigal,
Which droops its azure over all,
Is full of immortalities
That look on us with unseen eyes.
This sudden wind that hath come here,
With its low sobs of pain or fear,
It may be is a spirit kind
That loves the bruised flowers to bind,

Whose task it is to shake the dew
From the sad violet's eye of blue,
Or chase the honey-making thieves
From off the rose, and shut its leaves
Against the cold of April eves.
Perhaps its dainty, pink-tipt, hands
Have plied such tasks in far-off lands,
And now, perchance, some grim foe follows
The little wight to these green hollows."
Such gentle words had Emily
For the south wind in the tulip tree.

A runnel, hidden by the trees,
Gave out some natural melodies.
She said "The brook among the stones
Is solemn in its undertones:
How like a hymn! the singing creature
Is worshipping the God of Nature."
But I replied, "My dear—not so;
Thy solemn eyes, thy brow of snow,
And, more than these, thy maiden merit,
Have won Undine, that gentle spirit,
To sing her songs of love to thee."
Swift answered merry Emily,
"Undine is but a girl, you know,
And would not pine for love of me;
She has been peering from the brook
And glimpsed at you." She said, and shook
With a rare fit of silvery laughter.
I was more circumspect thereafter,
And dealt in homelier talk. A man
May call a white-browed girl *Dian*,
But likes not to be turned upon,
And nick-named *Young Endymion*.

My Emily loved very well,
At times, those ancient lays which tell
Rude natural tales; she had no lore
Of trouvere or of troubadour,
Nor knew what difference there might be
Between the tongues of *oc* and *oui*;

But hearing old tales, loved them all,
If truth but made them natural.
In our good talks, we oft went o'er
The little hoard of my quaint lore,
Culled out of old melodious fable.
She little cared for Arthur's Table,
For tales of doughty Launcelot,
Or Tristram, or of him who smote
The giant, Angoulafre hight,
And moaned for love by day and night;
She little cared for such as these.
But if I crossed the Pyrenees,
With the great peers of Charlemagne
Descending toward the Spanish plain,
Her eye would lighten at the strain.
And it would moisten with a tear
The sad end of that tale to hear;
How, all aweary, worn, and white,
Urging his foaming horse amain,
A courier from the south, one night,
Reached the great city of the Seine;
And how, at that same time and hour,
The bride of Roland lay in bower,
Wakeful, and quick of ear to win
Some rumour of her Paladin—
And how it came, in sudden cries
That shook the earth, and rent the skies;
And how the messenger of fate—
The courier who rode so late—
Was dragged on to her palace gate;
And how the lady sate in hall,
Moaning, among her damsels all,
At the wild tale of Ronceval.
That story sounds like solemn truth,
And she would hear it with such ruth
As sympathetic hearts will pay
To moving griefs of yesterday.

Pity looked lovely in the maiden;
Her eyes were softer when so laden

With the bright dew of tears unshed.
But I was somewhat envious
That other bards should move her thus,
And oft within myself had said,
"Yea—I will strive to touch her heart
With some fair songs of mine own art."
And, many days before the day
Whereof I speak, I made assay
At this bold labour. In the wells
Of Froissart's life-like chronicles,
I dipped for moving truths of old.
A thousand stories, soft and bold,
Of stately dames, and gentlemen,
Which good Lord Berners, with a pen
Pompous in its simplicity,
Yet tipt with charming courtesy,
Had put in English words, I learned;
And some of these I deftly turned
Into the forms of minstrel verse.
I know the good tales are the worse—
But, sooth to say, it seems to me
My verse has sense and melody—
Even that its measure sometimes flows
With the brave pomp of that old prose.

Beneath our trysting tree, that day,
With dubious face, I read one lay.
Young Emily quite understood
My fears, and gave me guerdon good
In well-timed praise, and cheered me on
Into full flow of heart and tone.
And when, in days of pleasant weather,
Thereafter, we were met together—
As our strong love oft made us meet—
I always took my cosy seat
Just at the damsel's little feet,
And read my tales. It was no friend
To me, that day that heard their end.
It had become a play of love
To watch the swift expression rove

Over the bright sky of her face,
To steal those upward looks, and trace
In every change of cheek and eye
The influence of my poesy.

I made my verse for Emily:
I give it, reader, now to thee.
The tales, which I have toiled to tell,
Of dame in hall, and knight in selle,
Of faithful love, and courage high—
Bright flower, strong staff of chivalry—
These tales, indeed, are old of date,
But why should Time their force abate?
Must we look back with vision dull
On the old brave and beautiful—
All careless of their joy or wo,
Because they lived so long ago?
If sympathy knows but to-day,
If time quite wears its nerve away—
If deeds majestically bold,
In words of ancient music told,
Are only food for studious minds,
And touch no hearts—if man but finds
An abstract virtue in the faith
Which clung to truth, and courted death—
If he can lift the dusky pall
With dainty hand artistical,
And smile at woes, because some years
Have swept between them and his tears—
I say, my friend, if this may be,
Then burn old books; antiquity
Is no more than a skeleton
Of painted vein, and polished bone.

Reader! the minstrel brotherhood,
Earnest to soothe thy listening mood,
Were wont to style thee *gentle, good,*
Noble or *gracious:* they could bow
With loyal knee, yet open brow—
They knew to temper thy decision
With graces of a proud submission.

That wont is changed. Yet I, a man
Of this new land republican,
Where insolence wins upward better
Than courtesy—that old dead letter—
And toil claims pay, with utterance sharp,
Follow the good lords of the harp,
And dub thee with each courtly phrase—
And ask indulgence for my lays.
            (*Graham's Magazine*, January, 1846)

THE MURDER OF CORNSTALK *

The miller sate at his cabin door—
A man of seventy years and more;
It was old Michael Beattison,
The gray-beard miller of Crooked Run.

The summer boughs of a chestnut spread
Over his white and reverend head,
And, catching the west wind in their leaves,
Rustled against his cabin eaves.
The wind that stirred the lintel tree
Touched the old man tenderly.

Serene of look the miller sate
Erect in his wicker chair of state,
And now and then a smile would grace
The pleasant lines of his fresh hale face.
Was it because his earnest mill,
With merry clank, and clamour shrill,
Discoursed so well beneath the hill?

---

* The Shawnee chief Cornstalk, head of the great northern confederacy of tribes, was murdered by the whites at Point Pleasant in 1777. The circumstances attending his death are given faithfully in the poem. See Kerchival's Virginia Valley, and Howe's Virginia Collections. Crooked Run is a small stream near and running parallel with the Ohio; it empties into the Kanawha. On the strip between this little stream and the Ohio was fought the battle of Point Pleasant between the Virginians under Andrew Lewis and the warriors of the northern tribes led by Cornstalk—October, 1774. At the date of the murder—three years after the battle —Arbuckle was captain of the fort at Point Pleasant. Tradition and history represent the Cornstalk chief as the greatest and wisest of the great Indian "kings."

Or was it because some thought swells high
Of happy scenes in the time gone by?

The miller's hoary pow has store
Of frontier deeds, and Indian lore,
And he can show old times as well
As any written chronicle.

I, with another, crossed the green,
Saying, "Old gentleman, good e'en,"
And Michael, with fair courtesy,
Gave the good even back to me.
"Michael," I said, "my friend is taking
Notes for a good book he is making
And much desires to hear you tell
The tale you bear in mind so well—
How the great sachem long ago
Was killed with Ellinipsico."

A happy man seemed Michael then.
"Good sirs," quoth he, "I was but ten,
When Cornstalk died; but older men
Have told me how the murder chanced.
My life is very far advanced,
But not enough that I should know,
Of things that chanced so long ago,
Like one who saw the very deed."

"Michael," I said, "there is no need
To parley so; pray tell the story."

Freely upspake the old man hoary,
"Sirs, I will tell what I have heard.
In seventy-seven some scouts brought word
That the great chief was coming down,
From his Chilicothe town,
To meet Arbuckle at the fort.
And shortly after this report
He came, myself was there that day,
For folk had come, from miles away,
In crowds to see the Shawnee king.
The Winnebago, Eagle-wing,

Came with him, for the two were friends,
And wrought together for their ends.
I saw them come, and can declare
What like of men the chieftains were.
The Shawnee was a man of care,
A grave, and quiet man, and old,
But upright in his gait, and bold,
And with a look about the eyes
Which said that he was good and wise.
He left his arms beyond the river,
And came up, like a sage lawgiver,
In flowing robes. The Eagle-wing
Was younger than the Shawnee king,
But a great chief and orator.
The two had fought in seventy-four
On that same spot, and Cornstalk's look
Calm survey of the country took.
He raised his robes, and touched a scar,
And said some words of Dunmore's war,
And smiled—and then, with thoughtful port,
Entered the gateway of the fort.

"His words and voice were soft, and low,
But there were men at hand who said
That it was craft that they were so;
For on the bloody day, and dread,
Of that great fight, when Lewis thinned
His lines, the old chief's cry rang out
As loud as any stormy wind;
There was a tempest in his shout
That drowned the guns. 'Be strong—be strong,'
Was Cornstalk's battle-cry, and long
The frontier bore its sound in mind,
Our women heard it in the wind
That swept the forests, bare and brown,
When autumn nights had settled down,
And fear sat by the chimney side;
And hushed their children when they cried,
In wantonness of baby grief,
With stories of the Cornstalk chief.

"What drew the Shawnee to the fort,
Indeed I cannot well report.
Some said he came down as a spy—
If so he merited to die.
But others have it that he came—
And this seems truer—to proclaim
That the great northern tribes were won
By British arts, and he must run
With the strong stream, unless we brought
Sure aid to him—and such he sought.
This sounds more like the Shawnee king.
However, after counselling,
Our men—to make my story short—
Refused to let him leave the fort.
A month passed by. The Eagle-wing,
Denied his freedom, seemed to pine;
But the stout-hearted Shawnee king—
They said who saw him—gave no sign
Of moodiness, but seemed to be
Careless of his captivity.
He kept his head, and heart, erect,
And, with courageous counsel, checked
The misery of his pining friend;
Saying, 'The oak should never bend'—
And to the white men—'We are here,
And helpless, but we have no fear;
I—weary and old and worn—am ready
To live or die.' His looks were steady—
Serene his voice—erect his head—
When valiant words like these he said.

"I said a long month passed away.
In the fifth week, one quiet day,
The Shawnee sachem, with a wand,
Was mapping, on a floor of sand,
The winding rivers of the west.
Arbuckle, Stuart, and the rest
Were looking on, when suddenly
The old chief paused with listening ear,
As one who catches some far cry,

Then raised his face with pleasant cheer,
And smiled, and said that he had heard
'The whistle of a Shawnee bird.'
These words to Eagle-wing he said,
And left the hut with stately tread.

"He stept three steps beyond the door.
The river* passed with a solemn roar,
But over its sounds from the westward shore,
Where the dark-green boughs of the forest hung,
He heard a call in the Shawnee tongue.
He shouted in turn—the voice replied—
And an Indian came to the water-side.
He looked on the current swift and clear,
For a little time, as a man in fear,
Then took to the stream like a mountain deer.
Sometime he waded, sometime he swam:
The chief looked on with a visage calm—
There was no light in his face to show
That he knew his son in the stream below,
His dear boy Ellinipsico.

"That night passed by; the guard who kept
Watch on the hut where the Indians slept,
Heard the voices of father and son,
And their falling footsteps, one by one,
For an hour beyond the middle night—
Himself then fell asleep outright.
He said the words—in that strange sweet tongue—
Of the ancient chief, and the boy so young,
Were like some music—so soft they were.
The day came on serene and fair,
And, side by side, in the open air,
With moving lips, and steps most slow,
The white men saw them come and go—
Cornstalk and Ellinipsico.

"That day, at rising of the sun,
Gilmer, and Robin Hamilton
Had left the fort to stalk for deer

* The Ohio.

On the Kanawha's southern side.
It chanced some Delawares lurked near—
These crouching Delawares espied
The hunters, from their screen of grass,
And lay in wait, to let them pass,
Then fired upon them; Gilmer fell,
And the red devils, with a yell,
Leapt out, and rushed on Hamilton.
But Robin turned, and ran to win
The river-side—which soon he won,
And in his fear plunged headlong in.
His friends came swiftly to his aid,
And plucked him from the stream half dead,
Half drowned and terribly dismayed.

"His comrades heard the hunter's story,
With vengeful threats, and curses loud;
But at sight of the dead man, scalped and gory,
A very fiend possessed the crowd.
John Hall, a desperate man and bad,
Said with an oath, 'The Shawnee lad
Brought down these Indians when he came.'
The crowd was grass—these words were flame.
Awful and stern outbrake the cry,
'The Indians in the fort must die.'

"Arbuckle strove, but strove in vain,
The fury of the crowd to rein—
Its fierce intent of blood to check.
Right little did the miscreants reck
Of such entreaty or command.
John Hall, with rifle in his hand,
And a wild devil in his eye,
Menaced his captain for reply.

"Meanwhile the Indians sat alone,
Nor knew what fate came swiftly on;
But Stuart broke in suddenly,
And warned them of the peril nigh.
The Winnebago glared around,

For refuge, but no refuge found,
And bent his dark brows to the ground.
The trembling Ellinipsico
His innocence essayed to show,
Saying, with utterance like a moan,
'Father, I came on my way alone.
My path was single in the wood.
Our people are white of the Long Knife's blood.'
But the great chief, the pale boy's sire,
Calmly arranged his wild attire;
Courage and pride were in his face,
And he stood in his robes with a stately grace,
And spoke with an air of majesty—
'My son,' he said, 'fear not to die.
The Mighty Spirit who loves our race
Looked on my old age tenderly,
And sent my son to die with me.'

"The mob surged onward with a roar.
The bristling guns are at the door!
'What Manitou wills is for the best,'
The old chief said, and bared his breast.
A click of locks!—and the rifles tore
The sachem's very heart, and bore
His body, drenched with its spouting blood,
Far back from where in life it stood.
The poor boy Ellinipsico—
His eyes saw not that scene of wo.
The courage of his race had come
To nerve him for the martydom,
But his weak vision could not brave
The face of murder, and he gave
His young life to the sacrifice
With bending head and cowering eyes.
The Winnebago stood at bay,
And, bloody from brow to knee, contended;
But his fierce life soon ebbed away,
And then the tragedy was ended.
And with it ends my old-world story."
So said, and sighed, the miller hoary.

My bookish friend—when he had done—
Gave thanks to Michael Beattison;
And said such tales were worth the printing,
And, with some fair art in the minting,
Would pass as well as many told
In the high chronicles of old.

          (*SLM,* June, 1846)

LOVE AND BE KIND

How hotly men will wrangle—
   One furious with another!
See how the strong hands mangle
   Some poor down-trodden brother.
Is this the lofty nature?
   Is this the lordly mind?
Can no poor human creature
   Love and be kind?

But if such strife be common,
   There still are nobler spirits
To rescue and illumine
   The mould that man inherits.
Such, with the lamp of goodness,
   A tranquil pathway find,
Such, in the raging rudeness,
   Are gentle and kind.

Strive boldly, human brother—
   Not with your fellow-creature
But in self-war—to smother
   All growth of evil nature.
Be of the nobler spirits!
   Forgive, forget, be blind
To others' faults—not merits;
   Love and be kind.

Then, if it chance such yielding
   Invite the rude aggression—
If patience gives no shielding

Against a base oppression;
Stand up, and dare the danger
    In armour manifold—
Defender, not avenger:
    Be strong and bold!

(SLM, July, 1846)

TO MY DAUGHTER LILY

Six changeful years are gone, Lily,
    Since you were born, to be
A darling to your mother good,
    A happiness to me;
A little, shivering, feeble thing
    You were to touch and view,
But we could see a promise in
    Your baby eyes of blue.

You fastened on our hearts, Lily,
    As day by day wore by,
And beauty grew upon your cheeks,
    And deepened in your eye;
A year made dimples in your hands,
    And plumped your little feet,
And you had learned some merry ways
    Which we thought very sweet.

And when the first sweet word, Lily,
    Your wee mouth learned to say,
Your mother kissed it fifty times,
    And marked the famous day.
I know not even now, my dear,
    If it were quite a word,
But your proud mother surely knew,
    For she the sound had heard.

When you were four years old, Lily,—
    You were my little friend,
And we had walks, and nightly plays,
    And talks without an end.

You little ones are sometimes wise,
    For you are undefiled;
A grave grown man will start to hear
    The strange words of a child.

When care pressed on our house, Lily,—
    Pressed with an iron hand—
I hated mankind for the wrong
    Which festered in the land;
But when I read your young frank face,—
    Its meanings, sweet and good,
My charities grew clear again,
    I felt my brotherhood.

And sometimes it would be, Lily,
    My faith in God grew cold,
For I saw virtue go in rags,
    And vice in cloth of gold;
But in your innocence, my child,
    And in your mother's love,
I learned those lessons of the heart
    Which fasten it above.

At last our cares are gone, Lily,
    And peace is back again,
As you have seen the sun shine out
    After the gloomy rain;
In the good land where we were born,
    We may be happy still,
A life of love will bless our home—
    The house upon the hill.

Thanks to your gentle face, Lily!
    Its innocence was strong
To keep me constant to the right,
    When tempted by the wrong.
The little ones were dear to Him
    Who died upon the Rood—
I ask his gentle care for you,
    And for your mother good.
                    (*Graham's Magazine*, August, 1846)

TO EDITH

Dear Edith, I am pondering now,
With the sweet south wind on my brow,
And thoughtful eyes, which only see
The past, in sky, and grass, and tree.

Into the past I go to seek
The lustre of thy maiden cheek,
And all thy graces debonair—
I go to seek, and find them there.

Canst thou revisit, as I do,
The time wherein I learned to woo?
The time when, young in thought and years,
We learned love's lore of smiles and tears?

Our early love found early cure,
But, cousin mine, of this be sure—
In that fair time we loved as well
As stateliest lord and damosell.

If thou didst not, pray tell me why
Thy soul stood beckoning in thine eye—*
Playing the sweet mime with my own,
And evermore with mine alone?

If I loved not, why should it be
That, quickened by a thought of thee,
My spirit goes forth fiery fast
To meet thee in the radiant past?

Ah! break not in thine ignorance
The golden rule of that romance,
But let it hold thy riper age,
As mine, in happy vassalage.

As mine!—by Eros, to be free
From bondage of that memory,

---

* I find that this line is almost identical with one in a poem addressed by Lord Carbery (1672) to his wife. My verses are too flimsy to be meddled with, or I would put another in its place.

Were but to wear a colder chain—
Were but to give my bliss for pain.
(*Graham's Magazine*, September, 1846)

THE STORY OF UGOLINO

[Some sentences from Cary's Dante will afford a proper introduction
to my translation of the famous story of Ugolino. Dante, conducted by
Virgil, has reached the ninth round of the frozen circle, and there—

"I beheld two spirits by the ice
Pent in one hollow, that the head of one
Was cowl unto the other; and as bread
Is ravened up through hunger, the uppermost
Did so apply his fangs to the other's brain
Where the spine joins it. Not more furiously
On Menalippus' temples Tydeus gnawed
Than on that skull and on its garbage he.
    'O thou! who showest so beastly sign of hate
'Gainst him thou preyest on, let me hear,' said I,
'The cause, on such condition, that if right
Warrant thy grievance, knowing who you are,
And what the colour of his sinning was,
I may repay thee in the world above,
If that, wherewith I speak, be moist so long.' "
                    Cary. Canto XXXII.—Inferno.

The "uppermost spirit" so entreated tells his story, which I trans-
late.]

His reeking jaws the sinner raised at last,
    And wiped them grimly on the skull's vile hair,
Seeking to cleanse them of their fell repast,
    Then said: "Thy will obeying, I declare
The story of my woes. If it may be
    That what I utter shall prove seed to bear
Fruit of eternal shame and infamy,
    To him, the traitor whom I mangle and tear,
Then will my earnestness speak weepingly.

"Who thou mayst be, or how art come beneath,
    I know not, but thou seemest Florentine

By thy sweet utterance. I, or ere my death,
   Was County Ugolino; this malign
Damned spirit was Ruggieri. Thou shalt hear,
   For reason strong my dire tale will assign,
Why in this place I neighbour him so near.—
   That trust in him wrought death to me and mine
Thou knowest and I need not make more clear.

"But what thou canst not know that will I tell—
   The ghastly secret of the Famine Tower!
Hear it, and judge thou if he loved me well.
   Mewed with my sons in that most horrible bower,
Which takes its title from our martyrdom,
   I watched the days creep onward, hour by hour,
Until my sense such watching did benumb;
   Then slept I that ill sleep which hath the power
To lift the curtain from the time to come.

"I saw mine enemy—this one—bedight
   As master of the sport, go out to sweep
The Julian mountain that forbids the sight
   Of Lucca to the Pisan. Up the steep,
His sons rode with him, ranging at his back;
   The boys shrill-voiced, their sire with halloo deep,
Urged on the fury of lean dog and brach—
   Keen brutes and questing. After that my sleep
Saw the fierce riders flagging on their track,
   And then their sides—tusk-rended—gape and weep.

"When as my sleep and dream were banished,
   Some voices in the darkness reached mine ear.
Sleeping, my children wept, and asked for bread.
   Right cruel art thou if thou hast no tear
At thought of my poor heart's foreboding load!
   Now had they wakened, and the hour drew near
Wherein it was the wont to dole us food,
   And each watched hungrily—but did appear
Some ghastly news, within himself, to bode.

"Then heard I harsh keys lock the outward gate
   O' the horrible tower: whence uttering not a word,
But staring on my murdered sons, I sate.

I wept not—so all stone I was—but heard
My boys weep: then my little Anselm cried,
  'Father, what ails thee?' and his wan face reared,
To read my looks. I turned my face aside,
  And shed no tear—nor anywise appeared
A man of pangs, but dumb and leaden-eyed.

"And I sate so until a second sun
  Made glad the freedom of the outer air.
But when a faint beam trembled in upon
  Four faces, imaging my own dumb care,
On either hand, in agony, I bit.
  My sons, who, in that motion of despair,
Saw but the craving of a hunger fit,
  Cried, 'Father, thou didst give this flesh we wear,
Resume it in thy want, and eat of it.'

"And, not to make them sadder, thence I sate
  Holding my spirit in stillness. Silently
Two days went by. Ah, earth most obdurate!
  Why didst not ope on our great misery?
The fourth day came, and Gaddo—my meek-eyed
  And best-loved Gaddo—sank and cried to me,
'Father, hast thou no help!'—and there he died.
  And plain as thou seest me, saw I the three,
Two days thereafter, fall down side by side.

"Thence I betook me, now grown blind, to grope
  Above them, and for three dark days made moan,
Calling upon the dead in wo, not hope;
  Then hunger of my grief fell mastery won."
Here ending, Ugolino turned to hug
  His skull, as a gaunt mastiff hugs a bone,
And, slavering fiercely as he fastened, dug
  His teeth into its scalp, and fed thereon
With many a mangling grip, and sidelong tug.

Pisa! thou burning shame of all who be
  Dwellers within that region of delight,
Where sweetest is the voice of Italy!
  Since man is slow to punish thee aright—
May firm Capraia and Gorgona rise
  From their isled roots, and dam to drowning height

The waves of Arno, till thy perishing cries
  Prove that thou payest, to the last bloody mite,
Even pang for pang, thy debt of cruelties.

Thou vile! thou murder-fronted! what if fame
  Reported that thy castles were betrayed
By that fierce sire? Doth it abate the shame
  Leprous upon thee for his children dead?
Brigata, Hugo, and the sweet ones—twin
  In gentleness—of whom my song hath said:
If sin there were, how might these join therein?
  Thou modern Thebes! their very childhood made
These tender ones incapable of sin!
[Published as "The Famine Tower" in article entitled
           "Dante," *SLM*, Sept., 1846—Editor]

GEOFFREY TETENOIRE

The Lady Jane, with urgent train,
  Comes trooping into Paris:
Her milk-white mule seems very proud
  Beneath the load he carries—
And, reason good, for fairer dame,
  Than lovely Lady Jane,
Is not between the Norman lands
  And mountain line of Spain.

The Lady Jane of Ventadore
  Is irritant of mood,
The dame is but a fugitive
  Before a robber rude;
Tetenoire, the Free Companion,
  Is master of her lands,
And castle strong, by hardy wrong,
  And holds them with his bands.

Thus is it that the Lady Jane
  Comes trooping into Paris—
Reining the little mule, so proud
  Beneath the load he carries.
Here may she be at liberty,
  And wisely meditate,

The wrong which she has undergone
    In pride, and in estate.

The countess came at June's sweet end,
    And, on an autumn day,
The County Gaston sought her side,
    His suit of love to pay:
"For thy dear love, all price above,
    And for thy hand so fair,
If win I may, sweet lady, say,
    What service shall I dare?"

The yielding dame made answer then:
    "The whisper of a lute,
Were not so dear a sound to hear,
    As this thy gentle suit.
But, like the dame who bade her lord
    Leap down, and win her glove
From forth a lion's jaws, I bind
    A service to thy love.

"Five years I dwelt, a widow lorn,
    In Castle Ventadore;
Tetenoire the Breton drove me forth,
    And wronged me much and sore;
If thou wilt slay the robber vile,
    And bring his head to me,
I freely vow, Sir Count, that thou,
    Shalt have my hand for fee."

*   *   *   *   *

It was the County Gaston
    Drew on to Ventadore,
His men-at-arms behind him,
    His trumpeters before;
And by his side did proudly ride
    Sir Anthony Bonlance,
A sweet Parisian gentleman
    Of dainty countenance.

Between St. Fleur and Ventadore,
    Fair in a forest glade,

The county rides, at stately pace,
  Before his cavalcade.
The autumn leaves, he well perceives,
  Have caught a beauty rare,
As if the rays of lovely days
  Had been entangled there.

And the near hills are ringing
  With joyous songs and sweet—
The birds are piping merrily
  The early day to greet:
The early day, for on their way
  As forth the riders pass,
The sparkling dews, which night renews,
  Are bright on tree and grass.

Some gentle praise of nature
  The gallant count was saying,
When he was ware of horsemen near—
  He heard their chargers neighing.
And then he spurred his good steed up
  A near acclivity,
From whose broad top a loving eye
  A lovely land might see.

But not upon the beauty rare
  Of that most lovely land,
The county gazed—beyond the hill
  He saw an armed band:
A band, I ween, fair to be seen,
  Of mail-clad cavaliers,
Holding their way, in close array,
  With sunlit helms and spears.

Lord Gaston's hand waved brief command,
  And straight an Auvergne guide
Obeyed his signal, from the troop,
  And galloped to his side.
"Now who be they on yonder way?
  Look freely and declare."
Whereto the guide in haste replied,
  "The man you seek is there.

"For mark you not the litter borne
  Amidst the armed band?
They call it Geoffrey's battle-horse
  In all this southern land.
The robber bold is waxing old,
  And therefore travels so."
Then said the lord, "By my good sword!
  I joy so much to know."

And now he wheels his champing steed,
  And hurries from the height,
And joins his willing men-at-arms,
  And orders them aright.
"The enemy rides here," quoth he,
  "Beneath us on the plain,
In bold array, athwart our way,
  His castle hold to gain."

Tetenoire was wending on his route,
  So in his litter borne,
When, from the wooded height above,
  Rang out a bugle horn.
And with the sound, shaking the ground,
  Rushed down the charging horse—
With level spears, the cavaliers
  Came thundering on their course.

Grim Geoffrey raised his head and gazed,
  Expectant of the shock,
And laughed to see its fury break
  Like sea-foam on a rock.
"These lords," quoth he, right scornfully,
  "Misjudge me overmuch,
They pounce as if my eagle brood
  Were quarries for their clutch."

And then his dark, keen eye did mark
  Lord Gaston's haughty crest,
Where, chafed and baffled, to and fro
  He rode amongst the rest.
Intent the gallant county seemed
  To rally back his host,

Like one whose courage would regain
    Some rose of honour lost.

"Give me a cross-bow in my hand,
    And place a bolt therein"—
Grim Geoffrey said—"and bend the bow,
    And let the bolt be keen."
And then he scanned the county's band,
    And bade his own hold place—
A perilous smile was fierce the while
    Upon his ancient face.

As leant he on his litter's side,
    An old and feeble man,
With raven locks so wonderful
    Above his visage wan,
And peered with keen and ferret eyes—
    So subtil in their guile—
You would have said a common wrath
    Was kinder than his smile.

He raised the cross-bow to his aim,
    And then with sudden twang,
The bolt flew forth, and angrily
    Upon its journey sang.
The sharp bolt flew so swift, and true,
    That, ere a man might speak,
It smote the County Gaston
    Betwixt the eye and cheek.

Ah, ill betide the bowyer's craft,
    That shaped that bolt so true!
And ill betide the heart of pride,
    From whose fierce will it flew!
The county tottered on his horse,
    His brain span round and round,
And then he lost his rein, and fell
    A dead man to the ground.

Sir Anthony scarce stayed to see
    The County Gaston slain,
But turned to face the homeward hill,

And urged his horse amain.
Now, by my troth, Sir Anthony
  Will surely win the race!
His knighthood claims, and holds, the van—
  Behind him bursts the chace.

Old Geoffrey in his litter lies,
  And marks his armed men
Come trooping back, in scattered groups,
  To win his side agen.
"Now who be these—our enemies—
  Who dare abroad to ride,
For foolish enterprise of arms,
  In this our country-side?"

In answer to his master's quest,
  A griesly wight and strong
Came leading, through the merry crowd,
  A captive, by a thong.
Leashed like a hound—his fine arms bound—
  Came pale Sir Anthony.
The hapless plight of that fine knight
  Was very sad to see.

"This gentleman"—his captor said—
  "Was riding with the rest,
And, yea indeed! he led the race—
  His charger was the best.
But as he rode so terribly
  Upon his dapple gray,
The good beast stumbled at a ditch,
  And left him by the way."

Sir Anthony is tremulous,
  For he is troubled sore:
Right awful are the icy looks,
  Of him of Ventadore.
Quoth Geoffrey, "Speak the truth, and show
  What errand brought you here."
And, quakingly, Sir Anthony
  Made all the truth appear.

"Who seeks my head had well beware,"
 The Breton sternly said,
"Lest, groping in the lion's den,
 He lose his own instead."
Then, lowering darkly on the knight,
 He deigned to say no more,
But bade his trumpets lead the way
 En route for Ventadore.

* * * * *

In a proud hall Parisian,
 With jewels quite a-blaze,
The Countess Jane was leading down
 The stately Polonaise,
When, like a discord, in the midst
 Of music proud, and dance,
In way-worn plight, stalked in the knight
 Sir Anthony Bonlance.

His beard defiled, his locks so wild,
 His garb in disarray—
Ah! can it be Sir Anthony,
 Who went so proud away?
A servitor behind him glides,
 And bears, as all may see,
A little casket, richly wrought
 Of gold and ebony.

"I bought my freedom at a price,"
 So said the haggard knight,
"Dearer than gold in red merks told—
 And I must pay aright
That ransome now, or break a vow
 Wherewith my soul is bound."
His sad, dark mien, and words, I ween,
 Have hushed the music's sound.

He came before the Countess Jane—
 Forlorn Sir Anthony!
And muttered, "I am sworn to bear
 This casket unto thee."

So said the haggard knight, and placed
   The casket in her hands;
And she, in marvel at his words,
   Unclasped the golden bands.

Ah! God and all good saints support
   The stricken Lady Jane!
Within is County Gaston's head—
   A bow-bolt in the brain!
She lost the casket from her hands—
   Out rolled the gory head—
And Lady Jane, with wandering arms,
   Fell down as fall the dead.

*   *   *   *   *

A convent crowns a gentle hill
   Above the bounding Rhone,
And to its shades, for health of soul,
   The Countess Jane is gone:
A sister of that holy house,
   Her griefs of earth are dead—
But, in her dreams, the sister sees
   A casket and a head.

                (*SLM*, March, 1847)

THE MASTER OF BOLTON

Part I

Young Gawen, from his castle wall,
Has heard the merry mavis call;
But Gawen better loves to hark
The warble of the morning lark.
That better bird is up to meet
The sun, with music proud and sweet.
A wonder is the song he sings—
And like the notes of charmed strings.
Just now his lay was all of earth,
Of sorrow intertoned with mirth,
But now, triumphant in his steven,

He mounts him to the ruddy heaven—
Making all humbler singers dumb
With his divine delirium.
Young Gawen views the fallow deer
Peopling the wide park far and near.
Some browse beneath the dewy shades,
Which edge the sunlight of the glades;
And some stare forth with earnest eyes
To greet a wandering hart whose cries
Break on the wild bird's melodies.
Kind nature, with a lavish hand,
Had poured her beauties on that land;
But Gawen, from his castle wall,
Looked moodily upon them all.
For he was born of gentle sires,
And in his bosom burned their fires,
And much it chafed his pride, to be
Shut from the pale of his degree,
By the base wants of poverty.
His sires, the knights of Bolton, were
Masters of spreading lands and fair.
Their lordly hold is stately still
On the green beauty of its hill;
But servitors, with busy din,
Break not the desert gloom within.
And over walls and portal towers
The ivy tod is weaving bowers.

A hundred steeds once fed in stall:
One freckled gray is left of all—
And he is stiff of joint and lean.
Once he was swift, and strong, and keen
As ever bore knight in harnasine.
White Raoull is his stately name,
And from a foreign land he came.
The master's sire, by dint of sword,
Won the brave steed at Castle Nord
From Raoull de Coucy, a Frankish lord.

Whilst Gawen mused in sombre cheer,
A noise of hoofs came on his ear;

And soon a goodly company
Over the lea came ambling by—
A horseman and two ladies gay.
Flaunting and brave was their array,
And they rode talking by the way.
The master, as the three drew on
Soon knew his neighbour stout Sir John,
And, in the flaunting ladies twain
His daughters Mistress Meg, and Jean.
A London knight was sleek Sir John
Who, lending gold, took lands in pawn.
The masters of Bolton had sometime made
Acquaintance with this knight of trade—
The dismal end need scarce be said.
The Boltons of Bolton have had their day;
Their wide fair lands have passed away.
Park, and meadow, and wood and lea—
As far as the circling hawk can see—
Sir John hath gotten them in fee.
Ah! Master Gawen brooks it ill,
That brave new mansion on the hill!
Ruddy Sir John, with jingling rein,
Ambled between his daughters twain;
Three spotted spaniels ran before;
Each damsel on her round wrist bore
A jessed and hooded sparrowhawk.
I say they cheered their way with talk,
And it rose clearly, from the bent,
Up to the master, where he leant
Over the frowning battlement.

Quoth Meg, "As proud as he may be,
The master's hall looks beggarly."
Quoth stout Sir John, "I prithee, dear,
Bridle thy tongue—the youth may hear."
But upspake Jean, the gentler maid,
And, scanning the grim pile, boldly said,
"Now, by my troth, were I as he,
A brave man lost in poverty,
The world a better tale should tell;

For I would vault into my selle
And shake my reins in proud farewell,
And bear my fortune on my lance
Over the narrow sea to France.
And where brave deeds were to be done
And lordly honours to be won,
Thither would I all odds to brave.
Better to win a gallant grave
Than cower to fortune like a slave."
The master turned him from the wall,
   Nor hearkened farther word.
He mused, and said, "I live in thrall,
   But I have freedom heard."
And more he said, with kindling eyes,
   "The burgher's little maid is wise!
Yea, I will take my sword and lance,
And ride into the realm of France,
And find in arms what meed I can,
For I am but a landless man.
In France my father won high fame,
And honour, to the Bolton name;
And even for his gallant sake,
As well as my good way to make,
Will I this journey undertake."

And when the news went up and down
That Gawen for the field was boune,
Ten varlets, and a little page,
Out of good love, and not for wage,
Gathered to Bolton speedily,
To ride with him beyond the sea.
The varlets were stalwart Kentishmen,
The page was Philip Hazelden—
A merry boy, with boyish skill
To rob hard fortune of its ill.
The boy had been a lady's page,
But that chain galled his riper age—
Such life seemed passing dull and tame,
And so the truant fled his dame,
And valiantly to Bolton came,

In velvet hose, and jerkin trim,
And gallant on a palfrey slim
Craving, for simple boon, that he
The valiant master's page might be.

Thirty leagues below Calais,
The Master of Bolton held his way,
Mounted upon his grim old gray.
White Raoull snuffed the wind that fanned
His stately crest—he knew that land.
The pleasant touch of his native ground
Quickened his hoofs to bold rebound.
Too proud for capricole or neigh,
He yet went snorting by the way.
And, comrade from the Kentish shore,
A tercel * hawk the master bore:
A gallant bird, but now of mood
Chafed by the darkness of his hood.

The master looked with thoughtful eye
Out on the fields of Picardy.
It was the time when autumn yields
Her riches from the browning fields—
What time the vineyard on the hill
Blushes the purple press to fill;
But bare were the lands of Picardy,
For there had been the Jacquerie,
With the wild curse of sword and fire.
The corn lay trampled in the mire,
The vineyards—pale and vine—were down,
And ruin lay on tower and town.
How sad to see those lovely lands
Made desolate by native hands!

As Gawen rode in stately wise,
The sunlight faded in the skies;
But wilder lights began to spread
Up to the blue vault overhead—
The baleful lights of dread Bon Homme.

---

* Tercel or Tercelet—the male falcon. The female was generally used in hawking, being larger and of brighter plumage.

So rode he downward from the Somme,
With none to check his valiant will.
But five leagues south of Abbeville,
Climbing a sudden ridge, he heard
Sounds terrible, and wild, and weird,
Upswelling from the farther plain.
He checked his course with instant rein;
And then he said, "Their howls begin:
These dread sounds are the nightly din
Of Laonois and Beauvosin.
The devils are loose; but let us ride
A little up this good hill side."

They reached the top and thence looked down.
Beneath them lay a burning town;
Spreading suburbs, and girdling wall—
The raging flames were over all.
Only by fits the wind broke through
And bared the town's red heart to view—
Showing the glare of roof and spire,
Through shifting lanes walled high with fire.
And strangely muffled by the flame,
Wailing upon the south wind came,
With alternating fall and swell,
The wild alarum of a bell.
The shades of night were darkling down,
But that red day still lit the town,
And shed its lustres, luridly,
Outward upon the heaving sea
Of the far crowding Jacquerie.

The master turned him from the sight,
And saw a castle on his right;
Westward, a league away, it stood
Rising above an autumn wood.
The forest shades lay dark, and deep,
At base of grisly tower, and keep,
But, glistering in the upper air,
Some turrets caught the ghastly glare.
The master looked forth earnestly,
And, "Comrades, we must make," quoth he,

"Yon castle strong our hostelrie."
He stayed no farther word to say,
But rode upon the westward way.

Downward he passed at gentle speed,
And came upon a little mead—
A meadow of the freshest green,
Its verdure bright with a dewy sheen,
For there no curse of strife had been—
And crossed the waters of a rill:
But ere he climbed the opposing hill,
His way again found check, for he
Heard in the gloaming suddenly
The sounding strokes of a courser's feet,
And then was ware of a horseman fleet
Coming his slower course to meet.
He checked his steed, and poised his lance
Awaiting the horseman's swift advance.
The coming, so heard, could not be seen,
For the broad hill that rose between;
But soon the rider drew in sight,
And Gawen saw, in the waning light,
A lithe young page on a palfrey white.
He rode on the way with turning head,
And body advanced, as one who fled
Ghastly, and white, and all adread;
Nor did he seem the band to see
As he came on so desperately.
And when as Gawen bade him stand,
The rein had well-nigh left his hand.
But when he marked the cavalier
And the mailed men-at-arms, his fear
Gave sudden way to bolder cheer.

Question abrupt brought quick reply;
The page recounted speedily
The story of his eager race.
He told the tale with reddening face;
How a right noble company,
Lords and ladies of high degree,
Riding in strength for Brennesville,

Were hard beset beyond the hill—
The lords of Roos, and Monthelesme,
And other lords of knightly fame,
And many a damosell, and dame,
Lovely ladies of noble name,
Beset in desperate case, pardie,
By a wild band of Jacquerie.
Quoth the young page, "I held aloof,
Then saved myself by speed of hoof."
"Craven!" said little Hazelden,
"The cause of dames should make us men"—
But the bold master checked his say,
And turned the strange page on his way:
Saying to all, "Good comrades, ride!
For, let all evil chance betide,
Foul breach it were of honour's laws
To strike no blow in such a cause."
With these bold words he took the lead,
And urged White Raoull to his speed.

So Gawen, with his following,
Drew on to where, in stubborn ring,
Fencing their dames as best they might,
The knights of France waged desperate fight.
He saw not, by the doubtful light,
How the ring held, but he might mark
The foe in masses dense and dark
Beating its iron fence amain.
Short space the daring youth drew rein;
Swiftly he ordered his merry men,
And placed in the midst young Hazelden,
(The stranger page had flown agen);
Then signing the cross upon his brow,
And saying, "St. George ride with me now!"
He struck the sharp spurs rowel-deep,
And, with a cry, charged down the steep.

The dark crowd swayed disorderly
Even from the master's battle cry,
And ere a lance bore stain of blood,
The nearer edge gave back a rood,

Confusedly pressing man on man;
But when the deadly work began—
When full in their midst the swift charge burst,
When lances ravened with fiery thirst,
When stroke of sword, and plunge of horse,
Bore their hardiest down perforce,
The whole dense mass gave way outright,
And covered the wold in howling flight.
Stout Gawen rode on their rear apace—
The Frankish knights joined in the chace;
The moon, so ghastly in the air,
The wide sky's universal glare
Lighted the rout, and clown on clown
Beneath the avenging hands went down:
To say the truth, for many a rood,
A steam went up from the shedden blood.
And so that noble Frankish band—
Lords and ladies of the land—
Were won from death and outrage dire,
By prowess of the wandering squire,
Young Gawen, and his merry-men bold.
As I have said, so is it told;
In the true chronicle, we read
That Gawen Bolton did that deed.
And when the bloody chace was done,
The master praise and honour won
From knightly tongues and radiant eyes;
He answered that his poor emprise
Had found most bountiful reward—
It was a man's best task to guard
Dames so gentle from dire mischance.
But then he said, "My Lords of France,
In God's name bide not longer here."
This counsel found right ready ear,
And the worn troop, without delay,
Resumed its interrupted way.
Ten men-at-arms were reft of life:
A score came wounded from the strife—
With bruise of club, and stab of knife—
But these found life and strength enow,

To sit their steeds, and ride, I trow;
Only the Lord of Reyneval
Was lorn of strength, among them all,
To ride beyond those perilous bounds,
And his worst hurt was not of wounds.
Time had stricken the ancient lord
With stroke more sure than stroke of sword.
But cloaked, from hoary head to spur,
In fur of stoat, and miniver,
And propped by grooms upon his horse,
The old man dared the darksome course.
Some space beyond the field of blood,
Rose the fair castle of the wood,
Whose towers had caught the master's eye;
But now the urgent train swept by,
And, crossing the line of Normandy,
Reached Brennesville, in weary plight,
After the middle watch of night.

Part II

It boots not here, at length to tell,
In full terms of the chronicle,
How lords and dames, of high degree,
Used all fair arts of courtesy,
To win the master to their will,
And stay his course in Brennesville:
How he gainsaid them, and would fain
Have journeyed into Aquitaine:
But how high revels bred delay,
And held him from his southward way.
In the true chronicle we learn
That the great lords made fair return
For the brave stranger's timely aid—
Such fair return as might be made
By puissant lords, of fame and worth,
To a poor squire of gentle birth.
The bounteous lord of Monthelesme—
Himself of high chivalric fame—
Gave from his stalls a sable steed,

Renowned for courage, strength, and speed.
Strong was Inguerrant of body and limb,
The toils of war were a joy to him;
The valleys of Auvergne bred his sire,
But Bessarabia gave him fire,
For he was born of a Servian dam.
A thousand florins of the Lamb
The good Lord Roos gave graciously—
A gift of love and not a fee—
And five full purses, of the ten,
The master lavished to his men.
But the old Lord of Reyneval,
The sooth to say, surpassed them all.
He gave a suit of knightly mail,
Tempered to hue of silver pale,
Inlaid with arabesques of gold,
And cunning traceries manifold—
All made by a famous artisan
Edme Paol of fair Milan:—
Adding, with courteous intent,
Some wealth of peaceful ornament,
A loop of pearls and turquoise band.
These gave he by his ward's white hand;
His ward, the Countess Jocelind,
Heiress of stately Rousillon,
Deigned in her courtesy to bind
The pearl-loop to his morion,
And clasped the band upon his throat.
Her fine fair fingers thrilled, I wot,
And the bold master said, "It were
A thing of less than naught to dare
Perils of earth, and sea, and air,
For a love touch from hands so white,
For a love look from eyes so bright."
The gifts, I know, were rare and proud,
But the good lords and knights avowed
To all who heard their words, that he,
By prowess of unbought chivalry,
Had rescued them from certain death
In harness on that bloody heath,

And high-born damosell and dame
From tortures of a hellish shame.

And then it chanced that, day by day,
The valiant master made delay,
From trial of his southward way;
Shunning all thought of fair Guienne—
Of his great Prince and countrymen—
Or, if he might not shun the thought,
Saying, "My master needs me not,
For there is present truce with France;
If the truce fail, as scarce may chance,
Then will I mount my steed agen,
And join his banner in Guienne."
But, I am bound to say the truth,
A lady's eyes enthralled the youth—
The dark blue eyes of Jocelind.
The days, like barques before the wind,
Flew swiftly by; and as they passed
The spell grew complicate and fast.
Sweet skill of undesigned art
Fettered the strong man, limb and heart.
Sore wrestled he, and stoutly strove
For freedom from a desperate love:
But feeble eld is stronger far
To wage such shrewd and subtil war
Than youth, whose very fire and force
Plunge into toils beyond recourse.
And so the master tarried still,
A thrall of love, in Brennesville.

Meanwhile the Duke of Normandy*
Upheld his banner, by the sea,
In leaguer of St. Valery.
For troubles of intestine war—
Hot feuds of Bourbon and Navarre—
Were rife in France, since good King John,

* Dauphin, and Regent of France—his father, King John, being prisoner of Edward III of England.

His ransom merks unpaid, had gone
Back to captivity, to bear—
Worse than captivity—despair—
Uncrowned, but kingly in his truth!
His son, of Normandy, a youth
Of gallant promise, ruled his realm,
Wearing for crown a soldier's helm,
And lay, I said, beside the sea,
In leaguer of St. Valery.
Proud Monthelesme and Roos rode forth
To join his standard in the North;
But the sick Lord of Reyneval
Tarried behind in peaceful hall.

The dames, deserted of their knights,
Grew weary of the tame delights
Of courtly life, and did decree
Divertisements of falconry.
And so one autumn morn it chanced
That, in fair train, these ladies pranced,
On gallant palfreys, from a port,
To spend the day abroad in sport.
Gawen beside the countess went,
And all sweet cares and service lent.
The lady heard him, and caressed
A falcon tercel on her wrist.
His speech, I say, the lady heard,
And so, I trow, did the stately bird,
And shook his hooded head, and screamed
In recognition glad, it seemed.
"Sieur Gawen, the bird," said Jocelind,
"So darkened by the hood, is blind,
But he is full of joy to hear,
And know, his former lord so near."
It was the bird the master bore
Over sea, from the Kentish shore.
The bird he had flown in calm and wind
On Kent's broad wealds in earlier days,
But now hath given to Jocelind:—
And she the courtesy repays,

And calls him by the master's name,
Which, sounded forth in mandate shrill,
Will ever the falcon's flight reclaim,
And bend his wild heart to her will.
The haughty bird is willing thrall,
And loves the lady's silver call.

Riding at amble, on a down,
A league beyond the trodden town,
Some object came to Gawen's ken,
And forth he called young Hazelden.
"Come hither, boy,"—the master said.
The page rode up unbonneted—
"Now ride to yonder knoll; I deem
I saw, just now, a banner gleam;
Use well thine eyes." The page turned rein,
And rode the distant knoll to gain.
"A comely page"—said Jocelind—
"And like mine own, whose fate unkind
I grieve. Poor Huon! since the night,
When thou didst find this wandering wight"—
"Forget," the modest master said,
"That peril, and my feeble aid.
But, noble lady, since the boy—
I trust he met with no annoy—
Hath scorned the lure, nor comes agen,
Take thou fair Philip Hazelden.
For his poor master's sake, and thine,
The boy, I think, will well incline
To serve thee; at his tender age,
The child should be a lady's page—
Not share the fortunes of my band."
The countess placed her gloved hand
Softly on Gawen's arm, and smiled;
Then said, "Sieur Gawen, I will take—
Thy rare and noble gift—the child,
And guard him for his master's sake.
But the boy loves such peril wild
Of camps and battle-fields, and he
May scorn my silken page to be."

Ere the good master made reply,
All heard a merry signal cry,
And a swift heron, from a marsh,
Mounted, with sudden scream, and harsh,
Beating the air in wild alarm.
Then hawks were cast from many an arm;
And it was a gallant sight to see
The fleet birds tower so valiantly,
Each for the vanguard challenging.
But none went forth so swift of wing—
Mounted so boldly on the wind,
As the brave bird of Jocelind.

With winnow, and soar, he won the height,
At point above the quarry's flight,
And balanced in air, and made his stoop;
But the swift heron shunned the swoop,
And, wheeling aside, a moment stayed
Just over the gazing cavalcade;
A wild-eyed, terror-stricken bird,
The Kentish hawk had canceliered,
But now drove back upon his prey,
Ire-whetted for the fresh assay.
The lady's heart with pity filled
The quarry's mortal dread to see,
And, in her gentleness, she willed
To ward its dire extremity.
With uplift hands, and eager eyes,
And cheeks bereft of their rosy dyes—
"Gawen, my Gawen, come back," she cried.
The hawk, true vassal, turned aside,
Doubtful upon his pinions wide,
Then, like the servant of a charm,
Sank to his perch on the lady's arm.
The damsel, in her loveliness,
Made lovelier by that kind distress,
Repaid the bold bird's loyalty,
With gentleness of hand, and eye.
That silver call, so sweet to hear,
When will it die on the master's ear?

"My Gawen—come back!"—the truth to say,
He pondered the words for many a day.
But he must win from his dream amain,
His page rides fast to join the train.

The boy's bright visage augured well
Of stirring news, and blithe, to tell.
He stopped his course at Gawen's side;
"What have your ousel eyes espied?"
"A gallant host," the boy replied,
"A royal army, foot and horse."
And Gawen said, "The regent's force
Is drawing from the northern sea,
As the news went, for Picardy."

And soon they mark the vanguard come
With trumpet blast, and storm of drum;
And proudly in the midst unrolled,
Blazoned with fleurs de lis of gold,
The royal standard woos the wind.
Pennon, and pennoncelle behind,
And crest of high-born cavalier,
And sheen of burnished helm, and spear,
Along the lengthened lines appear.
The son of France rode in the van,
With many a stately gentleman
Attendant on his presence high;
And when the fair train met his eye,
Brief pause he made, but left his post
In vanguard of the moving host,
And joined the dames, with greeting fair,
And a glad port and debonair.
Certes a gallant youth was he,
And owned chivalric fealty,
To the sweet powers of feminie.
Right pleasant were the words he spake,
And many a courtly jest he brake
With laughing damosell and dame.
And so, returning, slowly came
The host, and train, to reach the town.

The menzy saw them drawing down,
And with loud thunders rent the sky,
In welcome of their chivalry.

In the true chronicle of old,
We find the truth right fitly told,
That when the Dauphin heard aright
Of Gawen's deed, he dubbed him knight;
And that—the tale he heard so wrought
With his own valorous heart—he sought
Sir Gawen's service to engage,
At cost of lands, and annual wage.
To this, Sir Gawen, courteously,
Urged back his English fealty,
And still affirmed his purpose good—
With all fair show of gratitude—
To take horse with his Kentishmen,
And join the Black Prince in Guienne.

But whilst Sir Gawen held him still
In the proud court of Brennesville,
He found a limner great of skill,
And bought his art, with golden fee,
To paint a scene of falconry.
The limner painted Jocelind,
And that fleet falcon on the wind.
The lady's hands have lost the rein,
Which lies upon her jennet's mane,
And are uplifted whitherward
Her blue eyes fix their full regard;
Some tresses of her flaxen hair
Stream forth a little on the air;
There is no colour on her cheek,
Her quick lips seem to cry, not speak;
And the bold hawk, with downward eye,
Pauses to question of her cry.
A shining legend on a scroll
Beneath, gave meaning to the whole.
"Gawen, my Gawen, come back!"—such were
The golden words of the legend fair.

Ere Gawen went on pilgrimage,
He gave the picture, and his page,
To the sweet lady of his love.
And, fair return, her broidered glove
He wore upon his basnet bright.
The proudest dame may choose her knight—
Bold champion of her scarf or glove—
Yet deign no tender thought of love.
So Gawen deemed, and dared not speak
The passion glowing on his cheek.
Like a Chaldean to his star,
He poured his worship from afar.

It boots not now, in terms, to say
How the boy page was loth to stay
Behind, from trial of that way.
Suffice it, when the knight took rein
For the fair realm of Aquitaine,
Young Philip rode not with his train.
Nor boots it now in terms to tell
What on that course the knight befell;
Or how Black Edward—far the while
From solace of the happy isle—
Gave to his coming gladsome cheer,
And, of his fatherland to hear,
Much used the knight's society.
My story's progress may not be
Diverted from that single end,
Whither its steps, impatient, tend.

Part III

Attended by her happy hours,
    The maiden May walks garlanded;
The earth is beautiful with flowers,
    And birds are jocund overhead.
Wide valleys, verdant from the showers,
    By fertile cares of April shed,
Give promise, to the hungry towers,
    Of summer fruits, and autumn bread.

Look forth upon the hills, and see
    The dark-green umbrage of the vine!
This year she promises to be
    A liberal mother with her wine.
And mark the peasants on the lea,
    Dancing, in joyous intertwine
Of swift limbs, to the melody
    Of dull tambour, and viol fine.

Black Edward, and his isle-born men,
Have crowned the brows of peace agen,
And given her empery in Guienne;
To such fair land, to such sweet time,
Pass with the swift need of my rhyme.

The lists were closed at Castellon,
    And, in a palace high
Builded beside the broad Dordogne,
    That flower of chivalry—
Black Edward—sate, in careless state,
    At banquet with his knights,
Discoursing arms, and ladies' charms,
    Brave deeds, and soft delights.

Alone of all in banquet hall,
    Sir Gawen's troubled eyne
Denied the power of that high hour,
    Its flow of mirth and wine.
"Thou cloud upon our fellowship!"
    Such words his master said,
"What care is this upon thy lip
    To scorn the wine so red?"
Then Gawen made this answer true,
    "Ah! sire, some words of thine
Have lent the bitterness of rue
    Unto the ruddy wine.
Virgilius sings of one who shot
    An arrow at the sky,
And I, with like audacious thought,
    Have aimed my love too high."
Bold answer made the Prince, and laughed—

"If she, who quells thy glance,
Sits perched too high for flight of shaft,
   Essay her with thy lance.
Virgilius was a troubadour
   Of excellent renown;
But, nathless, brave deeds are a lure
   To win a princess down.
Take instance from another bard!
   A squire of low degree,
By prowess, won young Ermingarde,
   Princess of Hungary."

The Prince so answered and confessed
The swift wine's power: ungirded vest—
Bold cheeks empurpled by the dyes
Of jocund Bacchus—glittering eyes—
And volant speech—gave token free
Of the blithe god's supremacy.

Meantime a warder paced in state,
Clanking before the palace gate,
And humming, as he paced, a lay
Of the good island far away.
The notes were sad as sad could be,
For the brave warder Willoughby
Had looked upon the northern star
And thought him of his home afar,
His home by silver Wye's fair side;
And—softened from his warrior pride—
Of one who might have been his bride,
But for the wildness of his youth.
He sang, and sighed—and said, "Sweet Ruth!
There was a time when thou and I
Were happy on the banks of Wye;
But wayward was my youth and blind—
I broke thy gentle heart and kind.
Idle the wish, and worse than vain
But would that day were back again!"
And tears bedimmed the warder's sight
As he looked far into the night,
To watch the lodestar's silver light.

Whilst the stout warder paced in state,
Wheeling before the palace gate,
And mused his exile lot aright,
A horseman shouted from the night.
The warder bade him errand show,
And stayed his own proud pace and slow,
Fitting an arrow to his bow.
But the free rider blithely spake—
"Yon red lights show a princely wake:
Say if the knight of Bolton be
At banquet with the chivalry."
"That knight is at the wassail now,"
Said Willoughby, "but who art thou?"
Lightly the stranger left his steed—
A noble boy in way worn weed—
And pressed his suit, that he, with speed,
Might pass the gates—for that he bore
Hot errand to the knight: much more
His quick speech urged, and Willoughby
Gave to the stranger entrance free.

"Master"—a voice of slender sound
Reached Gawen's ear: he turned him round.
The low sweet voice he heard agen.
It was fair Philip Hazelden.
And now he stands, with beaming eyes,
Silent before the knight's surprise.
Amidst the flow of wine, it seemed
To good Sir Gawen that he dreamed.
But this soon passed, and in his joy
The knight embraced the gentle boy.
"Dear child," he said, "show now to me
Why thou art come from Normandy."
And Philip gave into his hands
A casket small with burnished bands.
A touch soon drew the bands asunder,
And then Sir Gawen saw, with wonder,
The picture, which the limner's skill
Had whilome made in Brennesville.
He marks the Lady Jocelind—

Her pity-beaming eyes—her hair
A little streaming on the air:
He marks the falcon on the wind—
Then letters of that legend fair:
"GAWEN—MY GAWEN—COME BACK!"—I trow
The words have flushed Sir Gawen's brow.
He marks them clearly by the gleam
Of the brave torches: doth he dream?
Doth that proud lady of the land
Utter to *him* the sweet command
To come again? Her messenger
Perchance may prove interpreter.
He turned him swiftly to the youth.
"Dear boy," he said, "say out the truth."
And the page said with earnest tone,
Which reached Sir Gawen's ear alone,
"My lady lies in grievous wo,
And, in her sorrow, bids me show
To brave Sir Gawen that her fate
Will poorly brook his coming late.
The dying Lord of Reyneval
Is vowed to hold a tourney high,
          Open to all
          True chivalry
Of England, Alemaigne, and France;
And, guerdon to the winning lance
In combat waged at utterance,
He firmly saith his ward shall be.
For he is in extremity
Of feeble age, and France is torn
          By discord dire;
He will not leave the damsel lorn,
          And meet her sire
Beyond the gates of death, which now
Ope for him, with a broken vow
          Vile on his soul;
And so fair field he will allow
          And free control
Of the good laws of chivalry;
And he who doth most valiantly,

Shall win the maid, and wide fair lands,
And he will gild the nuptial bands
With added wealth—for love, not hate,
Hath urged such course his ward to mate.

"And the sad lady bids me say,
In such fair phrases as I may,
That, if she errs not of thy love,
And thou wouldst win the hand whose glove
Is on thy basnet, thou must haste.
Something she said of maiden chaste
Constrained by fate such words to speak;
And blushes deepened on her cheek;
She knew not what thyself might deem,
And feared such course would ill beseem
A maiden in her purity:
But her true heart, and destiny,
Bade her forget observance fine
And rest her feeble hand in thine."

A red light streamed from Gawen's eyes,
His visage burned with sanguine dyes.
Himself, to hark, he did command,
But crushed a goblet in his hand.
And, when the tale was said, the boy
He seized, and wrought him sore annoy
With fury of his glad embrace.
"Now, by our blessed Lady's grace!"
He cried, "the tale thou tellest, child,
Hath reft my sense, and made me wild.
Thou art a herald brighter far
Than the blithe morning's vaward star,
And well hast driven my gloom away
With golden promise of the day."
"My Prince!"—he bowed at Edward's knee—
"My Prince, I crave a boon of thee.
I read not with my glooming eye
The omen of thy counsel high,
But now may read; it well may chance
That I, even I, with humble lance,

Wreathed by no splendours of renown,
Shall win my lofty lady down."

The board was hushed, and Gawen told
The truth, with joyous lip and bold,
To the brave Prince, and knights in hall—
How the good Lord of Reyneval
Was vowed to hold a tourney high,
Free to the gentle chivalry
Of England, Alemaigne, and France;
And guerdon to the winning lance,
In combat waged at utterance,
Would yield—he paused ere more he said,
And his brow darkened from its red:
But he spake on—"For guerdon good,
Prize to the stoutest man at arms—
Perchance some soldier, stern and rude—
That lord will yield the maid, whose charms
Are my soul's star. Grant, sire, that I
May ride to win that prize, or die."

The Prince unclasped his ruff's fine band,
Then leant his cheek upon his hand,
And read Sir Gawen with an eye
Wise with the wine's solemnity.
"I doubt," he said, "if knightly *laus*
Should gild success in such a cause.
A bugle horn may fitly be
Prize in a game of archerie;
A runlet, and a Lincoln gown
Guerdon the strife of clown with clown.
But, by St. George! it seems not well
That a true-hearted damosell,
In modesty of maidenhood,
Should bide the fate of jousting rude.
When the first Romans won that course
In tourney with the Sabine horse,
Each knight, for guerdon of his game,
Seized to himself a Sabine dame.
But this, sir knight, the clerks agree,
Covered the Roman chivalry

With the world's scorn and infamy.
I know it is the wont of France
To hang such issues on the lance,
Also of lands beyond the Rhine—
That river of the sapient vine;
But nathless, in our better land,
We win not so a lady's land.
Seeking the hand, we wile the heart
With strategies of manly art.
Besides, such wooing of the sword
Binds shrewish mate to wretched lord."

He ceased: Sir Gawen spake more low,
And the full truth essayed to show.
Black Edward heard him, and replied—
"If thou may'st win a willing bride,
Get thee to horse, good knight and tried;
And, certes, of these gentlemen,
            A band will ride,
To prove the prowess of Guienne
            By Seine's fair side.
The friend of Edward should not be
A needy child of errantry,
And leave his court, to journey forth
Like a Scots horseman of the north.
Strife for the maid of Rousillon—
Sir Gawen's mistress—be his own.
The knights of France—none worthier live
In any land—will doubtless give
To all, such entertainment good
Of arms, and feats of hardihood,
As well may stay the sturdiest mood.
By my own knighthood! I would fain
Myself join stout Sir Gawen's train,
And leave my cares of Aquitaine
To hark the bugles of the Seine."
And the brave knights, with blithe accord,
Welcomed the fair speech of their lord,
With thunders of the banquet board.

Felton, LaPoule, and Percy bold—
So is the old true story told—
With other knights of good renown,
By the next midday left the town.
Sir Gawen went upon the way,
Mounted upon his stately gray.
The sable steed, with haughty tread,
Came after, by a stout groom led:—
A charger worthy to uphold
A monarch, when his crown of gold
Totters upon his royal brows,
And he arrays, with muttered vows,
The broken remnants of his host
From turmoil of a battle lost,
To dare, in storm of final strife,
Issues of empire, death, and life.

So journeying earnestly, the band
Drew freely to the northern land;
And by the way, brave rumours heard—
For the wide country side was stirred—
Of open lists, and knightly sport,
In presence of the Regent's court,
At the good town of Bar-by-Seine.
The earnest horsemen rode amain—
Their swift desire brooked small delay—
And soon drew on to Fontenay.
There heard they certain news at last
That three days of the jousts were past;
That Eustace, Lord of Saimpi, held
Possession of the listed field.
That lord had done his devoir well;
Himself scarce shaken in his selle,
His lance nine knights had overthrown—
To bide his mighty brunt was none.
And, with the news, came doubtful tale
Of sorrows of the maiden pale,
Young Jocelind of Rousillon,
For whose fair hand such course was run.

For five days were the jousts decreed,
Three days were past, and urgent need
Was now to press their way with speed.

Past Cravant, riding in the land
Of fair Champaign, the English band,
Worn by the route, made brief delay
At a good hostel by the way.
Biding to mend their travel's want,
The knights sent on a pursuivant,
To Charles, the Regent, to declare
Their near approach, and purpose fair.

The lists were ordered, on a plain,
A little north of Bar-by-Seine,
And now, what time the band delay
At the good hostel by the way,
The barriers of the lists are down,
And Charles comes riding from the town.
Hark to the trumpet's shrill fanfare,
And the glad shouts that rend the air!
The sun is at his midday height,
But fleecy clouds half veil his light;
And breathing freshly of the main,
A far-flown wind sighs up the Seine.
So the glad riders all will say
Some words in honour of the day,
As marshalled onward by the din
They pass, in state, the lists to win.

The Regent on his hackney goes,
Crowned with a chaplet of the rose.
Such sportive wreath suits better far
Than crown of state, or helm of war
With the soft beauty of his brow.
And all who mark him will avow
That fate ne'er bound the weightier care
Of a realm's rule on locks so fair.
And stern men note his girlish bloom,
Mating so well with rose and plume,
And, softened from their sternness, say

"Now let him win, when as he may,
Pastime in sportive holiday,
And his proud ringol put away.
Our royal boy is wise with youth,
And well eludes the colder truth—
Cheating his cares, which are his foes,
With sweet deceptions of the rose."

So passing on his hackney stout,
Charles led the vanguard of the rout,
And reached the lists; then left his steed,
With a right gallant grace, to lead
The white-browed maid of Rousillon,
Queen of the tourney, to her throne.
Pale as a white flower is her cheek—
Pale and without one ruddy streak;
Her eyes are sad, but stern and proud—
Sad with a sorrow unavowed—
Stern with a strength of heart unbowed.
From her sweet lips, of late so bright,
Gone are the roses of delight.
The subtil tide which late distained
Their ripeness, wearying cares have drained,
And their wan lines are much compressed
With stern resolve and wild unrest.
Pray God the damsel's dark-blue eyes
May sparkle soon in happier wise,
And cheek and lip win back their dyes.

Part IV

Before his tent Lord Saimpi stood,
    And scornfully did say—
"Small hope is there, by holy rood!
    Of knightly sport to-day.
Will none of all take heart of grace
    To meet my swift career?
This countess, sure, is dark of face,
    Or I have bred a fear.
Go, page, and bid my bugler sound

A blast upon his horn."
He cast a jeering look around—
  He spake the words in scorn.

Of willing knights, who heard, I trow,
  There was not any want,
And many a scowl, and bended brow
  Answered Lord Saimpi's vaunt.
Much burned the lusty bachelours
  The boastful knight to tame;
But they were bound by their amours,
  And might not dare the game.
Upspake the Regent—"Is there none
  The course will undertake,
And meet this doughty champion
  For the sweet lady's sake?"
Even as he spoke, a winded horn
   Rang out with sudden sound,
And a stout courier, travel-worn,
  Entered the listed ground.

"Now, courier, say whence comest thou—
  What errand dost thou bear?"
Answer he made with covered brow,
  Nor deigned he preface fair.
Much lacked the wight of courtesy,
  He cast no word away,
But, upright in his saddle tree,
  Right stoutly said his say.
"Lord Arundel, Sir John Cathore,
  Of England, Sieur Herchaunce
Of Rhineland, from the northern shore
  Draw on to break a lance—
If France so will it—in the game
  For a fair lady's hand,
Whereof advertisement of fame
  Hath reached the northern land."
"Now, Lord of Clary! speed thee well—
  Ride with a gallant train,
And greet the good Lord Arundel,
  And greet his comrades twain.

Fail nothing of our state, pardie—
  Stint nothing of their due;
In honours of a welcome free
  Be thou our vicar true."
Even as he spoke, a winded horn
  Rang out with sudden sound:
Again a horseman, travel-worn,
  Entered the listed ground.
"Now, horseman, say whence comest thou—
  What errand dost thou bear?"
Answered the wight with reverent brow,
  And after preface fair—
"My masters, gallant gentlemen
  Of the Duke Edward's court,
Have journeyed hither from Guienne
  For share of knightly sport.
The knights of Felton, Parthenay,
  La Poule, and Percy tried,
Sir Godfrey Hall, Sir Walter Grey,
  Have deigned, for love, to ride—
Hopeful of enterprise—in train
  Of a most worthy knight,
Young, but of note in Aquitaine,
  Sir Gawen Bolton hight.
The gentle knights now make delay
At a near hamlet by the way,
And bade me ride thus much to say."

Quoth Charles, "This purse of ruddy gold
Take thou, for fair news fairly told.
Felton, La Poule, and Parthenay,
Percy, stout Hall, and Walter Grey,
Renown hath loudly bruited them!
But Edward hath no goodlier gem,
In the bright ring of valour, which
Engirds his state with lustre rich,
Than Gawen Bolton, trusty knight.
We read the gentleman aright
Some months agone; good fortune made
His prowess instrument of aid

To many here, who now will show
Their love in grateful overflow.
Brave Lord of Clisson! make array,
And go thou forth upon the way
With a proud train of gentlemen,
To meet the worthies of Guienne.
And bear in mind, right trusty lord—
What Christian lands, with fair accord,
Avow unquestioned truth to be—
That the sweet virtue courtesy
Hath chosen our Frankish hearts for bowers,
Wherein to rear her loveliest flowers."

I ween the maid of Rousillon—
Bending, to listen, from her throne—
Heard, with a flutter of the heart,
The messenger his tale impart,
Sir Gawen's name wrought like a spell
The maiden's dire despair to quell.
To God in heaven, with upward gaze,
And aspect beaming with the rays
Of a sweet trembling hope, she prays,
As one late rescued from despair,
And heart-assured of granted prayer.
If her fair thought had utterance won
Thus would its hopeful speech have run—
"Sir Gawen's heart is true and bold,
And, cased in armour manifold,
Of a good cause, can take no harm;
And stalwart is the knight of arm,
Sturdy in brunt of man and horse,
And skill'd to run chivalric course.
Love, kind to all who love—the right,
Dear to high heaven—his own proud might,
These to my heart, so beating, bear
Assurance strong of issue fair."

And ere the lady's courage fell
From the high tone it held so well,
The gentlemen of Aquitaine
Appeared in distance on the plain.

The knights had taken respite brief—
For dalliance wrought Sir Gawen grief—
And, mounting, came so close behind
Their messenger, that as the wind
Shifted to meet them, they might hear
The hoof-strokes of his swift career.
Under proud escort of a band,
The noblest of the Frankish land,
The knights of merry England came.
Welcome of lord and smile of dame,
And flying tongues subdued of tone,
As the proud men-at-arms drew on,
Greeted their presence graciously.
In van of all, great Normandy
Expended many a phrase of love,
The fulness of his joy to prove.
At stately height among the rest,
His mistress saw Sir Gawen's crest,
And caught the triumph of his eye,
And read the silent speech, whereby
He spake his gallant hope and love.
She saw, and read the truth, and strove
Dominion of her mood to gain;
But the sweet lady strove in vain.
Her utmost art might not repress
Tears of a hopeful happiness.
Love, in a gentle nature, rears
His home beside the fount of tears
And scouts the art which fain would quell
The sweet flow of the crystal well.

The English cavaliers were spent
With the way's toil, and Charles, intent
To do them pleasure, did adjourn
All feats of arms until the morn.
But for my lengthened lay, I fain
Would say how sped in Bar-by-Seine
A night of revel; how the day
Broke timeless in on banquet gay;
How Arundel—who reached the town

An hour before the sun went down,
With John Cathore, and stout Herchaunce,—
Surpassed the gayest wits of France,
And, solemnly installed high-priest
Of the blithe wine-god, ruled the feast
Until the lighting of the east.
Sir Gawen feasted not that night,
But husbanded his force aright.
At dawn, ere yet the festive mirth
Had found an end, he sallied forth,
Saw that his steeds were brave of trim,
Healthful of mettle and of limb;
And then, returning, meekly made
His orisons for Mary's aid;
And, after, with observance shrewd,
His knightly arms and armour viewed,
For more to him than death and life
Rested on issue of the strife.
I know not if the earnest knight
Passed greeting with his lady bright.
But, rumour said, the Kentish page,
With sober step, and aspect sage,
Did pass, and errand seem to bear
Betwixt the knight and lady fair.

Now to fair field! with mandate loud
Heralds make order in the crowd,
And clear free space for man and steed.
The last day of the five decreed
Is climbing onward to its noon:
The knightly sports will ope full soon.
Where, orderly, the crowd divides,
Into the lists Sir Gawen rides
Manful upon his charger black;
Percy and Hall ride at his back,
And the bold three pass slowly round
The circle of the tourney ground,
Beneath the eyes of ladies gay,
Greeting and greeted by the way.
This done, Sir Gawen did desire

Stout Thomelyn of Kent, his squire,
To strike Lord Saimpi's shield in sign
Of gage accepted. Thomelyn
Drew to the lord's pavilion,
Where, glistering bravely in the sun,
The broad shield hung: and, winning near,
Smote on its face, with point of spear.
Lord Saimpi issued forth with speed,
And donned his helm, and took his steed.

Now Gawen Bolton! fortune yield
    To love, and to the right,
The shelter of her magic shield;
    There is no sturdier knight,
In the wide realm of lovely France,
    Or any Christian land,
Than Saimpi's lord—in war of lance,
    Or battle-axe and brand.
But the stout islander, I trow,
    Has not a heart to faint;
In hope, not fear, he made his vow
    To his kind patron saint.
Once looked he to the golden sun—
    Once to his lady dear—
Then like a willing champion,
    Took ground for his career.

At signal of a bugle blast,
    Sharp and of sudden sound,
The knights set forward, fiery fast,
    And met in middle ground:
Met with stern shock of man and horse,
    And din of crashing spears;—
But neither champion won the course,
    They parted there like peers.
Again—again! and respite none
    Will hot Lord Saimpi yield:
Swift he demands with haughty tone
    Renewal of the field.
Whereto, Sir Gawen, urged to speak,
    Answers, as haughtily,

"By God! proud knight—I nothing seek
  So much as strife with thee."
Thus spake he, and his visor closed,
  As to his post he passed.
Again the armed men, opposed,
  Await the signal blast.
Sudden it came! with hearts of flame,
  The champions, at the sound,
Drove each his steed to furious speed;
  And met in middle ground.
The Frankish champion struck amain—
  Struck with a force so dire
On Gawen's helmet, that his brain
  Streamed with a flood of fire.
But Gawen smote the knight of France
  Full on his sturdy breast,
And, driven perforce, the trusty lance
  Through shield and corslet prest—
Crashing through steel, the weapon good
  Lord Saimpi's bosom found,
Nor broke until the sudden blood
  Gushed darkly from the wound.
Manful against the lance's force
  Lord Saimpi bore him well,
And passed Sir Gawen in the course,
  All upright in his selle:
But, with the gallop of his horse,
  He reeled—and swayed—and fell.

"Now yield thee, Lord of Saimpi, yield!"
  No word Lord Saimpi said;
The fount of haughty speech was sealed,
  Lord Saimpi's life was sped—
Sped gallantly: and on his shield,
  Distained so bloody red,
His servants bore him from the field,
  At slow and solemn tread.

With the lord's death, a hush of awe
  Fell down on tongue and heart,

And you might mark the nobles draw
  In sombre groups apart.
Few were who loved the haughty lord,
And vauntful port and jeering word
  Prefaced the stroke of doom;
But none reck now of these—the proud
Beauty, and valour, of the crowd,
  One aspect wear of gloom.
Said gentle Charles, "A woful end!
May Jesu's potent love befriend
The brave Lord Saimpi in his want.
  A rude audacity defaced—
Audacity and sins of vaunt—
  His prowess, but the knight was graced
With gallant virtues. Better lance—
Despite that taint of arrogance—
Or stouter heart, was not in France.
Sir Gawen Bolton—all will say—
Hath borne him gallantly to-day,
And we, as right is, willingly
Perforce of our fair powers, decree
That—Saimpi dead—this champion bold,
And proved of valiant worth, shall hold
Possession of the knightly ring,
All armed comers challenging.
All rights of field by Saimpi won,
Transferred by Saimpi, now undone,
Rest with his victor. Cheerfully,
So much of course we now decree.
And, gallants! hearken what we say—
Who holds this field at set of day
Will bear the game's fair prize away."

Into the lists Lord Arundel—
A gay, glad knight, known passing well
In courts of kings, and famed for skill
To vanquish woman to his will,
And trained in all accomplishments
Of dance, and song, and martial fence,

And master too of dexterous art
With the sweet harp to reach the heart—
This worthy gentleman, I say,
Entered the lists with bearing gay,
And said: "For the fair lady's sake,
I humbly crave a spear to break,
When the good knight of Bolton's force
Is mended from his double course."
Whereto Sir Gawen answer made,
Gallant and fair, and nothing stayed,
But, with high heart of hopeful cheer,
And proud glance to his lady dear,
Took post again, and couched his spear.

Part V

At signal of a bugle blast,
    Sharp and of sudden sound,
The knights set forward, fiery fast,
    And met in middle ground.
Lord Arundel struck Gawen's shield,
    And broke his spear in three—
Struck with such force that Gawen reeled
    Wild in his saddle-tree.
But Gawen smote Lord Arundel
    Full on his helmet's front,
And bowed him to his horse's tail,
    So mighty was the brunt.
And when the lord firm posture won,
    And from the shock upreared
His comely brow—his helm was gone,
    And bloody was his beard.
"Small thanks, Sir Gawen, for thy stroke"—
    Right merrily said the lord—
"And, ere a second I provoke,
    I crave one gentle word
Of the fair Lady Jocelind,
    For whose white hand we ride.
I care not with a doubting mind
    This battle to abide."

Then passing, frank of courtesy,
   He came before the maid,
And, gallantly, from bended knee,
   In pleasant accents said,
"Sweet majesty! an humble knight,
   Led on by brave report
Of splendours of thy beauty bright,
   I sought this Frankish court.
The real beauty, whereof fame
   So spake, outshines as far
Her best report, as Dian's flame
   Outshines a twinkling star.
Now speak a frank fair truth, and say,
   If playing well my part,
I win success, wilt thou repay
   My toil with willing heart?"

"Sir knight," said Jocelind, "thy words
   Are gently toned, but ill.
The prouder strength of man accords
   Naught to a maiden's will.
But, for frank answer, elsewhere seek;
   Thy skill of lance and lute
May surely win a brighter cheek,
   To redden to thy suit."
Uprose the lord: "Then will I ride
   No more to-day," quoth he,
"Lord Saimpi's fate—unwilling bride,
   Neither seems good to me."
And so the gentleman passed forth,
   And put his helm away,
And better pastime found in mirth,
   And converse light and gay.
Meantime, this controversy done,
   Sir Gawen, nothing loth,
Passed to a fair pavilion
   Of silk and samite cloth;
And doffed his casque, and rested there,
   Whereof was earnest need,
Whilst his swift grooms, with willing care,
   Recruited well his steed.

Now who is he, so haught of head,
  Who enters on the field—
Curbs his white steed to stately tread,
  And smites Sir Gawen's shield?
All marked the giant, as he passed
  At slow and stern advance,
All marked his charger strong and vast—
  All knew the knight Herchaunce.
The growing hope of Jocelind
  Before his coming bends,
And, like a taper in the wind,
  For feeble life contends.
How may her chosen knight endure
  The more than human force
Of such a foe—how hold before
  Such giant man and horse?
With beating heart, fixed eye, and cheek
  As very marble pale,
She sits, too wild of thought to seek
  Concealment of her veil.
But from his tent, Sir Gawen steps
  With gallant countenance,
And cheerfully to saddle leaps,
  And grasps his trusty lance.
At signal of a bugle blast,
  Sharp and of sudden sound,
The knights set forward, fiery fast,
  And met in middle ground.
Herchaunce, who ran the course as he
  His foe would overwhelm,
At meeting did unskilfully,
  And missed Sir Gawen's helm.
Sir Gawen struck the Rhenish knight,
  A stroke of truest force,
And bore him from his seat, outright,
  And hurled him from his horse.
Sir Gawen sprang from saddle-tree,
  And drew his dagger bright;
"Now yield, Sir Knight, or die," quoth he.
  "I yield me," said the knight.

What time this goodly end befell,
    A wondrous scene and rare—
So read we in the chronicle—
    Was clearly witnessed there.
From mastery of his rider freed,
    Inguerrant onset made
Against Herchaunce's Rhenish steed,
    Who met him naught afraid.
With clamping teeth, and nostrils wide,
    And crests right proud to see,
Rearing, and striking, in their pride,
    The steeds fought wrathfully.
Their yellow mail—their glossy skins
    Sable and snowy white,
Gleamed grandly, as the Paladins
    So waged their wondrous fight.
Before the crowding grooms might staunch
    The fury of their feud,
Both steeds, from quivering crest to haunch
    I ween, were crimson-hued.
The Black, sore wounded, may not bear
    His master more to-day;
And Gawen bids his grooms prepare,
    And gird, his English gray.

The long day wanes—short time remains
    Ere falling of the night—
Sir Gawen bold, if fortune hold,
    Will win his lady bright.
One champion more—Sir John Cathore—
    The combat will assay:
If evil chance weigh on *his* lance,
    Sir Gawen wins the day.
Of gentle birth, this John Cathore
    Was but a chevalier
Who sought his wage on every shore,
    And won gold with his spear.
The knight had lost his dexter eye,
    By flight of shaft, or dart,
In the King's train of Hungary,

At hunting of the hart.
Past middle life—gray-haired—of face
    Swart from an orient sun—
Was never wight so lacked of grace
    As this stout champion.
Now—signal of accepted gage—
    He strikes with ready lance
Sir Gawen's shield, intent to wage
    Combat at utterance.

At signal of a bugle blast,
    Sharp and of sudden sound,
The knights set forward, fiery fast,
    And met in middle ground.
Sir Gawen struck Sir John Cathore
    And bore his helm away—
But stout Sir John so rudely bore,
    That down went Gawen's gray:
Down went he wildly overthrown
    Before the stroke of force—
Down went he with a horrent groan,
    That grim and ancient horse.
His lady's cry reached Gawen's ear,
    Above the sounding strife:
That piercing cry, so wild to hear,
    Has nerved him into life.
From saddle-tree leapt John Cathore,
    But ere he touched the sand,
Sir Gawen stood the knight before,
    His good sword in his hand.
Now foot to foot, and hand to hand,
    The champions will contend:
By dint of honest blow of brand,
    The best will win his end.
But first Sir Gawen doffed, and threw
    His knightly helm away—
Still to his fame, and honour, true,
    However fare the day.
At vantage it were base to fight,

And helmless is Sir John;
But now the knights in equal plight
  To battle dire press on.

Sir John smote first, but with a bound
  Sir Gawen shunned the blow,
And giving ground, and taking ground,
  About the lists they go.
On young Sir Gawen's flowing hair,
  And bright and manly brow—
On John Cathore's gray pow, half bare,
  The level sun shines now.
Sir Gawen saw the flight so fast
  All of the golden sun,
And lowly said, "This trial past,
  And more than life is won."
His heart of valour seized the thought,
  Enflamed anew thereby,
And the bold youth his battle fought,
  Intent to win or die.

With blows, and thrusts, that seek a door
  At every rivet fine,
They fight until Sir John Cathore
  Bleeds like a cask of Rhine.
Griesly and grim have waxed his looks,
  Right hotly mounts his ire,
Rebuke of steel he badly brooks—
  His one eye glows like fire.

Be wary, Gawen—mind thy life!
  Sir John comes stormily.
"Close stroke of sword shall end this strife"—
  In stormy tone quoth he.
Down fell his blows like iron hail,
  With clangour loud and dread;
They struck the fire from Gawen's mail,
  They gleamed about his head.
With bound, and ward, and ready guard,

Sir Gawen held his own,
While to and fro all saw them go—
Sir Gawen and Sir John.
But now, forsooth, the sturdy youth,
Sir Gawen, onset makes;
With brand or spear, the truth is clear,
He gives as well as takes.
From first sweep of Sir Gawen's blade
Sir John his safety found—
The next blow that Sir Gawen made,
Down went he to the ground:
Down went Sir John with cloven brow,
And nevermore to rise.
And Gawen Bolton, victor now,
Is winner of the prize!
Peace to the soul of John Cathore:
A bolder cavalier,
Or better captain, never bore
His fortune on his spear.

With John Cathore cast down, and slain,
Ended the jousts of Bar-by-Seine.
And Charles, the regent, now will say
Who bears the lovely prize away.
Fronting the sunset's purple pride,
And hill tops with the glory dyed,
Charles watches, from his steed, to see
The burning disk sink utterly.
With the last flicker of its beams,
Dying amongst surrounding gleams,
He dropped his baton from his hand,
And forth bade good Sir Gawen stand.
"Brave knight," he said, "we do decree
All honours of this day to thee—
A chaplet for thy gallant head,
A countess for thy marriage bed.
This say we now—hereafter more.
Thy brows—and manlier never wore
Love's garland, won in front of death—
Will now receive the victor's wreath.

Haply—and, by our faith, we guess
So much—the lady's great distress,
Whereof the recent show made all
Condemn the good Lord Reyneval,
Will yield, in somewhat, when she finds
How frank and bold a brow she binds.
We know not of that shrewd surmise
Which speaks thy favour in her eyes;
But sure the countess, soon or late,
Will find contentment in her fate,
Nor rue this wooing of the sword
If gallant heart makes loving lord."

Sir Gawen, at his lady's feet,
Bends, harking to her words so sweet—
Some words of course, and which alone
Take meaning from their trembling tone.
But now her little hand, so fair,
Touches his brow, and lingers there.
Place, and that presence, speak him nay,
But Gawen wins the hand away,
And seals it to his lips, the while
The countess chides him with a smile.

The formal truth is clearly told
In the good chronicle of old,
How nuptial rites, and feasts, attended
By pomp and ceremony splendid,
Followed the jousts; how by decree
Watchful in points of fealty,
Sir Gawen, with his lady's hand,
Gained stately castles, gold and land;
And, with the rest, in fair requital
Of worthy deeds, a lordly title.
Such was his meed; and never one
Of the great counts of Rousillon
Such honour to his honours gave
As Gawen—gentle, truthful, brave,
Since the proud founder of their line,
With bands Franconian, crossed the Rhine.

(Froissart Ballads)

ORTHONE

It was the Bastot Maulion
  Who told this tale to me,
At Ortaise, by an ingle side,
  In gossip frank and free,
At the good hostel of the Moon,
  Where I sometime attended
The will of Gaston Earl of Foix,
  That potent lord, and splendid.

The Lord Corasse—the Bastot said—
  Had taken on his hands
Feud with a Catalonian clerk,
  Who sought to tithe his lands;
And dealt so rudely by the priest
  That he was fain to fly—
For the lord's wrath had put his life,
  He deemed, in jeopardy.

But ere the priest went forth, he came
  And yielded to the lord,
In formal wise, the cause of feud;
  And then, at parting word,
Quoth he, "Corasse, your greater strength
  Has robbed me of my right:
I yield not to your argument,
  But only to your might."

"Ah, Master Martin!" said the lord,
  "I care not for your rage;
Free living shall you never have
  From my fair heritage."
"So much I know;" the clerk replied,
  "You violate the laws;
But, swift as may be, I will send
  A champion of my cause.

"And he shall deal so by your peace,
  That you will sorely rue
That you have borne against the right,

And robbed me of my due."
And, with such words, the angry clerk
   Departed on his way:
The baron never saw him more
   From forth that summer day.

Three nights thereafter, Lord Corasse
   Lay quietly abed,
When, suddenly, the castle rung
   With wondrous sounds and dread;
A clatter in the kitchens—
   A thunder on the stair—
And shrillest voices screaming
   Around it in the air.

The Lord Corasse sate up, and stared,
   And seemed in trouble sore;
Then heard unmannered knocking
   All at his chamber door.
His lady drew the curtains
   In fear about her head,
But to his sword reached forth the lord,
   And, full of courage, said—

"Now who be ye who thunder so?
   Pray let your names be shown."
And at the word, reply he heard,
   "They call my name Orthone."
"Orthone," replied the baron,
   "Who sent you here to me?"
"Your enemy, the Spanish clerk,
   Whose work I do"—quoth he.

"Orthone," said on the baron stout,
   "A beggar like the clerk
Will give you little thanks, or wage,
   For moiling at his work:
I pray you be my servant!"—
   With this the clamour ceased,
And Orthone said, "So let it be—
   I weary of the priest."

Thereafter Orthone served the lord,
  Invisible to him;
Would seek his chamber nightly,
  When lights were burning dim,
And bring him news of distant lands,
  Of battle-field, and court;
Did never post so little cost,
  Or bear such swift report.

One day the baron came to join
  A banquet at Ortaise,
And some loose speech of his did strike
  Earl Gaston with amaze.
"Brother!" quoth he, "how may it be—
  This thing thou dost declare—
Unless thou hast a messenger
  To fly upon the air?"

And then the baron answer made,
  For he was glad with wine,
And told the earl the story—
  Who thereof did opine
As of a marvel deep, and said,
  "If ever thou hast seen
This messenger, in any shape,
  Pray tell me of his mien."

"I have not seen him," said Corasse,
  "Small use it were to see;
Sufficient that he comes, and goes,
  And serves me faithfully."
Then said the earl, "When next he comes,
  I pray thee bid him show
What look he wears—what shape he bears—
  So much I fain would know."

The Lord Corasse is now abed,
  And merry Orthone seeks
His side again, and plucks his ear,
  And toys upon his cheeks.
"Orthone—Orthone!" said Lord Corasse—
  "Good servant, prithee, show

What look you wear—what shape you bear—
   So much I fain would know."

"Sir," said Orthone, "I plainly see
   That you are bent to lose
A willing servant: but, for once,
   I grant the thing you choose.
Whatever, when you leave this bed,
   Your eyes first rest upon—
Observe it well, for certainly
   That thing will be Orthone."

The sun is shining yellowly,
   And dazzles on the bed;
And Lord Corasse laughs loud to see
   His lady hide her head.
He sits upright, and laughs, and peers
   Around him everywhere,
But he may mark no living thing,
   No matter how he stare.

Uprose he then, and placed his foot
   Out on the rushes, strewn
So soft upon his chamber floor—
   Nor saw he yet Orthone.
But as he puts his foot abroad,
   A quick keen tickle goes,
Athwart the sole, and tingles
   Betwixt the wincing toes.

And as his foot he lifted,
   A single straw fell down,
And rested not, but skipped about,
   Over the rushes brown,
With somersets, and other feats—
   The like, man never saw,
And Lord Corasse looked on, and said,
   "The devil is in the straw."

But never deemed the Lord Corasse
   That he had seen Orthone;
That day went by, he sought his bed

When as its toils were done;
And, at the middle watch of night,
Orthone drew nigh again,
And plucked the baron by the ear,
And plucked the counterpane.

"Orthone—Orthone!" his master said,
"You err in coming here;
You broke that promise made to me—
So much is surely clear."
"I made a promise," said Orthone,
"And truly held thereby:
The tumbling straw, whose feats you saw,
That little straw was I."

"Ah!" quoth the lord, "I deemed the straw
Was surely out of nature:
But prithee take some other form
Of greater bulk and stature."
And so, again, the voice has said,
"What first you look upon,
Observe it well, for certainly
That thing will be Orthone."

The baron rose up with the sun,
And looking up and down—
Now here, now there—and everywhere—
Saw but the rushes brown,
And oaken stools, and cabinets—
The room's appurtenances:
No semblance of his servant met
His shrewd and roving glances.

Then to a lattice broad, he stept,
And cast it open wide;
And, looking down upon the court,
He presently espied
A gaunt wild-sow, with ears, I trow,
As long as of a hound,
And bristled back, and loathly dugs
That trailed upon the ground.

The baron shouted to his men—
  It moved him so to see
That loathly beast—and bade them loose
  His bandogs speedily.
The mastiffs came out ramping,
  But eager-eyed and mute,
They snuffed the air, and flew to tear,
  And yell around the brute.

The wild-sow never tarried
  For bay, or roaring chace,
But gave a cry unearthly,
  And vanished from the place.
And then the baron knew the beast
  Was certainly Orthone,
And turned within, lamenting
  The thing that he had done.

Quoth he, "It would be merely just
  If Orthone left me now—
But certainly I deemed the beast
  Was but a loathly sow."
That night Corasse lay long awake,
  But lay awake in vain:
Orthone came not, and truly,
  He never came again.

So said the Bastot Maulion,
  And I have given his story
Fair place amongst my braver tales,
  Of policy and glory.
If it be true, or haply false,
  So much I cannot say:
But mysteries as great surround
  Our life by night and day.
                    (*Froissart Ballads*)

SIR PETER OF BEARN

I met the knight Sir Ernalton
  In those right pleasant days,

When, in attendance on the earl,
I tarried at Ortaise.
A wise and worthy knight was he—
Sir Ernalton of Pine *—
And pleasant converse oft we held
Above our cups of wine.

Sir Ernalton had much to say
Whereof I loved to learn,
And once, it chanced, the converse turned
Upon the knight of Bearn.
No man was near, our speech to hear,
And we were frank with wine,
And therefore freely spake my friend,
Sir Ernalton of Pine.

Quoth he, "The king, Don Pedro, slew,
Some twenty years ago,
The Count of Biscay, for a cause
Of which I nothing know.
His daughter, Lady Florens, fled
To seek Earl Gaston here,
And came in grief before the earl,
And made her story clear.

"Earl Gaston heard her grievous tale
With generous concern,
And matched her with his kinsman young,
The gallant knight of Bearn.
Sir Peter found sufficient art
To quell his lady's tears,
And happily, as man and wife,
They lived for many years.

"Now comes my tale: ten months ago,
One pleasant winter morn,
The knight from Languedudon rode
To hunt, with hound and horn;
And it befell that in a dell,

---

* I have given the English pronunciation to this name, as to most of the French names in these poems. In this I follow Lord Berners—if any evidence of pronunciation may be drawn from the various and capricious spelling of the old translator.

That most unlucky day,
The hounds of good Sir Peter brought
    A mighty boar to bay.

"Sir Peter heard their yells from far,
    And rode the greenwood fast:
And, drawing on, espied the boar—
    A monster fell and vast.
His fiery eyes, and foaming tusks
    Were fearful to be seen,
As in his wrath he ripped the dogs,
    And slew them on the green.

" 'Now, by St. Hubert!' said the knight,
    'This thing must have an end:
It seems but pastime to the boar
    My gallant dogs to rend.'
And then he urged his horse amain,
    And dashed, in full career,
To bring that battle to an end
    With one true stroke of spear.

"But coming near, his charger swerved,
    And would not front the beast,
Whereat, I trow, Sir Peter's wrath
    Was mightily increased.
'Ah craven!' quoth he to his horse,
    'Dost thou so fail thy lord?'—
And, leaping from his seat, he drew
    His trusty Bordeaux sword.

"An hour the knight waged battle hot,
    Against his foaming foe,
And sought his life with utmost skill
    Of cunning stab and blow.
An hour he fought, and verily
    The mighty boar he slew:
And, standing by the carcass vast,
    His merry bugle blew.

"His servants of the hunt came in,
    And they were in amaze,

And scrutinized the monster fell
  With wonder in their gaze.
'This boar,' said they, 'is sure the same
  That, twenty years ago,
Just here, in this same dell, alarmed
  Our lady's father so.'

" 'What say you?' said the knight of Bearn,
  And then an aged wight
Came forth before the rest, and made
  Free answer to the knight;
'Just twenty years ago,' quoth he,
  'In this same month, and day,
The count, our lady's father, brought
  A boar like this to bay.

" 'And pressing hard upon the beast,
  In this green valley here,
Some devil's voice came suddenly,
  And strangely, to his ear.
Whether it came from ground, or air,
  Our lord could never tell:
But certainly the voice he heard—
  And others heard as well.

" '*Why woundest thou a creature weak,*
  Whose comfort harms thee not?
The cruel shall die cruelly'—
  Such were the words, I wot;
And, with their sound, the churning boar
  Passed free of spear and sword:
Within a year Don Pedro slew
  Our well-beloved lord!'

" 'Grammercy,' quoth Sir Peter then,
  'My dame's unhappy sire
By the mere battle, proved the beast
  No better than a liar.
A hind may be a creature weak—
  Not so this giant boar:
But, certes, if he ever spake,
  The beast will speak no more!'

"Then back to Languedudon rode
    The knight, his halls to win,
Leaving the strongest of his train
    To bear the wild boar in;
And when the men had cast their load
    Upon the paved court,
Sir Peter called his dame to see
    The trophy of his sport.

"Fair Lady Florens left her bower,
    And came forth readily,
And with a smile upon her face,
    The slaughtered boar to see:
But when she saw the gory beast,
    Her face grew wondrous pale,
And, lifting up her lily hand,
    She sought her eyes to veil.

"But presently she put away
    Her white hand from her eyes,
And freely gazed, and mused as one
    Who deals with mysteries.
Sometimes she mused, then wended back
    Her lonely bower to seek—
Her right hand pressed upon her breast,
    Her left upon her cheek.

"A lonely hour she passed in bower,
    Then came, with honeyed word,
And face quite cunning in its smiles,
    And thus addressed her lord:
'I owe a vow to good St. James,
    And, husband, I would fain
Take our dear daughter Adrienne,
    And journey into Spain.'

"Sir Peter heard his dame's request,
    And said, 'So let it be:'
And Lady Florens, with the word,
    Departed speedily.
From Castle Languedudon, forth
    She journeyed with her train;

And, by my troth, the wily dame,
  Came never back again.

"That night, when all were sound asleep,
  Sir Peter left his bed,
And seized his naked sword, and placed
  His basnet on his head;
Fierce smote he right and left, and cried
  His sounding battle-cry:
I trow he deemed himself a-field,
  And in sore jeopardy.

"A little page, who shared his room,
  Fled from his blows aghast,
And reached the door, and flitted out,
  And made the strong bolt fast.
Long, from without, boy Gracien heard
  The knight that battle wage—
Heard wild Sir Peter's slashing blows,
  And cries of valiant rage.

"As sweet as summer did he seem—
  The gallant knight of Bearn!—
When, on the morrow, from his page,
  He came the truth to learn.
'Certes, dear boy,'—he smiled, and said—
  'I toiled to slay the boar,
And so my dreams were fever-wild:
  The thing will chance no more.'

"But, with the second night, once more
  Sir Peter left his bed,
And seized his naked sword, and placed
  His basnet on his head;
And shouted forth his battle-cry,
  And waged his fight amain;
While little Gracien, quite aghast,
  Escaped the room again.

"So passed his nights, until he pined;
  And now, as all may see,

By his wan looks, the gallant knight
   Is stricken mortally.
Ten months agone he slew the boar,
   And there are men who say
His wife, who augurs of his death,
   Can name his dying day.

"He here at Ortaise, with the earl—
   She with her friends in Spain—
Such thing, Sir John, should hardly be;
   The wife should come again.
But she is versed in mysteries,
   Of necromantic art,
And such give cunning to the brain,
   But poison to the heart."

So said my friend Sir Ernalton:
   I mused his story's wonder—
It was a complex web, which I
   Might scarcely win asunder.
"Doubtless," I said at last, "the dame
   Knew more than she would say
Of the great beast Sir Peter slew
   On that unlucky day.

"Perchance, enlightened by her art,
   She knew the mighty boar
Was some fair knight, who rode that land
   In merry days of yore,
And angered some old forest god,
   Whose terrible decree
Thus brutalized the gentleman
   From his humanity.

"This seems quite strange—nay, wonderful—
   But, nathless, we are told
Of many cases similar
   In chronicles of old.
For instance—and a score of such
   My reading could impart—

The cavalier, young Acteon,*
    Was changed into a hart."

"Sir John"—said good Sir Ernalton—
    "Pray make that story clear:
I have not heard of Acteon,
    And much desire to hear."
Then I replied, "This Acteon,
    Of whom you seek to know,
Was a right valiant gentleman,
    Who flourished long ago.

"The youth was fond of hound and horn,
    And all fair forest sport:
And, one day, riding in the woods—
    As chronicles report—
He roused a very noble hart,
    And pressed so eagerly
Upon that chase, that soon he lost
    His hounds and company.

"Holding his way for all that day,
    With speed and courage keen,
At setting of the sun he reached
    A meadow close and green—
A meadow with a pleasant brook,
    Shut in with beechen shades—
And caught Diana bathing there
    With all her snowy maids.

"The goddess was confused enough,
    But, towering in her pride,
Refused her naked loveliness
    By any art to hide,
And chid her blushing girls, who sought,
    By crouching or by flying,
To shun the youth who sate his horse
    Their naked charms espying.

* Shakespeare, and the old writers generally,—Lord Berners among the rest,—
spell Actaeon as I have done above; the delay on the diphthong, in pronunciation,
is discordant in verse of rapid measure, and for that reason I have retained the
ancient English spelling.

" 'Ah, hunter vile!'—Diana said—
   'Whoever sent you here
Was not your friend, as presently
   Shall very well appear.
I will not that your tongue shall speak
   The secret of your eyes:
Your speech shall never put to shame
   Our maiden modesties.

" 'Take shape and likeness of the hart
   Which you have chased to-day!
It is my will: so let it be.'
   And, sir, old writers say,
Young Acteon, with Diana's words,
   Assumed the horned looks
Of the wood-hart, whose natural love
   Is for the water-brooks.

"And finally, Sir Ernalton,
   The same old writers show,
That as the human quadruped
   Went plaining to and fro,
And gazing on his slender knees,
   His hounds came up with him,
And, urged on by the cruel maids,
   Soon tore him limb from limb.

"This is the tale of Acteon:
   And sad Sir Peter's dame,
I nothing doubt, from all you say,
   Knows more than she will name
Of that great boar her husband slew—
   And so, perhaps, should be
Excused, in somewhat, for her flight,
   And seeming cruelty."

"It may be," said Sir Ernalton,
   "That what you say is true:
But, sure, the dame deals cruelly
   Where tenderness is due.
The husband is a dying man,
   And, sir—I must maintain—

If he had slain St. Hubert's self,
   The wife should come again."
                (Froissart Ballads)

OUR LADY'S DOG

The Genoese had crossed the seas,
   And, with a mighty host,
Besieged a stately city,
   Upon the Moorish coast.
What time they lay at leaguer there,
   A strange event befell,
Whereof in this fair book of mine,
   I deem it good to tell.

It was at holy Easter—
   An hour before the day:—
The Christian host, with watches set,
   In heavy slumber lay,
When, pouring from the city's ports,
   The Paynim army came,
Led by the Moslem Afringor,
   A prince of valiant fame.

With night, and cloud, their march to shroud,
   And stealthy as the sea
When as its waters seek the shore,
   And gird it silently,
The enemies of God drew on
   To smite our slumbering host—
Drew on unwitnessed by the watch
   Asleep at every post.

But for a holy miracle,
   In mercy deigned to us,
The Cross had sunk that night before
   The Crescent orgillous.
But as the Paynim host drew on,
   A train of damsels bright,
Led by a lady fair of brow,
   Stood clearly in their sight.

And in her right hand, by a leash
    Of twisted silk and gold,
A milk-white dog, of mighty thews,
    The lady bright did hold.
Brave sentinel! with bay, and yell,
    The beast alarum made,
Until the Christian host were roused
    And gallantly arrayed.

The Christian knights see with amaze
    The lady and her train,
As visible as if by day,
    Before them on the plain:
And cross their brows in holy awe,
    As steadily they go
To do the lady's battle
    Against the Paynim foe.

The Moors, aghast, in terror passed
    To win back to their town;
But glaive and spear assailed their rear,
    And bore their strongest down.
And, it is said, the milk-white hound
    Was foremost in the fight,
And with his bristling jaws slew more
    Than any armed knight.

With rise of sun, and battle done,
    No man saw longer there
The lady of the shining brow,
    Or train of damsels fair.
But the white hound, without a wound,
    Snuffing the slaughter strode,
And came back to the Christian tents
    And with the host abode.

And then the men-at-arms who saw
    The wonders of that night,
Called the brave beast OUR LADY'S DOG:—
    For sure, the lady bright,
All said, was Mary Mother,
    Who bare the blessed Lord,

And hates the race of Mahoun,
And loves the Holy Word.

And thenceforth did our Lady's dog
Keep constant watch and good,
And gentle nurture had he,
And sweet and dainty food;
Our Christians saw, with pious awe,
The white crest of the hound,
As nightly, in his watchfulness,
He went upon his round.

(Froissart Ballads)

IMAGINARY ILLS

I have read of a man encompassed *
By phantoms dire and grim;
In an ancient park,
As the day grew dark,
They came about his pathway dim,
And with weird eyes encompassed him.

It was the Roundhead captain,
The dreamer Harrison.
With carnal might
He strove to smite
The ghosts, that closed his blade upon
Like thin folds of a vapour dun.

In such an Armageddon
Do not all mortals strive?
Our timorous wills
Create vague ills
Whereat we strike—but they survive
The many-spending blows we give.

Good friend! waste not your prowess
Against such phantom woes.
Be stout of heart,

* The reader will recollect the scene, in Woodstock, in which the enthusiast Colonel Harrison does battle with his imaginary enemies.

Bring courage, and art,
Against your real sorrows:—those
Are often vanquishable foes.
                    (*Froissart Ballads*)

PAN AND ECHO

Into my thought, as wakefully I lay
    On a green sod of June,
At a sweet hour when Night stole down on Day,
    Led by a crescent moon,
Came, clear as life, an old Arcadian scene—
Valleys of shrubby herbage traced between
Hills, forested with oaks of glorious green.

Among brown rocks, high up a bold hill side,
    I saw the ancient Pan;
His vest of glossy hair was opened wide,
    And light winds flew to fan
His dripping breast, and brow as red as wine,
Above the curls of whose low-arching line
Two little spikes of horns peered, round and fine.

Pan panted on his rocks; and well indeed
    Should he be worn away;
For he had chased that nymph of subtle speed,
    Young Echo, all the day—
Chased supple Echo who, his craft defying,
And ever, as he reached to seize her, flying
Yet drew him onward with her coy replying.

The panting God, at last, found utterance:
    "Nymph, I will chase you down
With divine dogs; deceive your vigilance
    With my sharp Satyrs; drown
Your haunts with rains—rive them with thunder shocks.
Must a God sue in vain?" A fine voice mocks—
"In vain!" rings clearly from the hiding rocks.

"Echo!" quoth Pan, "forgive these windy threats.
    Change love for love with me.
In this new dream, my beating heart forgets

Syrinx, and Omphale.
Be kind to Pan, or he will surely die:
Behold me, Echo, how I weep." Close by,
"I weep!" was answered very tenderly.

The round eyes of the Goat-God spoke their wonder;
   He mused the change, and said:
"Sweet mocker, weep you now in pity?" Under
   An arch, whose spanned way led
Into a cavern near, the fine voice sighed,
"In pity"—and the God, quite eager-eyed,
Passed after it, with strong arms groping wide.

Into the silence of the cavern old
   He went, with such wide arms,
Ardent, and swift with sanguine hope, to fold
   Young Echo's airy charms.
But still, although his steps knew well to trace
The involutions of that grottoed place,
No round young bosom filled his poised embrace.

Then Pan lay sadly down, and groaned, and said:
   "Was ever God or man
By arts of any minion so misled,
   As I, the cunning Pan?"
Even as he ended, the dusk air was stirred
Beside his cheek, and "Pan!" low-sighed he heard,
And a soft breathing fanned him, with the word.

His arms flew forth with sudden certainty,
   And, fast within their fold,
The lithe young Echo lay, while, beatingly,
   Her heart its tremors told.
The wild God's eyes flashed down a quivering splendour,
Making betrayal of her beauties tender,
And the warm meekness of her fond surrender.

*   *   *   *   *

Now the old times are changed. 'Tis many a day
   Since winds Ionian sped
To the third Caesar, off Tarento bay,

The cry "Great Pan is dead!"
But Echo lives; and when the midnight gleams
Silver the ramparts of our mountain streams,
I often question her of Ovid's dreams.
    (*The Illustrated Monthly Courier*, Nov. 1, 1848)

II FICTION

A   Foreword   117

B   Tales

   John Carper, The Hunter of Lost River   121

   The Gregories of Hackwood   162

   The Crime of Andrew Blair   199

   Joseph Jenkin's Researches into Antiquity:
      Erisicthon   244

   The Turkey-Hunter in His Closet   258

Foreword

Fiction as a medium for creative expression had interested Cooke at least as early as 1839. His letter to Poe dated December 29 of that year mentions a projected book whose title, "Maurice Weterbern," suggests a historical romance, perhaps something resembling Scott's *Quentin Durward*. But nothing, apparently, came of it, or of another title, "Lutzen," referred to in a letter to John R. Cooke dated February 4, 1847, although the first may have been ancestral in concept to the second and both to the unfinished *The Chevalier Merlin*.

Before appearance of the first installment of that narrative in the *Messenger* for June, 1849, Cooke had composed four short fictions and four long tales. Two of the former—"A Morning With Cagliostro" and "The Turkey-Hunter in His Closet"—were published posthumously. Like the other two, they are diverting. The first amusingly satirizes the method of producing fiction in quantity employed by Dumas, whose native talents Cooke admired; and like "Captain Guy; or the Unpardonable Sin," whose freebooting protagonist invites the reader's fancy to the age of Froissart, it is told almost entirely in briskly moving dialogue. "Erisicthon," fourth of the short pieces, and "The Turkey-Hunter . . ." are presented below.

For the four long tales Cooke found material in that region of Virginia which to him was home. He had turned to it in "Mary Hunter of Cotsworth," begun no later than 1843 but apparently put aside until circumstances could create a favorable atmosphere for literary activity. When it appeared in the *Messenger* in 1848, it bore the title *The Two Country Houses;* and perhaps in other and more important respects it had undergone alteration, though as to that no positive evidence has been found. Like *The Gregories of Hackwood* and *The Crime of Andrew Blair*, it depicts characters probably modeled on originals within the range of Cooke's observation and experience in a society dominated by an aristocratic-minded gentry but far from rigid in structure.

In variety of setting, character, and incident, *The Two Country*

Houses exceeds the other three. For example, it evidently makes use of persons and experiences observed during Cooke's trip to Missouri. It takes its cavalier hero to Paris in the improbable role of a brilliant commentator for journals on important public affairs. It is the longest of the four. It is, however, the least well-jointed in structure; and it is also the least credible, despite the realism of particular scenes, perhaps because the betrothed heirs of the two country houses too strongly reflect the more immoderate among the romantic fancies of Cooke's own high-spirited youth.

The Gregories of Hackwood, The Crime of Andrew Blair, and *John Carper* are restricted in background to Virginia, the first two to the society of the lower Shenandoah Valley before 1850, the third to frontier Virginia during the Revolution. Since in most respects they seem superior to *The Two Country Houses,* they have been selected to represent the longer fictional tales.

As is true of his verse, the merits of Cooke's fiction will be obscured for the reader who tries to judge it by criteria that do not apply. Cooke was writing his stories while Henry James was still in, or fresh from, the cradle. Most of the significant novels published in English since 1900 probably would seem to him as odd in structure and perhaps in other respects as his tales would seem naive to the reader whose literary horizon is bounded by the turn of the century. This is not to imply that they are free of blemish. Even when judged by the lax standards of the tradition to which they belong, the tradition perhaps best exampled in the English language by the novels of Scott and of the Cooper of the Leatherstocking Tales—the tradition followed at some distance by John Pendleton Kennedy and William Gilmore Simms— the observer will discover flaws which a more practised hand would have corrected. Cooke had a flair for using literary allusions, and he indulged it too liberally. Like most novelists from Richardson to Dickens and beyond, he liked to halt narrative movement in order to chat with his readers; and some pauses are perhaps too awkward. On the other hand, an occasional passage of summarized action suggests impatience to get along with the story. Other points may attract the eye of an exacting critic.

Blemishes, however, though they mar the performance of an author, do not necessarily outweigh its merits. Cooke's portrayals of characters are graphic, fresh, and occasionally illuminated by a play of wit more than a little suggesting that he had read with profit Jane Austen. His dialogue seems appropriate to character and situation. His plots, though simple and concerned largely with external action—nothing in the work of Cooke implies that he had been importantly influenced by the examples either of Hawthorne, whom he nowhere mentions, or of Poe, whom he praised—usually move along briskly without employment of incidents that take unfair advantage of the reader's suspension of disbelief. His style has the commendable qualities noted in discussion of his mature verse and essays: clarity, economy, fluency, vigor, liveliness, informality of tone. Moreover, along with his talent for choosing the vividly image-making detail, Cooke possessed to appreciable degree a gift superbly manifested in the novels of Dickens and Conrad: the power to create the illusion that before eye and ear of the spectator moved flesh-and-blood beings engaged in an engrossing drama.

The fact that Western Virginia provided setting and content for the four completed long tales may, but should not, suggest that Cooke was parochial in outlook or interested mainly in manners of the gentry or in local color. Nor should absence in the tales of specific evidence of concern with the great issues of the day, or with the "isms" flourishing north of the Potomac during the Fabulous Forties, although from his reading if not otherwise Cooke certainly was aware of them. By predilection and endowment a composer of romances in the primary sense of the term, he had found in a familiar locale and society materials suitable for imaginative treatment; and he used them. That his interest as artist could transcend not only Virginia but America, the short fictions and the unfinished historical romance attest.

But if the four tales suggest an artist's disengagement from matters beyond Virginia, Cooke was not indifferent to what was happening nearby. He knew and regretted that many of the older families, impoverished by chronic agricultural depression and a too carefree and lavish mode of life, were yielding in place and power to a different breed. The two older Herries, mother and son, in *The Crime of Andrew Blair* might with reason be thought of as prototypes of the Snopes in Faulkner's Yoknapatawpha County. Nor was Cooke blind, as Hubbell remarked in *The South in American Literature*, to "the strain of violence in American life which has figured so conspicuously in American fiction." This awareness of the real world, within and beyond Virginia, qualified the point of view from which character and behavior were conceived. It did not, fortunately, inhibit Cooke's talent for telling absorbing tales.

That his latest, and longest, tale was to be no less exciting, the opening paragraph must serve to suggest:

Merlin Brand, a Norwegian, entered the service of Charles the twelfth of Sweden a short time before the battle of Pultowa, and remained with his royal master quite to the end of the mad comedy of Bender. He saw the czar Peter, he came in contact with the rival Kings of Poland, he traversed the parched plains between the Boristhenes and Otzacow with Mazeppa the Hetman, he witnessed the state of three viziers, and the muster of Turkish armies on the beautiful levels of Adrianople, he was brought into daily intercourse with brave and distinguished gentlemen of many countries, he was much about the person of the king his master and read the nature of that most remarkable of the monarchs of the time closely: some chapters of his life, therefore, cannot fail to interest the reader, if they are written with even a small degree of skill. Apart from these adjuncts of a higher and more widely interesting character, his private adventures were not wanting in romantic incident. With so much of prologue, I begin my narrative of some passages in the life of the Chevalier Merlin.

How it would have ranked had Cooke lived to finish *The Chevalier Merlin* must be no more than matter of speculation. Completed chapters give evidence, however, that in turning to the past and an alien setting, his talent as raconteur had in no degree declined.

Asterisks indicate notes by Cooke. With few exceptions, spellings and marks of punctuation are also his—or perhaps a printer's interpretation of what the author intended.

John Carper, the Hunter of Lost River

There are many smaller valleys lying beyond the mountains which make the western limit of the great valley of Virginia. For instance, in the counties of Berkeley and Morgan, are Back creek, Sleepy creek, and Cacapon valleys, not to speak of many still smaller, which channelled by mere rivulets, narrow in places into glens, sometimes indeed into ravines. This alternation of mountain and vale extends along the western side of the great valley, very generally, from the northern to the southern line of Virginia.

One of the prettiest, and most fertile, of these subordinate valleys is that of Lost River. It commences near Brock's gap in the county of Shenandoah, extends twenty-five miles in a northern direction, and terminates at the foot of Sandy ridge, under which the river disappears, to rise again, three miles farther on, as the head-spring of the Cacapon. The name "Lost River" suggests the idea of a great chasm, and of the plunge and mysterious disappearance of a turbulent stream into it. We are apt to imagine something like the strange picture which Coleridge has given us in Kubla Khan:

"And from this chasm, with ceaseless turmoil seething,
As if this earth in fast thick pants were breathing,
A mighty fountain momently was forced:
Amid whose swift half-intermitted burst
Huge fragments vaulted like rebounding hail,
Or chaffy grain beneath the thresher's flail:
And 'mid these dancing rocks at once and ever
It flung up momently the sacred river.
Five miles meandering with a mazy motion,
Through wood and dale the sacred river ran,
Then reached the caverns measureless to man
And sank in tumult to a lifeless ocean."

Whoever imagines anything so grand of Lost River, will find the reality very disappointing. It has indeed its spring-head, course, and termination all amongst mountains, like the "sacred river Alph," but there is no "seething," and there are no "caverns measureless to man." An inconsiderable stream rising quietly, running in no remarkable manner, and sneaking away, at last, through a number of little holes in the ground, with a noise no louder than a gurgle—this is all that Lost River really is. I need scarcely say, after this, that the historian of the valley, my old friend Mr. Kerchival—a rare lover of traditions, and as earnest an itinerant as ever hunted out natural curiosities—is a little hyperbolical in calling Lost River "a stupendous evidence of the all-powerful arm of God."

On an instep, if I may so speak, of the mountains, west of Lost River, and within a few hundred yards of it, lived in the year 1781 a substantial Quaker named Joshua Blake. His house was a log cabin of one story, divided into two large rooms by a great central stone chimney. The roof was of clap-boards, held in their places by poles pinned across them. A long porch fronted the river. In this porch, hanging from pegs driven into the hewn logs of the cabin, were generally ranged the Quaker's saddle, the side-saddle of his niece, Nelly Blake, sets of plough or wagon harness, linsey hunting-frocks, and other minor articles of house-wifery, or farm-thrift. Here, too, Nelly Blake's spinning wheel had its permanent summer-place. A few young and vigorous apple and other fruit trees flanked the house. A wide meadow lay in front, between the foot of the hill and the tree-skirted river; and on the line between hill and low-ground, just within the yard enclosure, was a range of bee-gums, whose busy occupants, at the date of my story, were in full enjoyment of the apple-blooms. In the rear of his rude, but comfortable dwelling-house, Joshua had expended his entire stock of taste in the erection of a barn, with high blank gables, painted into a perfect blaze of Dutch red.

It was late in April, 1781, that Nelly Blake, the little Quakeress, worked at her spinning-wheel on the porch, in the sunshine of a very pleasant morning. Whilst she worked away, intent only, as it seemed, upon her thread and the fitting of the coil to the spindle, a young countryman, dressed in homespun, came to the bannister at her back, and leaning an arm on it whilst the other held a rifle in its curve, looked at her for some minutes without letting his presence be known. A tall, brindled dog, with a sharp nose and feathered tail, stood at his heels, as motionless as if he had the cue to be quiet. Forward passed the Quakeress with a spring of the instep, and a bend of her pretty neck; back she came, her little feet fairly twinkling as ankle passed ankle, her bust expanded, and her dimpled chin thrown up; whilst the surly wheel, shifting from a dismal groan to a furious roar, accompanied with such variations her coming and going. In the midst of this din which her industry made, she heard her name called. The wheel stopped with a clatter of the check-stick upon its spokes, and Nelly, assuming a prim look, turned to face the young countryman.

"Is it thee, John?"

"I have some doubts as to that, Nelly."

"As to what, John?"

"As to whether or no I am John Carper."

"Thee is in a gay humor this morning, John."

"No, Nelly, only out of my head with thinking of you. But listen to me for a little while. I left Broad-brim salting his cattle in the hills, and came down to have a word or two with you. This is what I have to say; I love you, and you love me—"

"Thee is not overstocked with modesty to say as much as that."

"Come, Nelly: you know that I am only speaking the truth. It is not so long since you gave me to understand that you did love me; to be sure you did not say so, which, as an honest girl, I think you might do without doing any harm—but you did enough, and I kissed you, which made it a bargain. Now Nell, I am as grave as the lean parson at Morefield; so put off that pretty bantering humor, and hear me like a true-hearted girl as you are. I have tried to live without you, but I find it isn't possible. Old Broad-brim has three hundred pounds of yours which he must give up when you are married, or come of age. Now he puts himself between you and me, and gives me the cold shoulder, because if we are married, the law will make him give up the money. You are hardly eighteen; three years are an age to wait; besides, something may happen to keep us from ever getting married. Now, Nelly, let Broad-brim have the three hundred pounds, and let me have you—or you have me—it is the same thing. I will work for you, and we will never miss the money. It would buy cattle to bring money in again, but I and Sharpnose here can find you venison enough, and keep the wolves from the sheep, and you can spin the wool, and sing at your spinning. How I should like to hear you singing in my cabin, Nelly!" The speaker had by this time left his position outside of the porch, and stood very near the Quakeress. "Nelly—dear Nelly," he said in a coaxing tone, as he took her hand, "do say yes—give up the money to Broad-brim, and be my wife at once: be my dear little wife. I will take such good care of you, and love you so much."

"John Carper," said the girl, become now quite grave, "thee knows very well that there is love between us. If uncle Blake will take the money, and thee will take me without it—here is my hand. But John, uncle Blake will hardly do so wicked a thing. He will be ashamed to rob the child of his brother. He will be ashamed to take the money; and not generous enough to give it up before the end of the three years. I am afraid that thee will have to wait for me. Is that so hard to do John?"

"Hard? yes, Nelly, impossible. If you love me, and Blake is such an old hunks as to refuse the offer to take the money, and give you up, run away with me. We can ride in a night to Morefield—be married—come back—beg Broad-brim's pardon—go to house-keeping, and be as happy as the bees here in the apple blossoms. Say the word, Nell, or if you mean yes, but can't say it for smothering the crying fit that makes your eyes look away from me, turn your mouth a little, and let me kiss you."

"It is a grave word, John, to speak between a kiss and a cry. Thee must not be so swift and peremptory with me. My duty is not clearly before me. The thread is tangled. Give me a little time, John. We can speak of this when thee has sounded uncle Blake upon the matter of giving up the money. Thee must leave me now."

After some farther speech, and a kiss, John Carper called to his dog Sharpnose, who had gone off on a foraging expedition amongst the outhouses, shouldered his rifle, and was about to depart. Nelly, however, called him back.

"John," she said in a low tone, "I have my troubles to-day; and thee seems to me to be a fitting person to communicate them to."

"Speak out, Nelly."

"Thee remembers the Indian boy, Girty?"

"To be sure. I remember all about him, from the time that drunken scoundrel, old Girty, brought him in and bound him prentice to Blake, to the time Broad-brim gave him a beating and drove him off. Old Girty was the arrantest white rascal west of the mountains, and the boy's mother was a squaw; so that, if young leather-face didn't deserve the beating, there is nothing in blood."

"He did deserve the beating, John. But does thee not know the cause of it? The boy showed me disrespect."

"How? I never heard of that."

"He asked me to be his squaw, John," said Nelly with a laugh and a blush.

"The infernal copper-skin—the leather-faced rascal! Why didn't you tell me all about it, before he ran away? By the—"

"Thee should not swear, John, and there is no use to be so savage. But this is what I have to say: I think young Girty has come back, and is hiding in the neighborhood."

Carper pricked up his ears, as did his dog Sharpnose. The dog had shown a singular attention at the calling of the Indian boy's name.

"Why I think that the lad is here," continued Nelly, "is this: I went this morning to the sycamore spring, to fill uncle Blake's pitcher; I saw, in the mud the print of a moccasin."

"But I wear moccasins myself, Nelly, and was at the spring yesterday."

Nelly looked down at her hunter's feet and laughed. "Thee has a larger foot, John—as well befits so strong and large a person. Besides thee has not the skill to make moccasins like the slim-fingered lad. There is the difference between the track of Girty and such as thee would make, that there is between the tracks of a buck and an ox."

"Hum!" grunted John, not much pleased with the illustration.

"But this is not all," continued Nelly; "I picked up this knife at the spring." Here she pulled a knife from the pocket of her dimity apron. "I knew it at once as Girty's knife. He bought it of the pedlar when he came on his rounds, last fall, a little before uncle Blake drove the lad away. What advice, John, does thee give in these matters?"

"My advice, Nelly, is that you keep in-doors, unless it is pleasant to have the lad asking you to be his squaw. I can't see any danger of worse. The Indians have not come in on us for ten years; since the peace was made with chiefs. They are killing and stealing on the Ohio again, but it is a long way from there here. Smith, the surveyor, is to be at my cabin to day; but I will take Sharpnose to-morrow, and scout in the hills until I learn something of the lad."

"There is another matter, John," said the Quakeress, but then paused, and seemed to consider very busily for a minute.

"Speak it out, Nelly, like an honest girl."

"Does thee know anything of the movements up the river? Uncle Blake is riding to William Mace's, and elsewhere, in a very unusual manner. I heard him tell William Mace, who was here last night, that the young men must fight it out here, if they were interrupted, but that the movements ought to be very quiet, and the companies ought to get down over the Blue Ridge, and join the *true men* in some county there; that Cornwallis was in those parts. William Mace laughed and called uncle Blake the 'fighting Quaker,' but uncle said that it was for putting down arms that arms were taken up, and besides, that he had no idea of fighting himself. What is the meaning of it all, John?"

John Carper laughed. "For a knowing man, I must say that Broadbrim is working into a considerable difficulty. You remember the twelve Philadelphia Quakers that Congress sent to Winchester, because they were so hot in preaching against our fighting,* that at last it looked as if they were ready to fight us for fighting?"

"Yes," said Nelly. "Uncle Blake took me with him to Winchester, whilst they were there. Thee should have seen the respectable persons. John Pemberton was a grave, great-looking, elderly man. There was a Master Swift, a dancing master, came on with them, whom they admonished sharply for teaching the people frivolous things. Master Swift was dressed in pink and blue, and was a very light, frolicksome person."

"You were something of a little minx then, Nelly, and no doubt admired the dancing man very much. But it would have been much better if your uncle Broad-brim had put his slim shanks under the fiddle of Master Swift, instead of slipping his crafty head into John Pemberton's noose. He has been an evil wisher to the country ever since, and now, Quaker as he is, there is no man doing more than he does to stir up a tory insurrection."

Nelly Blake looked greatly surprised, and then infinitely distressed. The word *tory* had in that day, and indeed retains to this, a horror of its own as a mere word, apart from the horrors of the bloody civil

---

* Some of our politicians, when measures go against them, are as ready with their "protests" as notaries public. But the most extraordinary case of protesting on record is furnished in the conduct of Mr. Fisher, one of these arrested Quakers. "Among the prisoners were three of the Pembertons, two of the Fishers, an old Quaker preacher named Hunt, and several others, amounting in all to twelve, and with the druggist and dancing master, fourteen. One of the Fishers was a lawyer by profession. He *protested* in his own name, and on behalf of his fellow prisoners, against being taken into custody by Col. Smith; stated that they had *protested* against being sent from Philadelphia; that they had again *protested* at the Pennsylvania line against being sent out of the State; had repeated their *protest* at the Maryland line against being taken into Virginia, etc., etc." Kerchival's History of the Valley, p. 191. It was a natural remark of one of the Pembertons— "Friend Fisher, thy protests are unavailing; thee should dispense with them." The stout-hearted Quaker, requiring to be lifted over state lines, and, clamoring out his protests, would make a good comic picture.

strife of which it was a type. An intense popular feeling will consecrate or desecrate words, until, from sounds, they become *things*—saving or fatal things, as the case may be.

"And is uncle Blake a tory, John?" said Nelly, with a pale face and unsteady eye.

"A sort of half-tory, Nellie; because he is principled against fighting with his own hands—which may mean that he is principled against being shot at. But he is doing his best to make full tories, and is likely to get himself into trouble. General Morgan is at home, down below Winchester, and there can be no rising here that he could not put down with a pile of stones * at a cross-roads. At any rate the crack of his rifles would clear Lost River."

"What would thee advise me to do in this, as in the rest, John?"

"To attend to your spinning, Nelly, until the day comes for running away with me."

CHAPTER II

John Carper gained his cabin, found Smith, the surveyor, there, spent the day in running the lines of his farm, to set at rest a dispute which had arisen with a neighboring land-holder, slept from dark to dawn in so hearty and sound a manner as to cast some doubt on the reality of that unhappiness which he had pleaded in his suit to his Quakeress, and by sunrise was well-advanced on his way back to the house of Joshua Blake. Sharpnose followed the long swinging walk of his master at a brisk trot, and was evidently greatly disturbed by something. Carper saw, without much observing, the whimsical passion of his dog; he was very intent on a speech which he intended to make to the Quaker. "First," said he to himself, "I must drop the Broad-brim and call him Mr. Blake; we must not set the old man horns foremost. Then I must smooth down that matter of the money. It would be barefaced knavery to take Nelly's portion just so. Blake is not a downright rascal—only too close to be always fair. I must propose a

---

* General Morgan fought a great many battles after the Revolution with these homely weapons. "Peace hath her victories," etc. Battletown, a village within a few miles of this spot, acquired its name from Morgan's street-fights in it. He would take post at a central spot, with a pile of stones at his feet, and throw them with such effect as to put all hostile comers to rout. His residence, to which John Carper alludes, was Saratoga, six miles south of Battletown—at present the seat of Mr. N. Burwell, senr.

loan of the money to him, without interest or security—something of that sort. What's the matter, Sharpnose?"

The hunter and his dog had approached within sight of Blake's house. No smoke issued from the pyramid of a chimney. There seemed to be no movement about the barn or stables. Joshua Blake was striding up and down on the long porch, his coat tails straightened by the rapidity of his motion. Sharpnose bristled, crept in front of his master, nosed the ground eagerly, gave a low whine, and looked up into his face.

"What are you telling me, dog?" said Carper, beginning to feel an alarm for which he could not account. The dog, in answer, moved away rapidly toward a gorge in the western mountain, evidently carrying a scent breast high. Carper called him in and hurried to the house. Joshua Blake gave him no time for the first question.

"Thee is slow, John Carper—slow. Does thee know the truth? Fire off thy gun, and raise the country."

"What's in the wind, Broad-brim?—Mr. Blake, I mean."

"The Indians have stolen away Nelly—killed old Abel in his loft— carried off the boy Tobe—killed my six fat beeves in the cattle pen—robbed my chest—ruined me. Fire thy gun, John Carper, and raise the country."

The Quaker's speech told the truth, which Carper was slow to comprehend in its full force.

"Where have you been all night, Mr. Blake?"

"Up at Mace's. But why does thee stay to question? Fire thy gun."

Carper roused himself, and rapidly, but with extraordinary calmness, made an examination of the premises. Nelly was gone. Her little closet, boarded off in a corner of one of the two great rooms, like a college dormitory, was empty, and stripped of its few articles of ornament. Abel, an old working man, crippled with rheumatism, and bed-ridden, was certainly dead, and lay horribly mutilated and scalped, upon the floor of his loft, in an outhouse. Tobe, his grandson, was missing. An oaken chest had been dragged from under Joshua Blake's bed, forced open, and rifled of its contents—amongst the rest, Joshua said, of a bag of dollars. The wooden trenchers, and other utensils of the kitchen had been broken and tossed about. The servant girl, to whose province they belonged, had fortunately gone, the evening before, to spend the night with her mother, on the other side of the river. Her brother, a half-witted lad, who had been in the house, and present throughout the visit of the Indians, had been spared, probably from the superstitious reverence, common amongst the tribes, for such unfortunates. He now sat in the kitchen, upon a wicker-chair, mending the broken trenchers and wooden bowls, with an awl and shoe-maker's thread. Carper gained no information from him, except that Girty was one of the party, that there were many others, and that Nelly and the boy Tobe were trudged off loaded with bundles. He examined the cattle pen. Six large beeves, culled from Joshua's herd, and penned and housed for grain fattening, were killed; pieces of flesh were cut from them, and from some singular whim many of the colored spots had been carefully cut out from the skins, and carried off. The matted frontal skin and horns of one of the largest of the oxen had also been removed. The horses, except the Quaker's dun gelding, which he had ridden to Mace's, had been at pasture over the river, and were still visible, feeding quietly, knee-deep in the plentiful grass of the flats.

"Joshua Blake," said Carper, after making rapid but full examination of the premises, "I am about to set off after Nelly. You can raise the country and follow on. But before I go, one thing must be settled. If I bring her back, I must have her for my wife."

"Thee may surely have her, John, and an old man's blessing if thee bring the child back. But, John, whilst thee is up and doing, thee will do well to get back also the bag of silver dollars. Thee shall have a just portion for compensation of thy trouble."

"D—n the dollars," exclaimed Carper rather irreverently; "this mixing up of your money bags with poor Nelly is not decent, and it makes me bold to ask for a word from under your pen giving her to me for my wife if I bring her back."

Blake assented to this, declaring, however, its unimportance, and suggesting to Carper that his suspicions lost him time and a mile of his journey.

"I will make it up with my legs," said the hunter, bringing a bit of dingy paper which he had torn from a blank book, and an ink horn from the adjoining room. "Whilst I am writing down the pot-hooks, do you cut me off ten pounds of jerked beef in strips of a pound, as near as you can come to it. I filled my powder horn last night, and put four dozen bullets in my pouch. The beef will make me ready."

Whilst the Quaker went to procure the beef, Carper cast about writing an agreement as to Nelly's hand.

"Every thing of this sort," said he, "should begin with 'in the name of God, amen'—no, that begins a will. This should begin with a 'whereas' I think," and he wrote—realizing the prodigious difference, to men like himself, between talking and writing.

"Whereas, Joshua Blake and John Carper are wishing to get back my dear Ellen Blake from the felonious Indians, in whose blood-thirsty hands she is fallen, and whereas John Carper mistrusts in my mind, the said Joshua Blake of a promise he has made of Nelly to me for a wife, if I bring her back; now the said Joshua Blake binds himself and his heirs to said John Carper, to give my dear Nelly Blake to said John Carper for a wife."

Carper mused over this production, which he wrote in a large, awkward hand, and for the punctuation of which he is indebted to his historian, for some moments as if not altogether satisfied with it. His countenance, however, presently became assured.

"There is a mixing up," he critically communed with himself, "somehow of *John Carper* and *me*, and me and *John Carper* that makes it a little clumsy, but the meaning is pretty straight, and when Broad-brim signs it, all will be right enough."

Blake presently brought the beef, and after formally reciting the paper, signed it. Carper stowed the provision about his person, pinched the agreement into the corner of a pocket, enjoined on the Quaker, whom his own steadiness had almost restored to a clear state of mind, to collect the neighbors without losing an hour, and put them on the way to the head waters of the Youheganey, shouldered his rifle, gave Sharpnose a sign to go before, and struck for the mountain.

CHAPTER III

The character of my hero has been gathered perhaps, by the reader, from his own lips in the preceding chapters. He was a brave, true-hearted, intelligent man, with much earnestness and simplicity of nature. In physical qualities he was a noble specimen of the best class of frontiersmen. He stood six feet two inches in his moccasins, was "as strong as a bear, and as long-winded as a wolf"—or, if not quite all this, yet near enough to it to give a color of justification to the rhodomon-tade of the hunters, his companions, who were in the habit of saying so much of him. It is very certain that a better man for the work before him—a more gallant, patient, trust-worthy hunter—never set heart and foot upon an Indian trail.

The mouth of the mountain hollow, which the dog, Sharpnose, had shown so strong a disposition to enter, on the approach to Blake's house, was near at hand, and Carper made directly for it. The country through which his travel was immediately to lead him, is broken up into a puzzle of ridges, knobs, spurs and gaps. Lost River mountain, Timber Ridge, and Sandy Ridge, now run together, now separate, now lower their crests in quite a bland and pacific manner, now rear and recoil in oppugnation, until to an ordinary eye all seems an incomprehensible confusion of sandstone, pine and laurel. But this country rugged, wild, and intractable as it is, has its passes, and even its strips of smooth meadow watered by the flow of clear mountain springs, and John Carper knew every foot of it.

Of these passes, the outlet of a chief one, into which many of the others converged, was near the Quaker's house. Into this, and rapidly up it, Carper took his way. He did not hesitate for a moment, but with his rifle on his shoulder, and his dog trotting before him with nose lowered, moved on at a speed which would have outstripped the ordinary gait of Joshua Blake's dun gelding. If he cast his eyes to the stony path under his feet, it was rather to assure his footing than to look for signs, which he well knew no eye could detect on such a way. It was evident that here, in these first stages of his undertaking, he relied solely on his dog.

This was especially apparent on his approach to a spot where the ravine forked. From this point a pass led away south of west, and was walled in by mountains until it opened, after a tortuous course, into the smoother country which edges the valley of the South Branch of the Potomac. If the Indians had taken this left hand pass, they would probably cross the South Branch above Morefield. The other pass, starting from the point of divergence, was most direct of the two, and led into the valley beyond in a course very little north of west. But there was a distance of many miles between the western outlets of the passes, occasioned by the southward inclination of the one on the left; and the after course of the Indians depended greatly upon the selection of courses made at the fork.

Carper held back and left his dog to make a choice for him. Sharp-nose, after going a little way up each hollow, wagged his tail, looked to his master, and resumed his trot up the northern one. The hunter turned to the right, and resumed his long swinging walk as if entirely satisfied with the dog's decision. His path soon became exceedingly rough; the sagacity of the deer, who had principally made it, led them across knolls to avoid curves of the ravine, and these knolls were heaps of sharp sand-stones, with scarcely soil enough to nourish a dog-wood or laurel. Here and there on these knolls, a pine thrown headlong by the winds, from the higher mountain side, lay in the way with its brush and turned the sharp stony path down some steep and critical surface.

In the bottom of the hollow itself, Carper's road was often a mere succession of stepping-stones with pits, worn by flowing water, between them. Altogether this most direct course to the valley of the South Branch was wholly impassable to horsemen. To the true hunter, who now trod it, the way was as easy as a shorn meadow in summer, and he held upon it with uniform speed. It was, however, several hours before he emerged from the mountains, and found himself upon a range of broad hilly barrens, covered with crab grass, and looking very much like deserted fields. Sharpnose had followed the trail of the Indians through the confined passes, into which the sun at that early hour only half penetrated, but lost it on these breezy hills.

Carper surveyed the country before him with a quick eye. Three or four hundred yards below, a little brook drew its line of running briars and thorn-bushes, in a zig-zag, about the foot of the up-grounds. "The trail will show there," he said to himself. "Nose up, dog—no time to be lost"—and bearing to the right, he hurried to the brook, reached it, turned to the left, and traced it upward.

He presently came to a deer path deeply worn into the banks, and here, to his great satisfaction, found numerous foot-marks. No care had been taken to conceal them. There were many moccasin prints, and in one place the toe-marks of a naked foot—doubtless that of the boy Tobe. Amongst the rest were shoe-prints. Carper recognized, in the small straight track, with the deep indentation made by the high narrow heel, the foot-mark of his dear Quakeress, and for a moment there was a blinding moisture in his eyes, and an uncertain motion of the hand that traced the dainty outline.

It was not the slight pressure of a kid slipper that gave token of Nelly Blake's recent presence, but a sharp-cut print with quite a filigree of small indentations near the edges, and around the curve of the heel, made by the tacks of an honest mountain shoe. It was well shaped, however, both slim and small, and did not belie the country-side opinion which gave the poor girl credit for possessing the prettiest foot in the Lost River settlements. There was little in the marks to show how long they had been made, but Carper, on close inspection found in one of them farthest from the water some beads of white frost.

"On, Sharpnose," he said, clearing the brook at a bound, "the tracks were made before day-break. We are seven long hours behind." On the low spotty ground beyond the brook, Sharpnose justified his name, and carried the trail with the certainty, but none of the clamor, of a fox-hound.

A little farther on began the alluvial bottom lands, and here abundant signs were to be readily caught by the untiring hunter. The passage of the Indians had left a visible enough wake in the high weeds which this soil, as fertile as any in the world, throws up like a thicket of canes. After breaking through this rank growth, Carper came upon the bank of the South Branch. Here he assured himself that all, at least, of the Indian party had not directly forded the river. Some tracks, the boy Tobe's amongst them, led directly to the water's edge, but there were others which turned to the right, and kept the bank. Sharpnose, after following the first tracks until they were lost in the water, came back and took the bank trail. Nelly's shoes had left no mark to show which course she had been made to take.

"They have lifted her into their arms," thought Carper, "and as she is rather too plump to be carried where there is no occasion for it, they have, no doubt, taken her up to carry her across the Branch. It is a civility of Girty's—very obliging in him!" Calling his dog from the trail along the bank, he at once entered the river. The stream he found languid and shallow, and with some difficulty in dragging through the mud on the other side, he shortly gained firm footing on the opposite bank.

Here it seemed that a first attempt had been made by the Indians to hide their trail. No foot-marks were visible in the muddy bank which the hunter had gained, but in looking up and down stream, he saw about two hundred yards above him, a flat rock which shelved into the water. The shore everywhere else within view was of soft and yielding soil, without turf, and indeed without vegetation of any kind except a few clumps of papaws. His woodcraft led him at once to this rock, and he presently detected some blotches, such as might be made by feet covered with wet buckskin, upon its surface. The sun, by this time nearing noon, had dried these away to a faint dull stain, but to Carper's quick eye, they were distinct enough.

From this rock the onward path was matter of more uncertainty than altogether suited his hasty humor. Sharpnose could make nothing of so old a trail in so sunny an exposure, and the hunter was thrown entirely upon his own resources. The Indians had not followed the bank either up stream or down. There were no signs in the papaw leaves and mud deposit, which would have retained foot-marks as distinctly as soft potter's clay. Directly from the rock, which quite cut in two this low muddy shelf of shore, a mountain rose very abruptly, with a face of grey sandstone, dotted with starved shrubs. Carper's eye scanned this rough ridge, and he saw, and recognized on its top half a mile off, southward, a spot where, sunk between two rocky knobs looking like cupolas, a patch of tall pines rested like the shadow of a cloud.

Large pines springing in this way on the spine of a mountain, generally denote a depression, for it is by the accumulation of soil from higher surrounding points that such islands of great timber are nourished and grown. Between these knobs, at this patch of pines, was in fact so considerable a depression as to have gained the name of gap—without being at all, however, the easy pass which a heavy-footed lowlander would imagine from the name. Unless the Indians had chosen to climb the rugged steep of a mountain several hundred feet high—dragging their female captive with them—they must have passed the ridge at this gap. There was, to be sure, a lower pass four or five miles down the river, but it was too distant to enter into the calculation of persons striking the mountain at the shelving rock.

Carper mounted the hill-side some thirty feet and soon put on a look of satisfaction. The grey sand-stones on the warmer slopes of our mountains, if not covered with the long beard-like moss of the cold northern exposures, have yet a vegetable covering of their own, a sort of coating of flat circular scales looking like the impressions of miniature river shells. The hunter found several of these stones lying with the side marked in this manner downward, and some faint remains of moisture, or rather of the dark color which moisture gives to stone on the upturned surfaces. A little farther on, also, he found the switches of a shrub compressed together, and bent, as if they had been seized and dragged through the hand of a person sustaining himself by them in falling.

Satisfied with these signs, which tended in the direction of the high pine-marked gap, he descended to the river bank, where the ground permitted swifter travelling, and hurried on up stream. In a short time he drew near the pines. On the nearer edge of them a wild gobler with splendid plumage was strutting in a circle about a clump of dogwoods, in amongst which two or three of his meek and shabbier looking wives were patiently scratching for their food. Sharpnose bounced in among the wild family and drove them clucking into the pines. He made several joyous efforts to storm their perches, and might under other circumstances have changed his obstreperous attempts into a blockade; but his master presently brought him to his graver duties, and after a little perplexed nosing and snuffling of the mingled scents, all lying well in so shady a spot, he found the human trail.

The hunter's first anxiety now was to ascertain if Nelly Blake was with this division of the Indian party. Getting upon his hands and knees, and prying amongst the tassels with which the dark boughs above him had covered the ground—prunings of their mountain wings—he searched long and earnestly. Near a log which the trail had crossed, and a little to one side of the confused marks of the party, the eyes of the hunter, brought to within a few inches of the ground distinguished a slightly curved line in the mat of pine leaves. It was indistinct, but it was so because the pressure had not been great enough to stamp deeply, and destroy the elasticity of the leaves, not because the outline of the substance making it had been blunt or yielding. Some of the pine tassels, in the line, had been cut in two; so Carper assured himself by ascertaining that they were too damp to break.

"It was Nelly's shoe," he said to himself as he rose; "she sprung from that foot in crossing the log, and had the heel up when the sole cut the line. Thank God her little instep had a spring left in it." He examined the opposite side of the log, but here he found that the wild turkeys had been before him, and had scratched away all signs. Satisfied, however, with what he had seen, he resumed his journey. Following the course which the shape of the mountain compelled, or at least made most easy, and which his dog went readily upon before him, he descended into an irregular valley. The trail, which with the aid of Sharpnose, he had been able to keep easily, led through this valley, and beyond it over a broken country, and at sunset he found himself between the headwaters of Looney's and Patterson's creeks, and near the base of the main or central chain of the Alleghaneys.

With the setting of the sun, the moon began to shine out low down in the western quarter of the heavens. Carper extended his journey several hours into the night, making poor speed however; and when the moon disappeared behind the dark mountain line before him, broke his fast, drank water from a little noisy brook, stretched himself upon a bed of leaves, and with Sharpnose, with whom he had shared his supper, for sentinel, slept the sleep of a way-worn man who puts his cares away from him.

CHAPTER IV

The dawn of the following day found Carper up, and preparing to resume his journey. He again ate of his jerked beef, denying a share of it now to his dog, whose powers of nose it was necessary that he should carefully preserve, drank of the brook, and continued upon his way. A mile from the spot where he had slept, he came upon a place a good deal trampled, and showing here and there the tracks of horses. A little examination showed him that two horsemen, and several men on foot had come in from the north and joined the party, whose course he had followed, at this point. Carper at once guessed the truth. The Indians, too wary to extend their depredations in the Lost River valley, had begun to grow bolder as they drew nearer to the Alleghaney wilderness—a region even at the present day as wild as the highlands of Oregon—and a part of their number had diverged down the South Branch, and fallen upon the settlements in the direction of Romney. The nearest settlement was Jacob Vanslaken's, and Carper conjectured that the homestead of this sturdy Dutchman had been the point of attack, and the scene of recent bloodshed and robbery. He had no close friendship with any of Jacob's household, and his own anxieties were clinging enough, but he gave a stern gesture of hand and head, as his imagination rapidly drew the scenes of this probable tragedy: a husband slain on his hearthstone—a wife carried away captive—their little children brained against the cabin lintels. These were imaginations to sharpen the edge of his war-knife. But he found matter of hope too in the midst of his conjectures of these things. The new outrages would muster the hunters of the South Branch and swell the pursuit.

"I trust in God," he said, "that in robbing Vanslaken's house, they have set fire to it, and made it blaze as high as the mountains, for news, and a brag, to the valley men. With myself nosing close on the trail, and the South Branch rifles coming on after me, and the Lost River party heading in at the Youheganey Springs, Nelly has too good a chance for a reasonable man to fall in his spirits about her."

With such reflections he kept upon his way. Following a wide and hoofmarked trail, he shortly came to a spring whose swampy ooze had killed the vegetation for some space around it. Near this spring there seemed to have been some delay and trouble on the part of the Indians; bushes were broken, and the ground was deeply dented by horse-hoofs. Whilst the hunter examined these unusual marks, his dog suddenly fixed his attention. A short distance down the ooze of the spring, at a spot where the fine thread of running water issuing from it, gained firmer ground and was arrested in a small basin, Sharpnose stood with his nose fixed to the earth. His hair was bristled along his back, and he gave alternately a sharp bark and a long melancholy howl.

On reaching this spot, Carper found blood, and what he took to be the impress of a man's body stretched at length upon the ground. There were marks, too, which the intelligent hunter was not slow to conjecture had been made by a wounded man struggling up, and dragging himself away from a spot where he had, for some time, been lying.

Along the course of these signs were a few scattered grains of parched corn.

Sharpnose presently left the blood, and went cautiously trailing down the stream. Carper followed him, finding the forest growth more open as he advanced. He had left the spring a few hundred yards behind him, when a rifle cracked from the top of a fallen pine tree a little before him, and a bullet whistled past his head. The "spit" of flame and fine wreath of smoke caught his eye in the incomplete light of the morning, and he was about to fire in return, when Sharpnose dashed into the pine top. In a moment the head and shoulders of an Indian appeared. The dog had fastened upon him, and he struggled to use his tomahawk. As quick as thought the white hunter fired at the Indian's breast, and the struggle of man and dog ceased.

Presently the dog came out from the pine. Carper, who had taken shelter behind the nearest tree and reloaded, advanced, and breaking away some of the boughs, drew the body of his enemy from its hiding place, and placed it upon the leaves of the open forest. The body was that of a powerful Indian, long-limbed, sinewy, and full-chested. The rifle ball had entered the centre of the breast, and passed out at the back, a little on one side of the spine. But in addition to this wound, was a very singular one upon the head which had discharged the blood very frightfully over the face. Carper was examining this wound, when the Indian opened his eyes, half raised his right hand as if attempting to make a gesture of peace, and spoke feebly.

"How do you do, broder?"

"Thank you," replied the single-minded hunter, "pretty well."

The Indian caught his hand from the wound upon which it was resting, and looked him wistfully in the face.

"I guess what you mean," said Carper, "but I am not feeling for your scalp-lock. What made the hurt on your head?"

The Indian endeavored to answer, but from his weakness, or his small stock of English, or both, Carper caught no sound nearer to an intelligible reply than "devil-horse." This he construed to mean that the man had been in some way hurt by a stolen horse. His mind ran on for a few moments in the train of this conjecture. "Ah!" he said to himself, "if the rascals have carried off Vanslakens' black stallion, he will give them the devil—sure enough." This horse was widely known as a fierce and vicious brute. Carper dropped the conjecture, however, and endeavored to gain from the Indian some knowledge of the movements of his party.

"Tell me," he said, "how many hours towards the great mountain," and he aided his speech with his hand, "have your men carried the white girl?"

The Indian seemed to understand him, but instead of answering, closed his eyes, dropped his hands, and assumed a look of death-like languor. Presently he roused himself again. Perhaps he intended this pantomime as an answer to the hunter's question. Carper seemed to take it for one. "He wishes to tell me," he muttered, "that he has been past keeping count of the hours." But if the sinking away into languor was assumed as a dumb show of answer to the hunter's question, it was presently followed by marks of a real and fatal lethargy. Death came on rapidly. Carper, disarmed by the condition of the dying man, and somewhat softened by his apparent gratitude for so slight a favor as that of leaving his scalp-lock upon his head, addressed him in an apologetic strain.

"If I had known that you were already half dead, I think it possible that I should not have shot you. But I was justified; and as a reasonable Indian you must admit it. Bullet for bullet is good law; and you did your endeavor to shoot me. However if you were the most infernal rascal that ever came over from the Muskingum or Hockhocking I would leave you with your scalp on your head, your rifle, tomahawk, knife, and pouch of parched corn by your side, and straighten your limbs decently. You have a religious notion about all this sort of thing, that is no doubt unreasonable; but it is of no use to argue it with a man three quarters dead, and who can't understand my language."

The Indian looked gratefully into Carper's face, muttered "broder," and in a few minutes, without farther attempts at speech, died.

The word "broder" * is, to be sure a barbarous corruption, when it is the result of an attempt to speak the English word "brother;" but to my ears, certain associations redeem it, and make it very touching. It was with the good German word, of like signification, and sound, upon his lips, that the last of the royal knights, Gustavus Adolphus, fell from his saddle on the field of Lutzen. And who does not remember the "Mein bruder" of the student of Weisenberg, as, throwing down his pistol, he flew to embrace the friend whom jealousies had alienated, but at whose heart he could not aim for "the haze which kindly recollections brought before his eyes?"

John Carper straightened the dead man's limbs, placed his rifle, knife, tomahawk, and pouch of corn by his side, and led by a purpose which gave no time for more than this simple care of the dead, resumed his journey. The horse-tracks rendered the trail clear from the point at which the Indian parties had united, and Carper followed it without difficulty, and rapidly. Sharpnose seemed to consider his functions at an end for the present, and made no effort to assist his master, but jogged on contentedly before.

For some ten miles the hunter held upon his way without interruption, and, at the end of this distance, the dog became again eager and excited. In fact, man and dog had reached the camping ground of the Indians. The spot which they had selected was in the centre of a kind of basin made by spurs of the Alleghaney. The mountain projections almost surrounded the hollow; the only gap in their circuit was a narrow one through which a slender stream from a mountain-spring escaped, making a humming noise, as it leaped the sandstones, or gurgled in narrow passes under them. This break in the rim of the mountain basin was on its southern side.

The fires which the Indians had kindled were still smouldering, and

* John Carper was singularly merciful to the poor devil who, measuring his deeds by his wild conscience, had done no wrong. An Indian shot by an old man named David Morgan, on the Monongahela, was treated very differently. "On the report of Morgan, a party went out from the fort and found the Indian at one hundred yards distant from the scene of action, hid in the top of a fallen tree, where he had picked the knife out of his body, after which had come out parched corn, &c., and had bound up his wound with the apron aforesaid; and on the first sight he saluted them with "How do, do, broder? how do, do, broder?" But alas! poor savage their brotherhood to him extended only to tomahawking, scalping, and, to gratify some peculiar feelings of their own, *skinning him*, and they have made drum-heads of his skin." Kerchival. Appendix.

the footmarks were as fresh as if just made. In fact the party could scarcely be two hours in advance; and Carper felt no little satisfaction, when, by this discovery of the camping-ground, he assured himself that five of the seven or eight hours by which, at first, the Indians led him, had been overcome by his greater speed. He examined carefully to ascertain, if possible, how Nelly had been permitted to pass the night, or so much of it as her captors had passed at the camp. He found at the distance of some twenty steps from the circle immediately about the fire, and on the side of the hollow opposite to its outlet, a bed of dry leaves, and hemlock branches, and the impress of a human form sunk deeply into it, as if the occupant had been nearly covered by the uprising of the light material on each side.

A hare never left a snugger "form" in a bunch of meadow grass. The length of the impression was less than the usual manly stature, and there was the wide pressure of skirts, instead of more definite marks of the lower limbs; from which the hunter was not slow to assure himself that the little Quakeress, or at least one of her sex, had here found a bed. There was nothing to show that her captors had used any other constraint with her than that imposed by her position at the side of the walled hollow most remote from the outlet, and the customary mainte-nance of watch. After Carper had made these examinations, which he did with no little feeling—for what lover ever scrutinized such dainty traces of his mistress without emotions of tenderness—he seated him-self and meditated upon his future course.

CHAPTER V

Carper had a good knowledge of the country about him, having hunted in it, and he took for granted that the Indians would ascend the Alleghaney at a place some miles to the south—the nearest point of practicable ascent to horsemen. On entering the hollow, indeed, he had seen the tracks of horses leading out of it and tending in a southerly direction. What course the party would pursue, after gaining the Alleghaney levels, was now matter of reflection. He at last made up his mind that their course could scarcely reach farther south than the difficulties of the mountain compelled, and that after gaining its ridge, a bend to the north corresponding with the present southern one, would be made, and a line of direction taken toward Horseshoe and Black-water runs—tributaries of Cheat River. Such a course would bring the party to the head of Youheganey, which he had appointed as the destination of the party to be gathered, and sent on by Joshua Blake. In accordance with these views, he determined to give up the trail of the Indians, climb the mountain at once, and either get before them, or resume the trail on the levels. I need not say in detail how he carried this plan into effect. We join travel with him again, many miles westward from the Indian camping ground—in fact upon the rocky highlands overlooking the valley of Cheat River. The hunter had reached a rocky point, from which his view took in a wide range of country, chiefly covered with forest, but spotted here and there with grassy glades. He overlooked the southern termination of the natural meadows of the Alleghaneys.

Very near him, but not at all fixing his attention, was a work of nature which, when this wilderness has been rendered penetrable to the world by good roads, and endurable by good inns, will draw crowds to admire its daring and novel beauty. Blackwater Run, a considerable stream to bear the humble name of run, after winding sluggishly along the mountain levels, takes a leap from a rocky ledge, down a precipice of two hundred feet, unbroken in the descent except by one step of rock, which drives it at a rebound into a second great curve. A basin of rock catches the waters below, and transmits them to other basins which descend in a series to the natural level of the valley. These basins are eternally shaded, and kept even in a twilight gloom by immense umbrella-topped evergreens, chiefly hemlocks, and the cold soil around them is entirely without undergrowth. The foot of this cascade, and the descending basins, I may as well say for the benefit of the trout fisher, abound in mountain trout of great size, perfect firmness, and unimpeachable flavor.

Carper stood upon the rocks, over this forest waterfall, which flashed and foamed in the light of the sun, (by this time near its setting,) and looked beyond into the valley dotted with glades. For some time no animate nature seemed to stir in the scene; but at last he saw a troop of nine elk * sweep across one of the largest of the glades at a brisk gallop. He could discover nothing to explain this flight of the elk; but at once conjectured that they were running from hunters of the Indian party. Below and before him, down Blackwater Run, he saw, at the distance of nearly a mile, a rugged, isolated hill, rising on one side with a gradual ascent dark with pines, and on the opposite

---

* The elk is still found, I have good authority for believing, in this singularly wild portion of Virginia—of course in small numbers.

presenting a precipitous surface to the stream. He determined to avail himself of this hill as a post of farther observation. Followed by his dog, he let himself down through the laurels of the mountain side, reached the shade of the hemlocks, followed the stream, gained the hill, and climbed to its top.

He found here an admirable hiding-place. Laurels grew in abundance amongst large masses of sandstone, and roofed in the chambers which these, lying loosely at some feet apart, made; and the pine trees growing on that side of the hill up which he had come, afforded with their tops that dark back-ground which, in woodcraft, is reckoned so useful in perfecting the hunter's concealment from his game. Carper hid himself between two squares of rock, near the edge of the precipice above the sun, and arranging the laurel so that he could see, without being seen, looked carefully out.

A glade of about an acre, extended from the other bank of the stream; and beyond this the forest gave way in many places to patches of grass, glimpses of which might be caught as the light wind moved, here and there, the screen of boughs. The hunter had scarcely run his eye over this broken scene of trees and grass, when he heard what he at first took to be the bleat of a fawn. Presently, upon a repetition of the sound, he became sure that it was a decoy bleat. This imitation of a fawn's cry is made with an instrument like the mouth-piece of a clarionet; or, in some cases of extraordinary imitative powers of the voice, without such aid. The echo of the second bleat had not died away, when a doe came bounding into the glade, with her flag up, and stood for an instant looking eagerly about her. A shot was fired from a thick part of the wood, and the poor dam, drawn by love and care for her young, gave a few leaps and fell.

Carper had seized his dog by the muzzle, at the first sound of the bleat, and still held him, whilst witnessing what followed. An Indian came from the wood, unsheathed his knife, cut the throat of the deer, and stood watching to see it die. Carper raised his rifle, but a moment's reflection enabled him to look upon the breast of the red hunter, as his blanket parted and displayed its swell—as fair a mark as temptation ever put in the way of a rifleman—with a quiet and patient eye. A few minutes convinced him of the wisdom of his forbearance. A second Indian came into the glade. The two proceeded to butcher the doe.

They were engaged at this work when the main body of the Indians came in sight. First came a strong athletic young warrior mounted upon a showy black horse, which the hunter recognized, at a glance, as the vicious stallion of Vanslaken, the Dutchman. The toilsome journey, or the skill and strength of the rider, had subdued the brute into a quiet gait. A little in the rear of this first horseman, came Girty, a slim, dark-skinned, and eager-eyed youth, mounted upon a pony; behind him with one arm about his waist, sat Nelly Blake. Bundles were fastened about both horses. Behind, in no particular order, came eight Indians on foot, and trudging heavily in the rear of these, with a bundle of immense size weighing him down, came the boy Tobe. No prisoner seemed to have been brought from the settlement of Vanslaken.

The party stopped in the glade, and made preparation for passing the night. Nelly was made to leap from behind Girty, and now stood in full view of Carper. Her face bore an expression of resolution, but was somewhat pale, in spite of mountain air and travel. She seemed to watch carefully, and obey readily, the signs of her captors, and to meet the dangers of her situation with a brave, but wise spirit. The boy Tobe, an uncouth, overgrown lad of fourteen, foot-sore and nearly dead with performing the part of Issachar to these wild Ishmaels, did not endure his lot with so much sagacious fortitude. Stumbling on, to the edge of the glade, he threw his load down, and seating himself beside it, began to weep bitterly.

He was presently roused from this condition by an order, followed by a blow over the shoulders, to get wood for building fires. The boy, instead of obeying, turned, caught the stick with which he had been struck, and with a sullen, dogged manner, kept his seat. The Indian who had given him the order, released his hold upon the stick, caught his tomahawk, and, without an instant of hesitation, drove the edge of it into the boy's skull. Poor Tobe fell like a calf under the axe of a butcher.

This tragedy was begun and ended so suddenly, that even the companions of the murderer were taken by surprise. The Quakeress uttered a sharp cry, and covered her face with her hands. Girty advanced with a clouded face and spoke to the Indian, who, tearing the scalp from the boy's head, fastened it to his belt, and, making no reply, joined the rest of the party. Presently he made a short speech, with a great deal of mouthing and gesticulation, and the nodding heads and grunted responses of his audience showed that he had satisfied them of the propriety of what he had done.

This final judgment given upon the homicide, the respectable judges seemed to forget it. As for Carper, he determined that when the time came for letting his presence be known by the crack of his rifle, its first bullet should crash into the skull of the murderer. With this resolution, he took patience, and afraid to expose himself too much, nestled amongst his rocks and kept his dog quiet. He had noted well the ornaments of the cruel warrior—a plume of eagle's feathers, and a broad stripe of white paint running like a bar sinister obliquely across his face from top to bottom.

By twilight the Indian party had hobbled the two horses, made a fire, cooked and eaten a great part of the venison, and as the supper ended, the white hunter, resuming observation, saw Girty gather boughs, and make a bed for the Quakeress; it was placed thirty or forty yards off, down the run, out of view of the party about the fire, and the half-breed seemed to make it with much care. Carper recollected having seen the arm of the Quakeress about Girty's waist, as she rode behind him, and that recollection coupled with the character of his present labor for her, excited more of ill-blood toward the youth, than of gratitude for services which, doubtless, rendered Nelly's condition one of less hardship. As he brooded, with something almost as savage as jealousy in his humor, over these things, he saw Nelly, after listening to some words from Girty, steal away to her little bower of fragrant branches, and there clasping her hands, turn her face upward, dim in the gloaming, as if she prayed to God for succor. A twitch of emotion moved his features, and even tears came to his eyes.

"I will lead you safely back, Nel, out of these dangers," he said within himself, "or never will I see Lost River again."

The Indians, when the Quakeress had left them, gathered around their fire and began an earnest consultation. They kept this up for an hour, and then one of their number assuming the post of watch, the others stretched themselves upon the grass, and wrapped in their blankets, fell asleep. The sentinel did not leave the circle, but merely sat upright in it, with his feet to the blaze.

Carper had seen the black horse moving in the direction of a patch of grass, which lay, as he had noticed before getting into his hiding-place, behind a projection of the hill; the patch of grass was beyond the run, and out of view from the Indian camp-fire. This, with the fortunate locality of Nelly's bed, also out of view, suggested to his mind a plan of escape which promised very well. He became seized with a fury of confidence and delight, as he turned the chances, arising from locality, over in his mind—chances such as he could scarcely have dared to hope would so soon present themselves. He determined to leave his post on the hill by the way he had ascended, so soon as the moon should have gone down, make a circuit, drag himself along the ground to Nelly's side, awake her gently, conduct her away noiselessly, and by a circuitous course, to the patch of grass where the black horse fed, cut his hobble, mount with the Quakeress behind him, and, striking north, ride for life toward the springs of the Youheganey. If the party from Lost River should have reached the Youheganey all would be well; if not, then he would continue on to the house of William Crawford, who had established a strong settlement at the Great Meadows, many miles farther north. Once mounted, he was sure that the speed and strength of the black would defeat pursuit. The principal peril, in this scheme, seemed to be in the difficulty of waking his mistress without noise; but he trusted to her courage and his own gentleness of approach. As for the danger of his dog's betraying him, Sharpnose, in spite of his obstreperous conduct in the case of the turkeys, would trail all day at his master's heels, and crouch like a lurcher at the simplest signal.

It was not long before the hour came for putting this plan into effect. The moon, trembling through a slight cloud, paled her fires, and at last went down, leaving nothing but a dim wake of light, to linger among the distant tree-tops. Carper left his post, awaiting, for doing so, a murmur of the light and capricious wind, that the rustle of the laurel leaves might not be heard by the Indian watch. He escaped into the more open ground of the pines and descended. He passed near the patch of grass toward which the stallion had been feeding, and found that he had reached it. The horse pricked his ears, but permitted the hunter to approach him. The bridle was still upon him, with the reins drawn up into loops about the head-stall, and it now occurred to Carper to fasten the animal to a tree. This he did, and, having done it, fell back, increased the sweep of his circuit, crossed the run more than a hundred yards below the Indians, and with great caution began creeping and dragging himself along the ground, in the direction of Nelly's sleeping place.

The Quakeress was lying upon her bed of leafy branches, with one round arm for pillow to her cheek. She was wide and sadly awake; no longer under the eyes of her savage captors, she gave free flow to her tears, and was indeed sunk into the depths of utter dejection. In the midst of her wakeful grief she heard a dull noise like the humming of honey-bees, but never guessing that the lips of John Carper made the familiar sound, she gave no heed to it. Presently the shrill cry of a katydid followed the murmur of the bees. This was a note of the pleasant evening music, which she had been wont to listen to, in the pensive humors of her girlhood; the fine chirp, one of the hunter's most effective imitations, reminded her all the more tenderly of her distant home, at the wooded mountain-base, whose shades were so sonorous, of summer nights, with the treble of this cicala of our groves; but it did not induce her to lift her head from its position. Then followed the creaking notes of a hearth cricket, and again the sum of her home-turning fancies received an addition. A pause in the hunter's performance followed the cessation of the cricket's cry. After a little, however, she heard the merry chuckle, and spinning hum of wings, with which the humming bird feeds amongst the bell-shaped flowers of the House-creeper. The combination of so many familiar sounds, rather than the singularity of any one of them in such a locality, induced her to rise a little in her nest and look over its edge. Had the very insects mustered and followed on, like some little army in fairy tales, to minister consolation to her? She saw a dark object crouching low to the ground.

"Nelly!" whispered a voice, "hush—hush—for God's sake. I am John Carper."

The girl's heart leaped, and her eyes started in their sockets; the faintest possible cry half escaped her lips. It was so faint that the prattle of the neighboring stream must have drowned it to any one not very near.

"If it is thee, John Carper," whispered the poor girl slowly, and in mingled love, hope, and terror, "let me see thy face, or hear thee speak some signal."

"Will you run away to Morefield, Nel, to the lean parson, and be my dear little wife?" This allusion to a past conversation assured the Quakeress fully.

"Surely," said she, "the God in whose name thee just now conjured me to be silent, has sent thee to save me, a poor child, and not deserving of the risk to thy safety. Let me feel thy strong hand in my weak one."

Her lover not only granted this moderate request but took her fairly into his arms, and, with a noiseless sort of blubber, kissed her mouth, cheeks, forehead, and eyes, with so continuous a fervor that the poor girl was in some danger of having the latter kissed out. In the stout, and somewhat coarse, hunter, the passion of love, even in circumstances of such peril, partook of the ridiculous; in the girl, honest and, if country-bred, still gentle and full of the grace which belongs to all beauty, it rose into earnest poetry.

"True—true"—she said in low and sweetly modulated tones, to which grateful love gave a tremor—"true as the love, and the strength, and the honor of a courageous man ever were to a weak child, or a sorrowful woman, so true has thee been to me, John Carper; and whether thee save me, or I am slain like the wretched boy, whose body lies cold, and stiff, yonder, for the wild beasts to tear, thee will surely be blessed of God."

Carper had given her lip-room for this speech. He kissed the mouth, yet trembling with its last earnest word, and then calmly replied, still in a whisper.

"I have done nothing very great, or unusual, Nelly. He would be a poor Joe, indeed, that would let his sweetheart be carried off without following on her trail. But time is pressing. You must creep along with me; I will guide you, and I hope to be mounted and riding away with you before a rascal of them all, at the fire yonder, stirs. We will have our talk out, where we can do it without whispering. Draw your petticoats about your knees, and stoop low to the ground. Mind your business, Sharpnose."

Precisely at this instant a stir took place amongst the Indians at the fire. Carper pressed Nelly back into her leafy nest, placing a finger on her lips as he did so, and then, as noiselessly as a snake, crept away into the densest shade of the wood—his dog following, and imitating his caution. The noises at the camp-fire became louder, and it seemed presently that the whole Indian party were rising, and preparing for travel as if day had dawned. It could not yet be midnight. The hunter was puzzled, and, for the better discovery of what the movement portended, dragged himself around some distance, to a spot near the edge of the glade, from which he could see what passed. Lying amongst the roots of an oak, he looked out safely. The fire, crackling with fresh brush, gave out a strong light; as it grew brighter he placed his hand over the shining eyes of his dog. In a few minutes he saw ten of the party, Girty one of them, leave the fire, and set off down the bank of the stream, fully equipped, and with the precision of step, and order of march of warriors setting out on the warpath. Their course led them near the bed of the Quakeress, and Girty, leaving the file, stooped for a moment over it, then went on with his companions.

The two Indians left at the fire, seemed to have no purpose of again going to sleep. They sat for half an hour talking, and occasionally kicking the ends of the half-burned brush into the blaze. After spending so much time in this way, one of the two got up, and going to where the bundles had been placed, brought back one of them to the fire. He opened it and spread the contents on the ground. He next singled out a little white night cap, and stuck it upon his head; then he tied a shawl around his neck with great bows projecting in front. Having equipped himself in this extraordinary manner, he walked several times around his companion, as if not a little vain of his fine appearance. The sitting Indian, as if emulous of cutting a finer figure, took, from under his blanket, the frontal skin and horns of an ox, (one of the trophies from Joshua Blake's cattle pen,) and placing it upon his head, with the horns erect, and the skin hanging over his face, began to strut about with as vain a carriage as the other. Finally both again sat down, laughing with the suppressed Indian chuckle at the pantomime just accomplished.

CHAPTER VI

The departure of ten of his twelve enemies led to a change in Carper's plan. He determined to wait long enough for the ten to get to a distance of many miles, for so far he conjectured they would travel —there being no habitation nearer than fifteen miles, and their errand being plainly of a predatory character—and then to deal boldly with the two left behind. A cattle grazer of the South Branch valley had established a man, named Daniel Ridgway, near some salt springs, in the mixed glade lands near Cheat River, about fifteen miles distant in a north-western direction. Ridgway had built his cabin only two or three years before, and Carper knew of it only from the report of hunters. The party of ten were striking, he supposed, for this homestead, as their march had been begun in that direction, and as there was no other habitation nearer than thirty miles, in that, or any other direction. It was impossible to know whether the two Indians were to await, where they were, the return of their comrades, or to reunite with them at some rendezvous on the general western route. More than an hour passed by. The hunter, finding that the two Indians had become quiet, and that the fire-light had died away into an occasional flicker, drew himself back, and regained the side of his mistress. She was on the alert, and welcomed him with a pressure of the hand. He inquired, in a whisper, if she could guess at the purpose of the party who had left the camp. She could give him no farther clue than he already possessed.

"Now again," he whispered, "roll out of your nest, and come with me. Be brave, but quiet. One to two is not odds for a true man to be afraid of in a good cause. We shall get back and be happy enough."

Nelly followed her hunter on her hands and knees; Sharpnose, crouching along close to the ground, came last. Carper soon reached a point for safely crossing the run. The Quakeress might have passed dry-shod upon the stones, but her stout lover would not miss the good excuse for his gallantry, and, lifting her in one arm, bore her to the other bank. Here, keeping upon his feet, he led the way and soon accomplished the necessary circuit, and approached the tree to which he had fastened the black horse.

Now had arrived the time for carrying into effect a stratagem which he had devised in his meditations under the oak. He led Nelly into the gloom of the wood, where he bade her remain concealed, and then, returning, unfastened the black from the tree. He next felt the priming in the pan of his rifle, and placed the handle of his knife within ready reach. Having done this, he took Sharpnose under one arm, and carrying him to the head of the horse, made him understand a familiar signal, and snap sharply at the animal's nostrils. The black stallion threw himself up with a simultaneous spring of all four feet from the ground, and snorted furiously. Carper pressed the neck of the dog under his left foot, and cocked his rifle, imitating at the same instant the snarl of a wolf. There was then a slight noise in the direction of the fire—a rustle of the bushes followed—and one of the Indians came stealthily out into the grassy area, and stooped to examine the hobble of the horse.

He was within ten feet of Carper, who had designed to shoot him, trusting that the Indian left at the fire would mistake the report of the rifle for that of a shot fired by his comrade, to scare the wolves from the horses. This was his first design, but the nearness and posture of his enemy invited an onset of a different character. He leaned his rifle against a tree, and drew his knife. He measured the distance with his eye, and threw himself at a bound upon the stooping man. The Indian fell with his face to the grass, under the onset, and before he could make an effort to rise, or even cry out, the long knife of the white hunter had ploughed its way upward from the fifth rib, dealing a terrible wound. Before the knife had sunk to its handle, the knees of the warrior had failed, and he was flat upon the ground; he quivered and gasped, and was a dead man. Carper seized Sharpnose promptly and prevented the noise with which this faithful friend might have signalized the victory.

The horse had plunged away as he leaped upon the Indian, but now stood still confined by the hobble; the hunter refastened him to the tree. Then he took his rifle and walked without caring whether he was heard or not, feeling sure that he would be mistaken for the Indian returning to the fire from an inspection of the horse, and so came within twenty paces of the comrade of the dead man. This poor devil still wore the night-cap and shawl. The failing fire now flickered up, now sunk, giving out an uncertain light. Carper raised his rifle; he found no small difficulty in getting his aim; the sights of the rifle were useless for want of light, and his eye had no better guide than the dusky line of the long barrel. At last he fired.

The Indian, instead of falling, jumped like a frog, from his sitting position over the fire, knocking the brands with his feet, and rising, without stopping to pick up his rifle, scudded off into the woods. Carper dashed into the glade and pressed after him. Sharpnose ran before and disappeared; the hunter heard the dog yelp, then whine piteously. Hurrying on as fast as he could in the darkness he met his dog returning. He at once gave up the chase and retraced his way to the fire. Here he discovered that Sharpnose was bleeding from a gash in his side. The Indian had beaten him off with his tomahawk. The cut was over the ribs and did not disable him or even hinder his seizing upon a venison bone from the refuse of the recent supper.

The escape of the Indian added to Carper's haste to be gone. He kicked the rifle of the fugitive into the run, called through the dark woods to Nelly, mounted the black horse, took her up behind him and rode away northward. He left the pony, upon which she had before travelled, still hobbled, feeding in a grassy opening near at hand. I leave the conversation of the lovers to be imagined by the reader, except so much of it as may be necessary to an understanding of certain matters requiring explanation.

"The horse seemed to kill the Indian of whom thee speaks," said Nelly in the midst of a dialogue occasionally interrupted by the bounding and irregular motion of the brute, of which she spoke, amongst the obstacles of their dark and often rough way. "When the party came in, bringing the beast, that Indian took charge of him, and soon began shaking a blanket at his head and tormenting him. The Indians laughed very much at this. The man held the reins, and the horse, after drawing back often, at last ran in upon him, beat him down with his knees, and ran around him kicking and making an angry noise. When the Indian's friends drove the horse from him he was apparently dead. They placed him on the ground, wrapped in his blanket, with his weapons by his side, and left him. Thee says that thee found him alive, but left him no longer so."

"Has Girty made love to you on the journey?" Carper asked at another stage of the conversation.

"Thee should scarcely care if he had done so. But he did do so. And I tell thee frankly, dear John, for between thee and me there should be frankness, I answered gently. The lad, from whatever cause, was my protection against worse men."

"You make a great mistake Nelly; there is no worse man in the party than Girty."

"More dangerous men, if not worse—if thee excepts to that word. He told me of his wigwam on a stream clearer than Lost River, and insinuated many things about my being his wife in the beautiful country, out in the west, where the earth is a field of grass and flowers. I did not say no to the youth, but, trusting in God, gravely listened to him. So Girty, wicked as he doubtless is, kept me safe from the rudeness of the others—placed the branches of trees for me to sleep upon, in places where the rude eyes did not watch me—and altogether behaved more after the manner of his civilized instruction at uncle Blake's than of his Indian blood and nature. Thee does not know me, John Carper, if from this seeming of yielding to the love-fancy of the youth, thee is of opinion that, in the end, succor being hopeless I would not have opposed the youth utterly—aye, even to such an act as slew Sisera."

"I believe every thing you say, Nelly," replied Carper, moved by her firm words. "In your conduct to the lad you were wise as you are pretty and good."

The mountain on their right guided their course, and riding as rapidly as the darkness and nature of the ground well permitted—and these in fact presented greater impediments to their speed than the hunter, who had never traversed the country on horse-back before, had imagined—Carper and the Quakeress came, a little after dawn, upon that large glade which modern travel first strikes in the route from Romney to Clarksburg. No traces of the Lost River hunters appeared. The Indian party, Carper supposed, were at a safe distance in the west. The fine rivulet of the Youheganey, recently sprung from its fountains, had been just crossed. He drew up his horse for a few minutes and meditated his future course. It seemed to him best to ride north to the residence of William Crawford. The house of this widely known person was in fact a fort, and his family, and the laborers in his employment, made up a force amply sufficient to prevent even an attempt of so small a party of Indians against it. Leaving Nelly at Crawford's he would return with all who were willing to assist him, pursue the Indians, and eventually recover the stolen horse and goods left on Blackwater Run, and see to a decent disposition of the remains of the murdered boy. The Lost River hunters might be up in time to join with Crawford's men in the pursuit of the Indians. These views and purposes passed swiftly through his mind, and he lifted his horse's head to ride northward. Nell, at this moment, drew her arm tightly around his waist, and exclaimed in a husky voice—

"Look—look!"

Her finger pointed westward. Carper instantly saw several mounted Indians dashing out from the wood that made the western boundary of the glade. They were coming at full speed directly toward him. Here was cause of speedy flight, and that too in the direction of Crawford's, where safety might, with a few hours of hard riding, be obtained—not in the direction of home, over a series of wild uninhabited mountains. He struck the black horse with his heels, shouted to him, and instead of riding directly away from his enemies, took a line across their course —Sharpnose running gallantly at his side. As he did so the Indians also turned as quickly as their speed would let them, and pursuers and pursued rode fast toward one point, an opening in the wood at the northern end of the glade. Carper's selection of this course of flight reduced the advantage which he had, at first, in the start; but he was still nearer, by more than two hundred yards, to the outlet, than his enemies.

"This comes," muttered the hunter, lifting his rifle angrily and urging his horse to full speed, "this comes of missing that whelp of the devil—missing a fair shot. I might have known that the rascal would dog us in the dark, and, after finding the course we took, be off on his long legs to bring the whole gang down on us. Nelly I must run more than is agreeable—to save not only myself but you. When running no longer answers, I must die game. It won't do for a man to give up and cry like a woman. If it comes to the worst, submit yourself quietly and trust to Providence, and the friends who must be coming on from home."

"Look," he said a moment after—"you sit in a way to see them well. How are they coming on?"

"One rides first on a horse that runs as fast as a bird flies. Two others ride much behind. Some are coming on far back on foot."

"Is the foremost man Girty?"

"No; he is much greater in size. Thee will scarcely outstrip the first rider. He gains upon us. John Carper, thee has fallen into ruin to save me. If thee dies I will die also."

Carper, fairly screaming to his horse, and striking him with both heels, drove on furiously to the outlet. He reached it nearly two hundred yards in advance of the first horseman of the enemy. The two behind, badly mounted, were a quarter of a mile in the rear, and still losing ground. If Carper could continue his pace, he had but one enemy to fear. A mile onward from the beginning of the outlet, after passing for that distance between thickets which occasionally met in his way, he gained a second glade. The earth here was wet and he turned a little to the right to gain firmer ground, and, in doing so, interposed a part of the thicket and wood between him and his pursuers. As he turned, a neigh was heard from behind. It came from the mouth of the leading Indian and not from his horse; it was a trick to arrest the speed of the stallion. It was successful. The black horse threw up his heels.

"Nelly, sit back, if you can," said Carper piteously. He was on the withers of his steed; the Quakeress had followed his forward motion. A second neigh—the black horse threw his heels yet higher into the air.

"Nel, if you can't sit back, we are gone." Carper had risen from the withers to the neck. Clinging to the mane, his rifle crossing the crest, Nelly fast locked about his waist, the young hunter, never very graceful or expert as a horseman, made anything but a gallant and heroic figure. A third toss of the brute's heels completed the work; the hunter was pitched some feet forward and struck the soft glade, with his Quakeress safe at his back. Her plump little person bounced off and rolled unhurt upon the grass. Sharpnose barked and snapped at the black's heels in revenge. Carper was almost instantly upon his feet—rifle in hand. The leading Indian dashed out of the narrow pass between the thickets. It was Tobe's murderer, with the eagle-plume and bar sinister of white paint. Carper fired and tumbled the warrior from his horse's back. It was one of those great shots which only the best of our fieldsmen, accustomed to strike a buck in his bound, can make. The Indian fell with the reins in his hands; he struggled in vain to rise; his horse pulled a little and then stood still, panting from the race. The black, making a gallant round, with crest lifted and tail streaming, thundered up to the strange horse and dying man. He yerked his heels in a hostile manner at the latter, but seemed to claim friendship with the animal of his own kind. Carper, without staying to load his rifle, approached his enemy, dragging Nelly, whom the fall had somewhat bewildered, after him; drove the black off with a blow, seized the reins of the strange horse, mounted, drew the stupefied girl up behind him, and resumed his flight.

"This is a good tame brute and a fast," he said as he urged the new horse to his speed; "only he is too low for my legs, and if he sinks at all in the mud will be apt to run from under me."

He had not ridden a minute, when he heard firing in the great glade in which the chase had begun. The shots were numerous. He drew up. On a current of the light wind came the shouts of men and other noises, which assured him that rescue had arrived and a battle, or new chase, begun. He was not long in putting this past doubt; and Nelly, within half an hour of her fall from the terrible black, was safe amongst her Lost River friends. They greeted her presence with shouts and every extravagant demonstration of joy. The flower of the Lost River maidens was well beloved, and would have been sorely missed if rescue had never overtaken her.

The newly arrived party had come within view of the great glade as the chase was going on; had attacked the Indians as soon as possible; had killed two or three of their number and driven the rest off. Girty was not among the killed. A part of the white force was still in pursuit, having pressed on so far as to be out of sight when the hunter and Nelly joined those least advanced. This pursuit Carper determined to join with ulterior views. He would press it at least to the banks of Cheat River; examine into the condition of things at Ridgway's settlement—from which the horses, recently in the possession of the Indians, must have been taken;—and, afterward, return to Lost River by the southern route, in order to bury the boy Tobe, and regain the horse and goods left on the banks of Blackwater Run. As for the black stallion, he sent a hunter after him, vowing never himself to mount him again in any extremity.

Nelly's return was to be begun without delay—except for a few hours for rest and refreshment. Four safe hunters, detached from the party, were to conduct her back, carrying her behind them on horse-back, by turns, by the direct route to Lost River.

Carper bade her an affectionate farewell, and the lovers parted in the glade.

CHAPTER VII

The reader will please go back with me to the house of Joshua Blake. He will suppose the little Quakeress to have been restored to her uncle, and all parties to have returned from the pursuit which had resulted so fortunately to her. A great fire was burning in the kitchen hearth and casting its light through the windows upon the fruit trees and out-houses, which were beginning to darken in the twilight of a pleasant evening. Joshua had a crowd of guests about him, William Mace and his five grown sons being of the number. Vanslaken, the Dutchman, was present from the valley of the South Branch. He had escaped massacre, having received timely notice, from a cow-boy, of the ap-proach of the Indians, and had sustained no eventual loss, his horses and goods being returned to him. He had been more fortunate than Daniel Ridgway, of Cheat River; the Lost River party had found that poor man dead in his door-way.

At the moment of time at which I resume my narrative, John Carper, who had returned the day before, was endeavoring to draw Joshua Blake aside, for greater privacy in the conversation which he wished to hold with him.

"It is not necessary, friend John," said the Quaker, "that thee should speak with me privately. The company is friendly, and thee and me may speak out."

"Well, then," said the hunter, no little annoyed that so many persons should be made to hear so delicate a demand as that for the hand of his mistress—"well, then, I saved Nelly from the Indians, Mr. Blake, and she is now safe and well."

"I am grateful to thee, friend John, for the manly services which thee has rendered the child, also for the redeeming of the money. Thee shall surely have a just proportion for thy services; to be computed at a time when we are at greater leisure."

I must mention here, that the bag of dollars had been found amongst the bundles, left by the Indians on Blackwater Run, and brought safely back to the Quaker.

"It is not of the money that I want to speak to you," said Carper: "in fact, I give up my part. But you gave me your written obligation, that if I brought Nelly back, I should have her for my wife. I want to know when we shall be married." As he spoke, he pulled the paper, which Joshua Blake had signed, from his pocket.

"If thee will read that paper, friend," said Joshua, "I will do as, on clear understanding, I find that I have promised."

Carper read the paper in the midst of a crowd of grave faces, which were turned up with looks of inquiry and interest. With some bashfulness, but a great deal of dogged resolution—for driven as he was to a public demand of what he considered his right, his courage came to his aid, and he determined to hold his ground stubbornly—he decyphered and read, in a loud tone, the bond, which he felt was conclusive.

"Whereas Joshua Blake and John Carper are wishing to get back my dear Ellen Blake from the felonious Indians, into whose blood-thirsty hands she is fallen, and whereas John Carper mistrusts in my mind, the said Joshua Blake of a promise he has made of Ellen to me for a wife, if I bring her back; now the said Joshua Blake binds himself and his heirs to said John Carper, to give my dear Nelly Blake to said John Carper for a wife."

"What do you say to that?" said the reader triumphantly.

"I say I will do by thee, as I am bound to do. Thee shall certainly marry the girl, if thee has won her own consent."

The hunter seized the Quaker's hand in rough ecstacy. "Well, that is downright dealing!" he exclaimed. "Your drab is true blue after all. When shall we have the wedding?"

"Well, that is another matter," answered Joshua, with an extremely innocent look and tone. "The child is young, at present. Thee must wait some three years, at which time she will be of a more marriageable age."

The hunter was utterly confounded. He stood before the Quaker with mouth and eyes wide open—the paper held at half-arm's length.

"Why," stammered he, "in three years, Nelly will be twenty-one, and then I won't want your consent. Do you mean to break your bond?"

"If thee will inspect the obligation, thee will find that no mention is made of the *time* at which thee and Ellen shall marry. Thee, in thy doubt of me, has overreached thyself. If thee had trusted to my bare word, thee should presently have married the girl. But thee took, instead of it, the bond, and by the bond thee must abide."

Carper looked again at the paper. His hand shook and his jaws were clamped together, whilst a flush of passion began to mount to his forehead.

"Do you mean to say," he at last quietly asked, "that you will take advantage of my not putting the time in the paper, and break the bargain as it must have been understood between us? Do you mean to say that?"

"Thee must not get into a heat on the subject," answered Joshua, who observed the hunter's rising colour, and construed the quiet of his manner aright. "Whether thee shall presently marry Nelly, or wait three years, depends upon additional matters. I have spoken thee publicly on this subject, because two or three of the friends here present know concerning it and are ready to advise thee forcibly into courses, which will give thee Nelly at once. If thee expects to be obliged, thee must thyself oblige."

The Quaker then proceeded to inform Carper of the meditated tory rising; that this rising would take place in a few days; that if he lent himself to their cause, to which they were anxious to bind him, as an able soldier and a man of influence with the young hunters of the region, he should be captain of a company, and, even before setting out for service in the lower country, marry Nelly Blake. These declarations and persuasions were strengthened by occasional words from the elders of the company; who, it seemed pretty clear, had put Joshua upon this plan of using his rightful power over his niece, to induce the young hunter to lend himself to their views. Carper, after hearing the whole, answered—

"You have your opinions, and I have mine. If you think it right to take the British side in the war, take it and stand up to the consequences; that is part of the business. I was at Saratoga, and elsewhere, with General Morgan, and it is likely that, having talked with more men, I know more of what our duty is than you; but whether I do or not, it is certain that, believing as I do, if I were to join your party, I should be an infernal rascal. Now I tell you three things: I *will* marry Nelly Blake in a very short time—I will *not* join your d—d insurrection—lastly, I *will* start for Winchester, to-night, to let General Morgan know what you are doing."

Saying these words, the hunter called loudly to Nelly, and she came to his call.

"Good bye, Nel," he said. "Broadbrim has cheated me in the transaction which we had about you. Don't mind it. We must take care of ourselves. I will see you again in a day or two."

He turned to the door, leaving the Quakeress embarrassed by the crowd and greatly distressed.

The elder Mace had exchanged whispers with his sons. As Carper stooped in the door-way, five strong men threw themselves from behind in a crowd upon him. After a fierce resistance, he was thrown down and disarmed. A consultation was held amongst the elders. The result of it was that the disarmed hunter was dragged, with his hands securely tied behind him, to the smokehouse, a strong building of heavy logs, and there locked up. This was quickly done, and just before the thick door, studded with wrought nails, closed upon him, he heard Joshua Blake say—

"This is distressing enough, friend John; but thee has threatened to endanger our safety. I think thee will hardly journey so far as Winchester to-night."

The hunter's answer was a most energetic, but useless oath.

It was near day-break. The house of the Quaker, still crowded with its company, had long been silent. Nelly Blake stood at the door of the smoke-house.

"John!" she called in a low voice.

"Nelly—is it you? God bless you. I thought you would be here some time or other."

As the girl received this answer, conveyed, as her own speech had been, through the key-hole, honest Sharpnose came around the house and gave her a cordial salutation. Carper whistled and the dog went back.

"He is digging me out," said the hunter. "But perhaps you have the key."

"No," said Nelly, "I have not. Uncle Blake took care that I should not get it. He knew that thee would not stay long if I got the key. Ah, John, thee has been poorly repaid for thy kindness to me. But thee is in no personal danger."

"Nelly, your friends are at open war with me now. Will you be true to me?"

"Surely thee need not ask that. Yes, thee will find me true to thee in all things, now and forever."

"I believe you, Nel. As soon as possible you must run away with me."

"Hush, John," said the Quakeress, "I hear a noise in the distance."

"What is it?"

"The noise of horses coming at a trot up the river."

"Listen well and tell me what you hear."

"They come more quietly. The trot is now a walk."

"Look out; probably they are in sight."

The Quakeress, stepping to a point of advantage, used her keen eyes, and then returning to the door, whispered

"It is a great number of men upon horses. Some are coming, by the road, to the house; and some are moving around under the shade of the mountain. I must get back."

The girl scampered off, looking like a ghost, in her white night-dress, and crept by an open window into her closet. She had scarcely done so, when Sharpnose, drawing his head from the hole, which he had been burrowing under the foundations of his master's prison, snuffed the dirt from his nostrils, gave a leap outward and barked furiously. The rush of shouting horsemen immediately followed. It was the force sent under Morgan to suppress this foolish tory movement in the valley of Lost River. News of such a movement had reached the lowlands some days before, and now the rough hero was present to deal with it.

By sunrise a scene of great confusion had closed at the house of Joshua Blake. His friends had been seized and were in the hands of the great captain of the Cowpens. One of the Maces had been needlessly shot. Morgan's bugler killed him. With this exception no blood was shed. As the hubbub subsided, thumps, kicks and shouts were heard in the direction of the smoke-house. Carper was presently led out, and came forward, with his hands still bound behind him, and with the most extraordinary mask of red dirt thick upon him from the top of his head to his shoulders. He had been attempting to force himself through the opening made by Sharpnose.

"Who the devil are you?" said Morgan, as the hunter approached. "Untie the man, and let him wash his face."

Carper, no little mortified at his uncouth appearance, contained himself before so important a person, until, his bonds being cut, he had used his freedom to cleanse his face of its disguise.

"Why, my brave fellow, I know you now. Eh! How do you do, Jack? What's the matter?"

Carper began to tell his story.

"Take a little grog to wash the mud out of your mouth," interposed the great man, handing him a gourd of whiskey-and-water.

The hunter's story was at last told. Morgan called up Joshua Blake —swore at him for ten minutes,—and then said:

"I know Jack Carper very well. He is a stout, respectable young man. I have seen him do good fighting. There is no law for making you give us a wedding to-night; but if you don't, I will tie you to my horse's tail, and lead you back to Winchester, for this bit of tory business. Do you hear?"

Joshua Blake did hear, and, after an interval of quiet stubbornness, consented. A messenger was sent in haste to Morefield for the parson. Morgan continued his route up Lost River, effectually exterminated the misjudged insurrection, seized a Scotchman by the name of Claypole, who was supposed to have been the originator of it, and before sunset had returned to Blake's house. The parson came in due season. Nelly Blake, "with a smile on her lip, and a tear in her eye," gave her hand to John Carper. If the reader wishes to know more of this wedding, at which so famous a man as General Morgan danced, drank whiskey, and swore uproariously, he may learn it in the right pleasant chapters which Doddridge—full of graphic power—has given us, descriptive of the merrymakings which border fashion made customary on such occasions. I steal away from so boisterous a wedding.

*   *   *   *   *

A year had elapsed from the day of the wedding. The groom had taken his wife home, received her three hundred pounds, increased the size and comfort of his house, bought cattle to sell again at a profit, and was, in country parlance, doing very well. It was near sunset of a May day. Carper and a laborer in his employment, named John Hogeland, had gone up amongst the mountain spurs, to look after their wolf-traps —each carrying with him his rifle, after the frontier custom. Nelly Carper sat in a wicker chair, near the door-way of her house. Her uncle, Joshua Blake, sat near her, making awkward efforts to hold, without damage to its tender person, a child of two or three months, which promised to become a pet of the softened old man. Nelly was laughing, with a gay face and light heart, at the unpractised Quaker's extraordinary motions. Sharpnose, just a little watching the glee of his mistress, lay basking in the evening sun. Breaking in upon the cheerfulness of this scene, came John Carper, with a hurried step and face somewhat pale. To the looks of inquiry, with which his wife received him, he answered—

"Jack Hogeland has killed Girty."

After a few moments, during which his wife and the Quaker remained silent, and in that awed expectancy with which we await the story of a death, he proceeded to a detail of the circumstances. The substance of his account was as follows. He and Hogeland were coming in from the hills, but had turned from their direct course to find, and drive in, the milch cows. Going up a green hollow, shaded with wild poplars and papaws, they heard the ringing of a cow bell. At first they held on their way in the direction of the sound, but on a repetition of it, came to a stand. The bell sounded as if it was *swinging*, and not in the tremulous tinkle commonly made by the motion of the feeding animal. Carper proposed to his companion that they should go over a hill, and, making a turn, come in at the upper end of the hollow.

While they were doing this, they heard the bell ringing, at intervals, in the same strange manner. They reached the upper end of the hollow, and crept on under the papaws, Carper giving the lead to his comrade. They had moved on a short distance in this way, when Hogeland saw a man, in the dress of an Indian, squatting as if to hide himself, and swinging a slim papaw, to which he had tied a cow bell. Beckoning to Carper to keep back, Hogeland crawled to a stump, fired and shot the bell-ringer through the head. "We went up," said Carper, "and found that it was Girty. He had killed the cow and was, no doubt, ringing the bell to bring me out, that he might do by me as Hogeland has done by him. I am sorry that the boy should have come to this end, and glad that it was Jack and not myself that shot him; for I do not like killing a man in that still way, in cold blood; and besides, although he carried you off, Nelly, he was decently civil and attentive to you in the wilderness." Here Carper kissed his wife.

"I am truly glad with thee, John, that thee did not kill the boy," said Nelly sadly. "Too much blood is not good for the conscience, and the poor youth was misguided."

Her husband continued—"Hogeland is with the body; Mr. Blake and myself must ride up the river, get some of the neighbors and go back to dispose of it. No Indians, I am sure, came with the boy this time."

Joshua, buttoning his coat to be gone, said:—"Thee has a cow the less, but I will replace it."

Carper added—"And an enemy the less."

"I hope," said Nelly, "that thee has not another left in the world."

The Gregories of Hackwood

An old stone house, of great dimensions, stands on a slight elevation in the midst of a champaign country. A stream with a musical Indian name, which our Virginia country folk have not benefitted in the pronunciation, bends aside from its course, to sweep the circular base of the unusual hill. Miles Gregory, at the date of my story, lived in this house, which he called Hackwood, and was the owner of many thousand acres of the lands around it: a great estate, but deplorably neglected, and reduced to the appearance of a barren.

It was near twilight of a summer evening. The walls of Hackwood were growing dusky and sombre. The grim high-peaked gables, darkening into deep cornices, had lost the glare of day, and were not yet yellow in the light of the harvest moon, which trembled on the line of the eastern landscape, tipping the dewy tops of the ash, dogwood, and redbud coverts which extended far away in an unbroken wilderness. These peaked gables were none the less gloomy for the desolate din of the martins and barn-swallows which swarmed about them.

At several hundred yards from the house, was a burial ground. It seemed to be very old. The wall about it was sinking into ruin. The stones had, in many places, fallen out, leaving their coping of plank to span wide gaps. A few locust trees, overrun with wild vines, grew amongst broken tombstones and sunken graves.

As twilight drew on, one might have seen a horseman approach this burial ground, dismount, fasten his horse outside, leap the broken wall, and seat himself upon a tombstone. He was a tall, well proportioned man of about five and twenty, with long dark hair, a ready and graceful carriage, and wore the dress of a gentleman. He sat until the moon began to give a more distinct light, and then left his seat and looked toward Hackwood.

As he did so, two female figures advanced from the shadows of the house, and approached him. One, a slender girl with a light step, came swiftly before the other. The last comer, a taller and statelier person, advanced at a more sedate pace. As they came near, the gentleman leaped the wall, and, with a few earnest words of welcome, caught the hands of the slender girl and kissed her lips. He then saluted, more moderately, her companion, who loitered behind.

These persons were Henry Grant, of Statton, a gentleman of honour and intelligence, who had inherited from a spendthrift father a great estate burthened with a perfect confusion of debts, and Joan and Anne, the two daughters of Miles Gregory, of Hackwood. Joan, the tall and sedate lady, walked away at a slow step, making a circuit of the burial-ground. Henry Grant and Anne Gregory, sitting side by side, conversed in low tones. They were lovers. After the conversation had continued for some time, the gentleman said—

"It is very annoying, dear Anne, to be driven to this questionable mode of meeting you. We are equals, we love each other, there is no good reason why we should not be man and wife"—here he pressed the girl's hand, and his tone became most serious and gentle—"and yet you compel me to lurk about your father's house and steal this sweet intercourse. Why should I not ride to Hackwood at noon-day, and meet you as equals meet?"

"Master Henry," replied the girl, with a sweet smile, "it is Joan that prevents your coming to Hackwood, and she must tell you why she does so."

As Anne spoke, the dark figure of her sister, with a black mantle drooping from the inclined head, became visible; her circuit of the graveyard had brought her near the speakers. She joined them, and said, as Anne ended—

"Yes, I have prevented your coming to Hackwood."

"There surely must be a good cause for it," said Henry Grant. "Your firm and just nature does not give wanton pain."

"Perhaps," said Joan, "my reasons will appear to you to be bad or insufficient; they are conclusive to me." The girl turned her thoughtful face to the moon, and was silent for a few moments. At last she spoke with a sad energy—

"It is our father's condition that has made me shut the doors of our house against you. Ah! he is a most miserable man. The evening of life which should bring with it calm affections, an equal mind, cheerfulness and contentment, has brought him nothing but wretchedness. It has increased a passion, which he once ruled, into a madness which now rules him. But surely you know what I would say."

"That your poor father, Miles Gregory—once an accomplished gentleman—is cursed in his old age with the insanity of avarice. I know it."

"But, master Henry," said Anne Gregory, greatly distressed, "Joan always sees things on their dark sides. Our father is kind and gentle."

"Gentle to you Anne—sometimes; not kind to any one," Joan answered. A sob moved her white throat, but controlling it, she continued resolutely, "None but his daughters know to what extreme wretchedness he has sunk; and only I of his daughters fully—for I have stood between Anne and the bitter knowledge of all—of details which could but have made her light heart as heavy as my own. I must speak even now in merely general terms. In the midst of wealth, he lives in a state of want. I have indeed, more than once, saved him from—from starvation. He has dismantled his house, driven out servant after servant, until but two or three feeble old creatures, who refuse to be driven away, remain. He wanders about his empty rooms half clothed. Ride at noon-day to Hackwood, and you will find a poor sad girl, clad like a nun in black serge, hiding from the cruel eyes of the world, even from her lighter-hearted sister, a miserable old man, wasted for want of food, and who, instead of greeting you as an honorable suitor for his daughter's hand, will insult you with wretched suspicions that you come to force yourself on his hospitality. From such a house, and such miseries, shame has made me exclude you."

At these words, uttered by Joan resolutely and with little apparent emotion—for the tides of the proud girl's nature were deep—Anne wept as if her heart would break. Henry Grant succeeded, after a time, in quieting her grief, and then said to Joan—

"You draw a dreary picture. Why not permit me to remove Anne as my wife, and yourself as her good and kind sister, to a condition of comfort and happiness?"

"Happiness!" said Joan Gregory. "How could I be happy under your roof, with the dreams of Hackwood haunting me? No: I must remain steadfast. I cannot leave my poor father. And it would be a fatal blow if Anne left him. She is the only one on earth whom he seems to love."

"We can unite to watch over him," said Henry Grant. "He can live in greater comfort with us at Stratton."

"It cannot be so," Joan answered. "If I have shrunk from admitting even you to our dismal home, because it would fill me with shame to have you look upon my father's weakness, how could I lead him to your great house—to be stared at—to be laughed at by your very servants? But this is not Anne's answer. If drawn by love, she answers otherwise, I cannot blame her."

"Ah! let us talk of these things at another time," said Anne Gregory, with a sort of sorrowful naivete. "Must we never have a good, dear talk? Joan is always unhappy; and you, master Henry, are always arguing about coming to decisions, and saying the time has come for this thing or that thing."

Henry Grant looked tenderly upon the beautiful girl and answered:

"I will not press you to a decision to-night; we will find a time when we are all more buoyant and hopeful. Your sister takes, as you say, dark views, and has depressed us a little."

As he spoke, he turned to Joan. Her face was pale; her lips were quivering; her large hazel eyes wore an expression of intense grief.

"You have some peculiar grief," he said kindly; "something beyond the common sorrows of your life, of which you have spoken, to disturb you tonight."

"Yes, a peculiar grief," Joan answered.

"Conceal nothing from me. Anne's love gives me a title to your confidence."

"I will confide everything to you," said Joan slowly, and confirming herself into the fixed calmness with which she had hitherto spoken. "The friendship that listens to grief lessens it. The condition of Lewis Gregory, our brother, is just now a source of infinite distress to me. How much or how little of his struggle with life do you know?"

"Speak as if I knew nothing," said Henry Grant.

Anne pressed close to her lover's side, and Joan told her brother's story.

"Lewis grew to manhood," she began, "full of rare promise. He came to his father and mine, and said—'It is not suitable that the son of a gentleman should sink from his position, and I have chosen an honorable calling; give me the means of beginning life, and I will take care of the rest.' Our poor father refused this just demand. Lewis became a schoolmaster; devoted such time as he could to the study of the law; finally came to the bar. He succeeded at once, and bade fair to become a distinguished man. He married a sweet and excellent woman. The world was full of good promise to him; but a change came. Two years ago, with many little children looking up to him for bread, and a

sick wife to be nursed and cheered, he suddenly found himself involved in debt. Perhaps the debts of others had fallen upon him—for
his nature is kindly and generous; perhaps his own want of worldly
prudence brought the misery upon him. But so it was. He found his
condition almost hopeless. He applied to his father. He was again
repulsed. Then he betook himself sternly to the labors of his profession. For one year he bore his burthen hopefully; it grew lighter as he
toiled on. In the beginning of the second year a terrible and fatal
calamity overtook him. He became blind. The race was run. Now he
sits a gentle, proud, but most helpless man, and sorrows are crowding
in upon him. His wife is sick, sheriffs are taking his property, his children are without protection. It is for this reason that I am so sad to-
night. Is it strange that I should be so?"

Joan turned her eyes upon her companions, as she ended, and smiled
so wretchedly, that weeping would have been more cheerful. Henry
Grant, deeply moved, said:

"Your brother shall not go down alone. I will save him, or be ruined
with him. You know well my own condition. When I became master
of Statton, I found the fortunes of our house in great danger. Since
then I have been fighting, yard arm to yard arm, with creditors, and am
beginning to hope for success. Energy will accomplish everything. But
your blind brother is now to be a care of mine. I will place half of such
a shield as I have before him."

"You are a true-hearted and brave man," said Joan with flashing
eyes. "It is Anne's rare good fortune that she has attached so excellent a
nature to her own. I know you well. But this burthen must not be
added to the load you already bear. There is a resource to be once
more tried. I have determined to make a final appeal to my poor father.
Lewis shall be brought to Hackwood, to join me in it. I think we shall
find words which must bring relief; and if we succeed, it will be a
double relief. For it will be the removal from my father's heart of a portion of the terrible infirmity which now destroys it. It will be a triumph
of right feeling over his insane love of riches. We will see. I have some
hope."

"And I hope," said Anne Gregory calmly, "that succeeding in these
just purposes, we may soon have a happier meeting than this has been."

The moon had climbed high before the sisters left the scene of this
interview and returned to the house. Henry Grant, reining his horse,
saw them, as he sat in his saddle, disappear in the shade of its walls, and
turning, rode away at a slow pace.

CHAPTER II

In a large room of Hackwood, with a most desolate look, for it possessed scarcely any furniture, rambled an old man. His appearance was singular. His body was thin and much stooped. His face had no flesh about it, and was peaked and sharp in the features. His eyes were keen and restless, with a blending of suspicion and alarm about them. His hair straggled in a thin line of white around his head, leaving the top bald and shining. His costume was antiquated, mean, and patched. I introduce him to the reader the day after the night scene between Henry Grant and the sisters.

"Jenkin," said the old man, in a peevish, sharp tone—"Jenkin."

A feeble old negro, scarcely in better physical condition than his master, came to the call. He stood leaning on a stock, but said nothing. Miles Gregory, the miser, who had called him, seemed to be seized with the same dearth of speech. At last, however, he said:

"When they come, Jenkin, don't leave me alone with them—do you hear?—don't leave me alone with them."

"Who are coming, master?" said Jenkin.

"Don't you know," said the miser, fixing his sharp eyes on the negro; "don't you know? Then they have not bought you over. Lewis is coming with the old story about want of money; and Joan will be pestering me. They want to ruin me, Jenkin, but the old man can take care of his own. They will find him sharp, Jenkin, sharp and careful."

Jenkin groaned, and fastened a look of extreme pity upon his master. Then a door opened, and Joan Gregory entered. Her cheeks were bloodless and her lips compressed. In spite of her noble person, and the extraordinary beauty of her melancholy face, there was something in the firmer moods of this high-spirited girl, to excite fear rather than love.

"Father," she said abruptly, "Lewis has come, and the time for action has come. He and his dear family—his wife and the little ones your grandchildren, will be cast upon the world if you do not aid him. Father, break this miserable spell that destroys you—that destroys us all—and save him."

"The old cry—the old cry," said the miser. "I am to pay money because Lewis is a fool." And he tightened his grasp of the frayed skirt of his threadbare coat, which he had fidgetted into his hands, as if, in tightening the grasp, he held his money safe.

"Lewis is most unhappy—not a fool. He is a blind man, beset by poverty and debt, which you can remove in a moment—hear me father—remove in a moment. Ah! that you should refuse to save your own son—so worthy a son—when his salvation would be so easy. I, father, would die to save him. As I hope for God's mercy, I think that I would be resolute enough to do so."

"What can I do?" said the old man querulously.

" 'What can I do?' I will tell you, Father, not only what you can do to save Lewis, but what you can do to gain happiness for yourself. Throw open your doors—cultivate your lands—live like a gentleman, the descendant of gentlemen—fill this desolate old house with the merry noises of children—your grandchildren. The wealth which you love will be trebled after every charge upon your love and duty as a parent. Is not this so?"

"Money ventured, money lost," muttered the old man.

"Well, suppose it were lost," said Joan Gregory, with tears rising to fill her eyes, "suppose that the aid to Lewis were but the casting of your riches into a gulf; if you save him by the sacrifice, do you not achieve the one thing for which wealth is alone to be greatly desired? You raise up the fallen, you make the unhappy happy. Father, how will you sleep when this day has passed, and you have sealed the fate of Lewis and his little children?"

The miser trembled. Dreams are the whips which scar the hearts of such men. Without farther words, Joan Gregory left the room. In a few moments she returned, leading Lewis, the blind man, gently by the hand. He came with the step of doubt which marks the blind; but his colourless face, dim for want of the bright fires of the eye, was yet very tranquil; a calm majesty ennobled the appearance of this unfortunate man. The miser looked upon his son at first with a sharp and resolute eye; presently a singular change came over his features. An expression of gentleness, wonderful in such a countenance, was plainly to be seen upon them. The old man almost sobbed.

"Jenkin, give the boy the chair." There was but one in the room, and whilst Lewis Gregory was led to this, his father rambled about from windows to doors, and from doors to windows, turning his eyes always away from him.

"Father," said the blind man.

"Now now—not now," said the miser.

In a few minutes he came to his son's side and took his hands into his own.

"Father," said Lewis Gregory, "this is a sad meeting, after so many years of separation. Your hands are thin with age, but they have more labor in them than mine. I am blind—utterly blind." And he turned his sightless eyes up to his father's face.

The old man, with the singular gentleness becoming more and more distinct upon his countenance, made no reply, but continued to hold his son's hands.

"Joan has spoken to you of my condition," said Lewis Gregory. "And, indeed, it has come to this extreme point, that unless you aid me, my wife and children will be beggars. I cannot bring my stubborn spirit to entreat you; God forgive my human pride; aid me, or deny me; the work, for safety, or for hopeless ruin, must be your own."

Here there was an interruption. A blue-eyed urchin, a noble looking little fellow, dashed a door open, which the recent entrances had left ajar, and entered the room. As he did so, a light step hurried after him, and Anne Gregory became visible at the door. We have not before seen her by daylight, and she is well worth looking at. She has a very young fresh face—too pale just now—large innocent eyes, and waving hair of so light and glossy a brown that you can scarcely distinguish its colour for its glitter. Her figure is lithe, but womanly and perfect. She is scarcely eighteen—four or five years younger than her taller, equally beautiful perhaps, but sadder sister.

Her pursuit of the child ended at the door, in which she stood undecided, looking from one to another. Joan did not seem to regard her as an available ally, notwithstanding the old man's love for this youngest and most cherished of his children. In fact, the resolute sister undervalued the soft and habitually yielding one, and misinterpreted a child-like gayety and simplicity into feebleness—a mistake very often made. "Anne might do much," Joan has mused, in preparing for the interview with her father, "if she used her influence; but she has no firmness, and would only weep like a child." And perhaps Anne would have done so, for she had never learned under the dominating vigor of her sister, to use the strength of her own nature. As she stood in the door-way, she caught a signal from Joan and slowly retired, leaving the child whom she had pursued.

The boy advanced towards the group in the centre of the room, saying, "Aunt Joan, I don't like this house."

Joan took him into her arms. "This, Father, is little Miles, your namesake," she said. "Look well at the beautiful boy, who, so soon, will want bread." There was a great deal of bitterness in the girl's tone as she said this; and she looked almost haughtily at her father.

"The child will never want bread," answered the old man; "we must see to that—we must see to that. A very little is enough for reasonable wants. Eh! Jenkin? Take the child away."

"Father," said Joan Gregory, who still retained her little nephew, his pretty head with its light curls pressed against the oval of her proud, earnest face, "Father, I hoped just now that you were relenting. You were moved, I saw, by looking again upon your son, whom you cast off long years ago. But the gentle look has left your face. You have shrunk back. You will do nothing. Now Father listen to me. You *must* aid your son, my brother. Do you hear?—you *must* aid him." The countenance of the girl was full of boldness, almost anger; her brows were drawn into sharp straight lines, and a red spot flushed out on each cheek.

"Be gentle, Joan," said Lewis Gregory. "It is our father to whom you speak."

"I think of that," replied Joan. "But there are things which we cannot endure from any hands. God knows, my own suffering—if it brought me to death—ah! how welcome death becomes to the miserable!—would never wring a word of anger or reproof from me. But it is you, and your little ones, and your poor wife. I am in despair. I will speak. I will control. The thing must, and shall be done. Father, if you were dying, and a medicine of sure virtues, which would at once restore you, were locked away near at hand, would I not use force to reach it, to procure it, to save you? Well, my brother and his dear ones are in deadly peril; the means of saving them lie yonder; you look alarmed—that is cause for it. I tell you, Father, that your hoards of money must be opened, aye emptied, if that is necessary, for this great purpose. You are destroying yourself—pining your body—and laying away stores of remorse to kill your very soul. Perhaps I should have been resolute, instead of sad, in my struggle to save you in past times. But now, surely, when the poison which destroys you is to destroy all, and our house is to be ruined—even to the little ones—even to the child here in my arms—I say my tears shall scorch their sources before I shed one of them; my hands shall act. Father, I will *rob you*—do you hear?—*rob you.*"

Lewis Gregory seemed infinitely shocked. The dove was showing the talons of the falcon. The old man became a picture of terror.

"Rob me—rob me of my money?" he half muttered, half gasped. "What money have I? The little would do no good. What would you have?"

"Many thousands of dollars: how many, Brother?" replied his daughter, her firm tone becoming yet firmer, her eyes fixed, the red spots upon her cheeks blazing.

"Joan," said Lewis Gregory, "this is dreadful. You carry your love for me too far. Lead me away; and then subdue your feelings. Be gentle, as you have always been, to our poor father."

"As surely as I live, and wish to die"—Joan Gregory answered, "I will take this money. If I am dragged away to prison for the deed, I will declare my motive and receive my punishment. I will say that I did the deed to save others—even the father whom I robbed; that I shuddered at the deed, and scorned to benefit by it; that I did my duty as I understood it."

"God help us," groaned Lewis Gregory. "Sorrows crowd upon us. Joan, your mind wanders."

"Wanders?" replied the excited girl, who had spoken, and still spoke, in tones all the more impressive for their unnatural calmness; "it does not wander. It clings to its purpose. I will do this thing which the world calls utterly vile. I will do it with a high intention, and pure hands."

"Jenkin," said Miles Gregory, the miser, in a husky whisper, "what shall we do?" But Jenkin was beyond giving counsel. He had been weeping, sighing, or groaning, continuously, since the arrival of his young master; and now, turning his shrivelled face from one to another, looked entreatingly, but said nothing.

"I have no money—none to speak of," said the miser at last, eagerly, as if he had caught a spar in the whirl of the sea of misery—"but there is a bond of Jeptha Smooth, and John Stanton—a great bond—a bond for nine thousand dollars."

Joan had become the principal director of the business of the interview. Looking doubtfully into the crafty eyes of her father, she said:

"These were the great speculators who are now ruined; is it not so?"

"Yes," said her brother, musing, "but the bond might be collected, in whole or in part. I know of certain funds left from the wreck of these men. If, sir, you place this bond at my disposal, it may give me much relief."

The miser groaned. The bond might, after all, be collected; but as he hesitated, a vision of possible results—a failure in the attempt to collect, with lawyers, clerks, sheriffs, turning and fastening like leeches upon his substance—came to the rescue. Then, too, the glowing eyes of his daughter were upon him, and she had shaken him with a terrible fear. How far parental love, which surely *was* in his heart, for from no heart can it be extirpated, and it had been visible in his old, unhappy face upon the entrance of his son, had to do with the questionable sacrifice he was about to make, I fear to conjecture. He promised to give up the bond to his son, but took no step to get it. His eyes wandered from a part of the room, in which nothing was visible, to its occupants.

"He fears to betray the hiding-place of his riches to his children; poor—poor Father!" muttered Joan Gregory, upon whom softer influences were beginning to work. "Come Brother; I will return for this bond." And Joan left the room, bearing the child, and leading the blind man. Jenkin hobbled after her. Left alone, Miles Gregory locked the doors of the great room, and presently put a key to a part of the wainscotting, which extended, in panels, as high as the chairboard. He unlocked a hidden door, which, opening, disclosed a spacious recess in the wall. Into this he thrust his hands, and presently drew them out with a parcel of papers in them. He hurriedly took one from the rest, put the others back, reclosed the door, locked it, slipped the key into his pocket, and, glancing about him, became quite a placid and kindly old gentleman to look upon.

Joan Gregory, on returning to her father's room found the door unlocked. She entered, passed swiftly to where the old man had seated himself in the wicker chair, received the paper from his hands, and, bending over him, burst into tears.

"Father," she said, "forgive me. I was most wretched. It was only a terrible necessity that made me speak such words to you. Forgive me, Father." The old man put an arm about his daughter's neck, and a tear ran down each cheek, slowly, and as if the eyes, fully open, and with no expression whatever, were unconscious of their escape.

"This is good," he said. "Now we wil be quiet. Love me, Nanny."

The girl seemed shocked. "Have I shaken your mind?" she said anxiously. "It is Joan, not Anne."

"I am not out of my mind," replied the old man, a crooked suspicion stealing in amongst his better emotions, and driving off the momentary torpor into which his mind had fallen. "I can look after my own without your helping me. You'll want some one—eh?—shortly, to take care of the old man's money."

Joan turned, with a sigh, and left the room. Again left alone, Miles Gregory looked long at the part of the wall in which his treasures were concealed. Doubt and distrust were evidently returning in undivided force upon him. Then he seemed to become peevish, and crushed, with the point of his stock, a large gray spider that came out upon the floor, and approached him with the confidence of a long established friendship.

CHAPTER III

A day or two had elapsed. Joan Gregory had gone to the house of her brother, in Casselton—a little neighbouring town. Lewis Gregory sat in the shade of a tree, which almost roofed, with its spreading boughs, the grassy enclosure before his cottage. An expression of hopefulness blended with the quiet resignation, which extreme pallor, and sightless eyes, usually gave such winning effect to, in his fine face. A great present danger would be met and overcome, by the means which his father had placed in his hands. His wife, indeed, lay upon a bed of sickness, from which she had not risen for a long time; but her malady was stealthy and gradual, cheating the fears of love by its very slowness, and especially by occasional bright reactions into apparent health. The good success, which the appeal to Miles Gregory had met, had been a restorative to the sick woman; and as her blind husband sat hopefully, under the summer tree, she called her children about her, and with flushed cheeks, and bright eyes, enjoyed their merriment, and caresses. Joan Gregory enjoyed this scene, yet stole from it, and joined her brother.

"We have a glimpse of happiness, to-day," said the girl, "and I think, Brother, that happiness is a great medicine. But the work is far from complete. We must, gradually, get rid of all debts, and secure some-provision for the future. I think that the least costly mode of doing so, will be to restore your sight. You could then labour, and achieve every thing."

"Restore my sight?" said Lewis Gregory, turning his dim eyes to his sister. "I despair of so great, so unspeakable a blessing. No—no—all that is beautiful in the outward world is forever lost to me, except in the visions which my memory supplies to me. Blindness is a terrible curse, my dear. It is captivity in a deep dungeon; and this, always terrible, becomes killing to the heart, when the bondman knows that, around him, beyond his prison-house, those dearest to him, his wife, his little innocent children, are calling upon him to help and sustain them. Wild beasts will contend with their bars, and crash their strong jaws against the iron, to escape to the aid of their young. The iron bars are not more impassable than the walls of darkness which press around, and shut me in, whilst my children—like little Anselm and Gaddo—call from beyond, upon me, for bread."

"The more terrible the calamity," said Joan, "the more we should strive to remove it. There are famous oculists in the world. Money will buy their skill. Money we must have for this great work. Let but the blessed sunshine gleam in through these shut gates, and you are free, safe, and happy. You liken yourself to a man in prison. If you were so in fact, I would tear my way through stone-walls, with bleeding hands, if there were no other means of restoring you to freedom. With the same devotion, I will extricate you from this dungeon of blindness, if God permits me to do so. Human obstacles shall not turn me aside. A portion of our father's misused wealth must be devoted to this good purpose. In saving you, and yours, it will make even himself happier. Brother, this present aid, which gives you so much relief, has already had its humanizing effect upon him. Tears were in his eyes, as I spoke with him. Tears are rain to the desert of such a poor old man's heart. And then, too, something must be done for dear Grace, who is quite happy now that her husband is relieved. The soft airs of some distant countries are healing, and saving, to such invalids. Our father's misused wealth must place this cure within her reach. I will not bend or yield until these great works are accomplished."

"You speak," said Lewis Gregory, "too hopefully. If we can vanquish the infirmity of our poor father, so far as to gain a payment of my remaining debts, and a safe provision for my family, it will be more than I dare now even to hope for; an unspeakable blessing—one to fill my heart with gratitude to God, who has won me nearer to him by this affliction."

As the blind man spoke, a horseman approached. The horseman was Henry Grant, of Statton. He dismounted, and joined Joan Gregory and her brother, on the grass in the shade of the tree. He came to make a direct offer of pecuniary aid to Lewis Gregory; a moderate present aid, to be increased in the future. Joan and her brother, aware of this generous man's struggles against the very evil of debt, which he was seeking to alleviate in another, heard his offer with much feeling, and told him of the successful application to Miles Gregory, which rendered his aid no longer necessary.

"The bond of Jeptha Smooth, and John Stanton, can be collected," said Lewis Gregory. "It will be taken in present discharge of executions against me. I have made an arrangement to this effect, and am to transfer it this evening. I have no pressing debts which this will not discharge."

"This is certainly a great success," said Henry Grant. "All will end well. Give us but time."

"Yes," said Joan Gregory—"time, and the blessing of God. We possess, already, resolute hearts. Do you know that this present success has made me very hopeful, and quite happy?"

"Who is it that rides so fast?" said Lewis Gregory, bending his head, and listening. "Some one comes, at a gallop, on the Hackwood road. He is now on the sounding flat, just over the hill."

In a minute, an old, strangely dressed man, mounted upon a grotesque old horse, passed the comb of a near hill, at a gallop which seemed a paroxysm of the rickets.

A cry escaped from the lips of Joan Gregory.

"Who is it that comes riding so?" asked Lewis Gregory.

"Listen," answered the girl with a white face.

As she spoke, some boys, who ran upon the sidewalks, imitating the spasmodic motions of the galloping horse, shouted:

"Old Miles—Old Miles—hurrah for the miser!"

CHAPTER IV

Let us go back to Hackwood, to ascertain the cause of the miser's ride. It was some hours before his appearance in Casselton, that, as he sat in his desolate room, ruminating variously—now embittered by his recollection of Joan's bold threat to lay violent hands upon his hoards, and again becoming placid with the reflection that he had relieved his son without parting with a dollar of his actual moneys—the arrival of a gentleman was announced to him by Jenkin. This gentleman was Achilles Wiley, Esq., a lawyer of distinction in that country—that is to say, a legal star shining, in a very noted manner, over some five counties, which his orbit embraced. He came in a great roomy, low-swinging coach, with spotless panels, and a splendid hammer-cloth. His coachman was excessively fat, his footman was excessively thin, and the tails of his sixteen hand bays swept their fetlocks.

This well-fed gentleman, rosy with abundance, and full of the condescending suavity of a man who always vanquishes, was presently front to front with the meagre and bloodless miser. Miles Gregory received him with a wintry welcome; and, but for Jenkin, the distinguished lawyer, fresh from the luxury of his sinking cushions, would have been left without so much as the comfort of a hard-bottomed chair. As, thanks to Jenkin, he seated himself, the slim footman placed a small but heavy box on the floor at his feet.

"Well—well—what is your business?" inquired the miser. This was in answer to some warm salutations with which Achilles Wiley met an "old friend."

"Ah!" answered the lawyer, "you were always an eccentric man. But perhaps you are right. Time is money. My business, my worthy old friend, concerns the bond of Jeptha Smooth and John Stanton—a bond which, I think, these persons gave upon their purchase of some of your Swan River lands."

"Yes: it is so. What of the bond?" said Miles Gregory.

"You are aware that Smooth and Stanton have failed," said the lawyer, "and that this bond for $9,000 is not worth six pence."

"May be so—may be so," commented the miser.

"You take your loss very coolly," Wiley resumed. "But although the bond is not worth six pence, Smooth and Stanton will pay you a fair sum. They have failed, but they are honest men; and their good reputation enables them to borrow the means of arranging this debt upon reasonable terms."

"If they are honest they will pay all—pay all," said Miles Gregory.

"This is a little too exacting," answered the lawyer; "and such a demand will defeat the contemplated arrangement. My dear old friend, you are a sagacious man. Half a loaf is better than no bread. If you go for the whole, you lose the whole. I am empowered to pay you one dollar in two of the debt."

"That will be well," said the miser; "and we can give some time—not too long—on the rest."

"No," said the lawyer, "the bond must be surrendered on payment of $4,500. Otherwise you get nothing for it."

A sharp, shrewd twinkle of the old man's small eyes answered this speech, before he answered it in words.

"You are cunning enough—cunning enough," he presently said, "but I see through you. Lewis, my son, has the bond, and can fasten it on some funds, which you keen dogs have found out. Jeptha Smooth and Jack Stanton have hired you to come, and make this offer of half—to tempt me—to tempt me to take back the bond from my son, who, they think, would give it up, if I said give it up. You are sly—very sly—but I am sharp."

"I admit," said the lawyer, not in the least shaken, "that my clients have heard of the assignment of the bond, and stand in fear of annoy-ance if not persecution, from your son's creditors, to whom it will soon pass. But there is no fund; the bond will not be collected; your son is mistaken. It is from an honest desire to pay their debts, combined with the fear of this annoyance and persecution, that they make you the present offer."

The miser began to lose his look of clear cunning, and to seem confused in understanding and purpose.

"May be the bond will be worth nothing to Lewis," he said, "whilst it is worth what you offer to me. But I could never take it back. Joan has her way. You can pay the money on the other bond. That is a good idea—very good."

"What other bond?" the lawyer asked. "I wrote the conveyance of the Swan River lands, and recollect the transaction. Smooth and Stan-ton paid you $10,000 in gold"—

"In silver mostly—in silver and gold," the miser interrupted him, with the gleam of a happy reminiscence streaking that wilted winter-apple, his old face.

"Yes: $10,000 in silver and gold. They assigned the bond of Henry Ireton, and Henry Grant, Snr., for $10,000 more of the purchase-money —an assignment made without recource against themselves. Finally they gave their own bond for $9,000, now in question. You hold no other bond of these parties, Smooth and Stanton?"

"It is Ireton's bond I meant," said the miser. "Pay me the moneys on that."

"My clients," responded the lawyer, with a pleasant lifting of the eyebrows, "have nothing to do with that bond of Ireton and Grant. By the way, old friend, you had better look about you in that matter."

"I look after it very well," answered the miser. "Ireton pays me, pays me on the day, six hundred per annum, in silver, punctually."

"Ireton wades in deep water, and the estate of Grant, the surety, is in quite a pretty condition."

This ambiguous remark upon the solvency of our friend Henry Grant, for the Henry Grant, Snr., of the bond, was his dead father, and the estate pronounced to be in quite a pretty condition was his inherit-ance, the lawyer made less ambiguous by a pretty shrewd look, and a wise shake of the head. The announcement of this peril, real or imaginary, to his interests, produced an immediate effect upon Miles Gregory. The evil principle began, at once, to rear its subtle head, and to shake its hideous scales.

"Danger—danger!" he muttered. "And is there danger? You keen dogs find out a great deal. I must have my money, every cent of it."

"A bold step or two, taken in time, may make you safe," answered the lawyer. "Ireton, I think, will be, even now, unable to pay the debt; but young Grant is so deeply involved, that he will quietly pay it, to save his credit, which is of vital importance to him. A little adroitness will make the debt without suit. Of course I do not advise you for any benefit of my own; I would be very reluctant to undertake the business, after advising you to proceed in it. It is but giving necessary counsel to an old and esteemed friend."

"The bond must be collected," said Miles Gregory, with a sharp accent. "All is roguery—roguery. Is nobody honest? You must sue— sue. Give no quarter. They want to ruin me in my old age—in my old age."

"Well, we will see after the matter," answered the lawyer. "You can place the bond in my hands before I go. My scruples shall not stand in the way of serving you. But let us reconsider the business of the other bond, which, it seems, your son holds. Smooth and Stanton offer $4,500 for its surrender; your son will find it impossible to collect a dollar of it; you are losing $4,500 for the pleasure of leaving a worthless piece of paper in his hands."

"You don't know," said the miser with a sort of sour fear in his look. "You are sharp, but you don't know. My daughter Joan has her way."

"Of course your excellent daughter," replied Wiley, "will be reasonable enough to perceive, in the end, that you have acted with wisdom, in resuming a paper of no earthly value to your son, but worth $4,500 to yourself."

"No—no," said the miser, but with a look which belied his words. "Let them find out; no fault of mine; let them find out that the bond comes to nothing. No fault of mine. I gave them the help. They were satisfied. Besides, it may come to something."

"Well, well," said Wiley, "I have made the offer, and explained its entire liberal character, as well as the positive folly of rejecting it. I knew the objection, which, as a cautious man, you entertained to bank notes, and was at the pains of procuring the sum, which I have offered you, in gold. But your mind is made up, and I may as well have the box returned to my carriage. Peterkin! Peterkin!"

As the lawyer called, Peterkin, the slim footman, entered. He received an order to take the box, which he had placed at his master's feet, back to the carriage; and proceeded to obey it. A glance was interchanged by master and man; and Peterkin, after raising the box with great apparent effort, as high as his shoulder, permitted it to fall upon the floor. The fall made the old warped flooring tremble, and the windows clatter. The miser jumped from his chair with a weakly agility; before him, in a yellow stream, he saw the bright gold pieces tremble, and rush, and spin upon the floor.

"Gather them up, gather them up; temptation!" muttered the old man, and, stooping down, he began to rake the coins together. As he did so, his eyes began to express the vile craving of his nature; his hands lingered upon the metal.

"And this was for me," he half moaned. "Fresh from the mint. Four thousand and five hundred dollars in gold—nine hundred pieces—all for me. And if I don't take it, the rascals are to keep it—keep it owing me. And Lewis is to be none the better. Joan—but—but," here he paused, and his voice, when he did speak again, had sunk into an inward whisper, "I can hide my moneys away where Joan, pry, pry, as she will, can never find them."

Turning presently to the lawyer he said: "Send your man away. We must see what can be done."

Wiley, his countenance expressive of innocent surprise at the sudden change of resolution on the part of his old and esteemed friend, dismissed Peterkin, whilst the gold still lay with a tempting glitter upon the floor.

"This is reasonable," he said. "It would be a great pity that so pretty a sum should be lost to you."

"We must get the bond back," said the miser, with the wrinkles of his face drawn into a fixed knot between his eyes.

"Assuredly. Your refusal, in the first instance, was quite unlike your customary sagacity."

It was presently decided that Miles Gregory should go in person to recover the bond from his son. He would gladly have taken the lawyer with him, as a body-guard, but that gentleman had insuperable private objections, and insisted, with some adroit reasons, upon remaining at Hackwood, until his return. The gold was restored to its box. Wiley was conducted to another room; Miles Gregory could leave no one so near his treasure-closet. Doors were made secure. Jenkin brought out the superannuated riding-horse. The miser mounted, the wrinkle still fixed between his eyes, and an internal one as tightly puckered about his heart. The miserable horse, an old friend, neglected as his powers waned, at first quite satisfied his master by his slow rickety amble; and Miles Gregory, like Tennyson's horseman—

> "A gray and gaptoothed man, as lean as death,
> Who slowly rode across a withered heath"—

went feebly, and at poor speed, upon his way. But presently came the fear that all might be defeated for want of haste; the bond might even now be passing into other hands; the glorious gold, with the magic of its yellow gleam, might be lost. With the fear, the rickety amble became a rickety gallop. The reader now understands why Miles Gregory, the recluse, galloped, amongst shouting boys, over the hill to the house of his blind son.

CHAPTER V

The miser drew up his horse at the gate of the little yard in which Lewis Gregory, his sister, and Henry Grant were met; and presently stood face to face with the three. Joan said nothing, but pressing an arm across her breast, awaited the result. Henry Grant saluted the old man with grave courtesy. Lewis Gregory said:

"Father, it is long since you did me so great a kindness. Thanks for a visit, which your infirmities make a serious labor to you. You see us quite happy again."

"Kindness—kindness?" replied the old man, possessed by his one idea. "No: it is not that. Give me back the bond."

His voice had a fatal earnestness in it. He fastened his keen eyes upon his son and said several times over, running the words into each other, —"Give me back the bond."

Lewis Gregory, astounded by this unexpected demand, turned from one to another, without answering. Joan stepped forward; her father thought that he saw the storm of her temper rising.

"Send Joan away," he exclaimed angrily. "I am not to be talked out of my own. You won't brow-beat me now. Go away: go away—you Jezebel."

"No; here I remain," Joan answered.

"Well, stay. I am not afraid. You are a bold hussy. Get out of the way. Give me back the bond; Lewis, I say, give me the bond."

"Is it possible, Father, that you require this?" said the blind man.

"Yes, yes: you are deceiving yourself," said his father. "The bond will be worth nothing to you. I know all about it. Give it back to me."

He said nothing of the fact, that a sum of money had been offered to himself for it; fearing that to let this be known would but increase the difficulty of recovering it.

Here the noise of some michievous lads, climbing upon the paling, made an interruption.

"Come," said Lewis Gregory, "let us leave this too public place. I have still a roof to shelter you from the derision of these poor children."

The miser, as he followed his blind son, who went led by Joan, only said, "Never mind—never mind."

Henry Grant, as the other entered, stopped upon the portico, and remained there, walking up and down.

"Now that we are alone," said Lewis Gregory, "tell me why it is that you recall an act of paternal bounty, which has brought back peace and cheerfulness to my household."

"I have my reasons," replied the old man with a dogged look. "You have a great many words. Give me back the bond. Are you going to be rebellious? You are an undutiful son. Do you want to rob me? I thought that was Joan's business."

"Be it so then," said Lewis Gregory, with infinite sadness. "My course is clear. What you gave, again take. But God forgive you for the wretchedness with which you overwhelm us. I feel that what you now do is fatal."

Joan stepped between father and son.

"This must not be," she said. "Father, you are mad."

"Hold your tongue, Jezebel," screamed the old man. "This is not your business. You have nothing to say."

"Nothing to say? I have much to say," Joan answered. "Father, you must not do this fatal deed. We had a terrible scene in getting this paper from you. Are we to have another? Am I to unsex myself daily? Almighty God preserve me from madness! What is there in this poor base paper, that all of safety, that life and reason, should depend upon it? Take it back, and I am no longer your daughter; Lewis, this blind man with the noble heart, is no longer your son; the little beggars, his children, must go out pleading to God and man against you. A gulf is sunk. We are landed on one side—you are left desolate on the other. Old man, you are insane to sacrifice all to this base craving to get your poor gift back again."

"Words—words! Hold your tongue," exclaimed the father, his ferret eyes gleaming.

"I will not," answered Joan. "I will speak; but not to threaten you as I did once. I have grieved over that. Is there no safety—no escape—no refuge? And we were just now dreaming of so much to be done to brighten the future. Father, this gift, which you have come, with the very children mocking you, to recall, opened a golden gate to us. We were all to be so happy. Even you were to be a cheerful old man, surrounded by hearts to love you, and hands to aid you. We were to be one united family. Lewis was to see again. Grace, his dear wife, was to be well again. The children were to grow up to be high-hearted men, and refined women. You come; you undo all; you sink us from great happiness to a wretchedness the more intense for the glimpse of better things. And it is all for this paper—this poor miserable shred. Father, forget that there is such a paper. Go back to Hackwood, and gather your moneys, and hug them in your old arms, and gladden your withered heart with them. You will never miss this gift. It is not silver, or gold; and why should you love it as you do silver and gold?"

The word "gold" sounded like the clear ring of the metal itself on the ear of the miser. The vision of the broken box and streaming coins, which had quickened the evil of his nature into furious action, and removed all checking fears by sharpening his invention into schemes for hiding his wealth surely, came clearly before him, and confirmed him into a stony obduracy. He replied to his daughter only by repeating, like some old grim parrot with a cracked voice, his one cry— "Give me back the bond."

Joan, deadly pale, not supported, as in the former scene, by a passion which made a bold crime appear a high duty, stood quivering, unnerved, and despairing. This girl, so bold, and so adamantine in her resolution, could now find nothing to resolve; no scope for action of any sort. She had brooded upon her former threat to take by force the means of relief—had come to perceive the enormity of that wild resolution—had dismissed it from her mind with a horror which made its return impossible—and so, now, she stood disarmed, without a purpose, despairing. She had promised not to yield, not to bend, until the full work, not only a present relief from debt, but eventual happiness bought at the cost of a full provision for the future, of expensive travel, of expensive skill of celebrated men, had been accomplished; she would never yield or bend, and yet what could she now do, when met

at the first step? Colin, in one of Spenser's pastorals, has an epigram—
"He that aimeth at a star, oft stumbles o'er a straw." The high designs
of poor Joan, providing for the good of many persons, fell at once
before the will of an old man whom children shouted after.

Meantime the loud speaking had startled the nest of young children,
and the happy mother who enjoyed their merriment and caresses, in
the adjoining room. Lewis Gregory heard a door open, and then a
feeble foot-fall. Only the blind man heard these sounds.

"It is Grace," he muttered—"it is Grace."

And, indeed, this was true. The sick woman, tottering as she walked,
came into the room. Her white feet were bare. Her face, much
emaciated, had the bright hectic spots. The veins were visible, in blue
lines, under her unnaturally transparent skin. Her eyes were singularly
large and prominent.

"Father," said Lewis Gregory, suddenly rising, "we must bring this
business to an end. I cannot assure you, or myself, that I am free from
anger. Nor am I sure that an honest anger is not called for. You sacrifice me, and worse, this poor wife, to an unworthy passion. But I must
not speak, I must not feel, a harsh censure of what you have done. God
clear your heart and mind of this weakness. I return the bond to you."
And he placed the bond in his father's hands.

"You do right, husband," said the sick woman, putting an arm upon
the blind man's shoulder. "Let us love each other, and trust in God."

What was it that changed the expression of the miser's countenance,
as his son placed the reclaimed gift in his hands—substituting, for the
look of resolute hardness, one of doubt, and inward debate? The
distress of the scene had seemed not to touch him, until his end was
gained. The end gained, was he giving way to feeling, about to undo
the cruelty, to which he had borne on stubbornly, at the cost of
broken ties, overthrown hopes, and old age made desolate? He held the
bond in his right hand. Now he would hold it loosely; again he would
tighten his grasp upon it. At last he said, but in so low a tone as to be
scarcely audible even to the quick ear of his blind son:

"We must see about it; he must be helped. This won't help him. We
must look about. We must find a way."

Without waiting to put together the fragments which he caught of
this speech, Lewis Gregory, kissing the bloodless lips of his wife, lifted
her readily with one arm, gave the other hand to his boy Miles, who
also had come to his side, and guided by the child, bore her back to her

room. Joan heard the sobbing of the sick woman, and consoling words uttered by the blind husband. Her father's relenting looks, and words holding out some promise, had been lost upon her.

"The work is done," said the despairing girl. "We are given over to perdition. I am no longer your daughter. We, your children, have no longer a father. His heart is dead. We will labour, beg, or die together. Go back and enjoy what you have done. Clutch that paper so much more valuable than happiness on earth and in heaven. Leer your delight over it. It is the price of your soul, and of your children, and of your grandchildren. You have sold all to ruin for it. Go now!"

Her face had become livid. Her voice, broken into short utterances, sounded like so many stabs of a blunt knife. Her arms hung without guidance or control. Her eyes were glassy.

Henry Grant, who had entered the room, approached her.

"Come," he said resolutely; "we are not obliged to despair. We will find some means of supplying the place of this gift, which your father has taken back. I can do something at once, and soon may be able to do all, for the relief of your brother."

This was very impolitic. The miser was angered to find another stepping in to do the good which he had himself refused to do. One would have supposed from his looks, that Grant had been guilty of a mortal offense. The sharp ferret eyes sparkled with passion; the old thin lips worked with a sort of pulsing motion of the lower against the upper.

"You—you—what business is it of yours?" he at last said. "You are to help them—are you? Pay me the moneys you owe me. Pay your own debts."

Henry Grant replied, in some astonishment, "I am not aware that I owe you any thing. I am certainly very much in debt, and can do less to relieve your son than I should wish. But how is it that I owe you money?"

"You know nothing about it? That is not so. You owe me $10,000. You must pay it, every cent, at once. I have taken advice. No quarter —no quarter."

"Ah!" exclaimed Joan, "what is this? Are we to be beaten down at every step?"

Henry Grant interposed:

"Dear Joan, these things affect you sadly. There ought to be an end of all discussion for the present. Be alone for some time, and collect your courage. I exasperate your father; he is certainly under some delusion; but we will clear it up hereafter. Farewell, for today."

Saying this, he left the house. He mounted his horse, and betrayed his humor by urging him to a swift gait with severe strokes of the spur.

"This is a terrible old man," he said. "He crushed the good, and the weak. He is pitiless and obdurate."

Muttering such words to himself, he rode fast upon his way.

CHAPTER VI

The road upon which Henry Grant travelled, was the same by which the miser had come to Casselton. In going from the village to Statton, you pursue this road very nearly to Hackwood before diverging. Riding at a gallop, Grant cleared the village hills, and came in view of the wide flats of the estate of the Gregories. The peaked gables of the old house were visible in the distance. Alas that its desolate walls should be the ring beyond which he could not bear the gentle and good Anne! As he thought of the tragedy of this family to which love bound him, a tragedy passing rapidly to a climax, if not to a conclusion, and struggled through crowding schemes, seeking relief with stubborn perseverance, the anger, which had been excited by contact with the miser, gave way gradually to calmer, and more profound, emotions. The gallop of his strong horse became a walk, and his head sank into the musing attitude. Riding in this way, he was not aware of the approach of a beautiful girl, who came to meet him with a light and quick step, until she had drawn quite near. A little handkerchief was pulled over her head, by a tight grasp at the chin. Her carriage was upright, her face bespoke an earnest purpose. This girl, walking alone upon the dusty highway, was Anne Gregory. Henry Grant was, in a moment, out of his saddle, and at her side.

"Master Henry," said Anne, in answer to his hurried and earnest inquiries, "I have come here, and am going to Casselton, because something very unusual has happened, and I am nervous, and these things frighten me very much."

"You mean that your father has mounted a horse, and galloped away to your brother's?" said Grant, as she paused.

"Yes; that is it," replied Anne. "We are not very happy. Indeed there is some dark fate about us all—is it not so? A noise, any sudden event, any change from the usual, makes me shake with dread of something—what I do not know. Now, it is a great relief to be with you. But has any thing terrible happened?"

"Nothing very terrible, Anne, when the nerves are strong," said Grant. "Your father gave your brother a bond a few days ago, and he has now reclaimed it. This is all. But Anne," he continued, "Hackwood is a house full of whispering terrors to you, and you must leave it, and be my wife. I love you as my wife now; and how can any one have peace of mind who knows that his wife, away from his side, is trembling with wretched fears, and even in a condition of physical suffering? You owe love to your father; but this you can feel for him without devoting yourself to a wretchedness which can be of no service to him. For God's sake, weigh these words of a plain honest man, and act reasonably upon them."

"I will weigh them," said Anne Gregory; "but I think my final answer will be the one which occurs to me at once. I love you truly, and with such devotion, that if the love be thwarted, I scarcely think I shall find anything in life worth living for. This may sound like some folly of a young and romantic person; but I do think that my love goes so far. And yet, master Henry, it is clearly my duty to do nothing unbecoming a pure lady—to become your wife in no secret or passionate manner—but openly, with consent of my friends, and at the cost of no rudely broken ties. I might listen to my heart, and go with you now, this very day, to be your wife; but to-morrow—to-morrow— what would be the scene at Hackwood? And reflection would make me unhappy for a long time. The recollection of violated duties is not sweet. Continue to love me; if you do not, all is lost for me; but do not urge me beyond a free use of my reason. And yet I will weigh what you have said, and if I can see my duty differently, I will yield to your wishes."

The innocent girl, whose every tone and look bespoke a charming maiden modesty, and a frank nature, looked upward with fully lifted eyelids into her lover's face, as she spoke.

"You are always good, and gentle," said Henry Grant. "But the obstacles that separate us must soon be overcome."

After a little reflection, he continued:

"We must break through this passive folly, to which your sister has confined us. I have seen your father, who instead of a drivelling and imbecile old man, whose miseries I could not be permitted to witness, has shown himself a terrible one, and may excite many emotions, but hardly that of contempt. He is too fully armed and too strong of will to leave us with a front of contempt. I will in a short time go to him and say boldly, 'Give me your daughter.' Perhaps he will yield. Perhaps not. The course is, at least, the course of duty."

"And I," said Anne, "will entreat him to consent. We may move him."

It was determined that Anne Gregory should return to Hackwood; and Henry Grant, leading his horse, walked by her side. The carriage of the lawyer, hitherto hidden by some sycamores, interposed by a bend of the tree-lined stream mentioned as washing the base of the Hackwood hill, became visible to them, as they drew near the tumbledown gateway in front of the house. When Anne, answering his enquiry, said that the fine carriage had brought Achilles Wiley to Hackwood, Grant became for a moment silent and thoughtful.

"This man has caused all of to-day's grief and trouble," he presently muttered. "I shall have something to say to him."

The fat coachman dozed on his seat. Peterkin, the lean footman, stood with a melancholy patience, his wrists crossed before him, and one hand holding a hat ornamented with a yellow band. A great fly buzzed about the fat coachman's nose, but its buzz lulled him. An occasional mosquito tasted the lean footman, and finding nothing savoury, retired in disgust. It was all very still; the gay equipage, and all belonging to it, had succumbed to the genius of the place—a dead old place, with only a life of barn swallows, martins, and the humming insects through whose swarms the swift birds would make paths of slaughter, in the humid calm of the mild evening. The lean automaton made but one practised step to one side, saluting with a motion of his hat; the fat coachman stirred a little in his slumbers, and then was again oblivious, as the gentleman and lady passed them, and entered the house.

Anne was soon in her chamber, and Grant in the presence of Achilles Wiley. Salutations, smooth and wordy on the part of the lawyer, reserved on the part of the young country gentleman, were interchanged. Then, losing no time, Grant said:

"I have just witnessed a distressing scene, with which I think you must have had something to do."

"Explain," said Wiley; "I profess I do not understand you."

"Miles Gregory made a valuable gift to his son Lewis Gregory. To-day he rode from this house which he has not left for some years, and came in haste, and as if at some sudden and unusual instigation, to his son, and obliged him to relinquish the gift. The persons who played losing parts in this scene were a blind man, a sick woman, a broken-hearted girl. I have some homely sympathies, and I confess that I have come from witnessing it with no little distress of mind, and with some disposition to hold the cause of it personally responsible."

The lawyer at once mastered the map of the honest mind before him. He answered with a subdued smile:

"I suppose, such being the case, that you desire me to bear a cartel to my old friend of Hackwood. That would be something quite interesting."

Angry blood mounted to Grant's cheeks. But he checked a rough insult which had nearly escaped him, and answered calmly, weighing his words:

"You are a cool, practised person, Mr. Wiley. You can divert an attack upon yourself very adroitly to the body of another; and you can sport with a supremely ridiculous notion, with quite a serious face. Possibly you will be amused by my simplicity in gravely declaring that I have no desire to send a cartel to the person of whom you speak. Possibly you will not be amused when I say that I look upon yourself as the true object of my resentment."

"You can scarcely be guilty, my dear sir, of so great an injustice," replied Achilles Wiley.

"If, like an honest man, you will inform me," said Grant, "what connection there is between your presence here and the sudden measures of which I have spoken, I may be able to discover that you are innocent."

Wiley looked, in spite of himself, a little chafed, but he presently answered in a calm manner:

"You involve your grave, slow sentences in suppositions very offensive to me. 'If, *like an honest man*'—and 'may be found innocent'—and so forth: these are not very pleasant observations."

"They were not meant for pleasant observations," said Grant.

Wiley bit his nether lip and resumed:

"I pass them by. The connection between my presence here, and the really distressing circumstances of which you have spoken, is easily and innocently explained. I came to effect the arrangement of a debt due from my clients, Smooth and Stanton, to Miles Gregory. I made an ultimate proposition from my insolvent clients, conditioned upon a surrender of their bond. It seems that Miles Gregory had given this bond to his son. Yielding to my offer—an advantageous one, made quite professionally, and with no disposition to wrong or distress one human being—my old friend saw fit to reclaim the bond: doubtless with the purpose of giving in another form the aid which natural affection must induce him to bestow upon his excellent son. Do you perceive a breach of honesty, or innocence, in this conduct of mine?"

"Scarcely, as you state it," Grant replied. "But you have, notoriously, very adroit powers of narrative. Leaving this matter for the present, there is another which perhaps you can explain. In the interview at the house of Lewis Gregory, his father spoke of a debt of $10,000 due to him from myself. I know nothing of such debt. Can you give me any light on the subject?"

The lawyer had stirred this debt into life, and had undertaken to propel it against the man before him; but his composure did not fail him in the least, as, armed with an apparent candor which the shrewdest men adopt as the very best means of deceiving, he answered:

"Yes, I can give you information about that debt. Your father joined Ireton, his neighbor, in a bond to Smooth and Stanton. These last named parties assigned the bond to Miles Gregory, in part payment for lands purchased of him. The debt is Ireton's; your father drew no advantage from the transaction. He was, in fact, merely a surety. Miles Gregory can hardly think of pressing this large debt against you; at least until measures against Ireton have failed. And of this there can be little danger. Ireton, of course, can discharge it."

"Perhaps so," said Grant musing. "But tell me how it happens that I hear of this thing for the first time now—just in connection with your presence here at Hackwood?"

The lawyer was somewhat at a loss for a reply; he however said:

"Coincidences occur. And perhaps peculiar circumstances—annoyance at some feeling interference of yours, in the recent interview, perhaps—led the old gentleman to speak of it."

Grant persevered:

"Did you, or did you not, suggest and advise as to this debt, in the conversation here, in this house, to-day?"

"My young friend," replied Achilles Wiley, "you must be aware that, as a man of honor, I can make no answer to your singularly offensive question. A gentleman scarcely endures to be catechised in so extraordinary a manner."

"I then take for granted that you did what you refuse to deny," said Grant. "You are not a man on the one hand to utter a direct lie, or on the other to withhold, for want of a certain etiquette in the mode of asking, a satisfactory answer, when truth will permit you to clear your skirts by giving it. I am persuaded that you have instigated the father of Lewis Gregory to measures of hardship against that good and suffering man." Here Achilles Wiley tapped loudly upon his snuff-box. "I am also persuaded that you have suggested and advised in the matter of this Ireton debt, and that but for you I should not have heard of it." Achilles Wiley took a profuse pinch of snuff. "These are wrongs to be atoned for; and yet I have no good ground to quarrel, in the estimation of the world, against you. You are specious, and perhaps the mere assertion of your professional duties and immunities would sustain you with the public, and make my course appear wanton and absurd. But where gentlemen desire one of these useful collisions: as I do for the occurrences of to-day, and as you must do for certain words which I have seen fit to use in my conversation with you: a little ingenuity can find a way. You comprehend me? It is understood then that you and I, meeting here at Hackwood, dissipated an hour's ennui with some spicy political discussions. It is understood that, becoming warm, you used certain very offensive expressions."

"Well: go on," said the lawyer filling up a slight pause.

"It is understood that you declined in the heat produced by the discussion, to retract these very offensive expressions, and that you chose rather to give me the manly satisfaction, which my wounded honor made it necessary that I should demand at your hands."

"You have turned the corners of an hypothesis quite prettily," said Achilles Wiley; "but you have stopped short of the end by one clause."

"What have I omitted" Grant asked.

"You have omitted to state that Mr. Wiley, the heat produced by the discussion having subsided, reconsidered his position, and after advising with honorable friends, retracted the offensive remarks, and apologized for them."

Grant smiled in spite of himself.

"I see," he said, "that you are not disposed heartily to such a meeting as I desire."

"Heartily? no," replied Wiley. "Upon my word, I have no disposition on earth to it, either hearty or lukewarm."

"Then," said Grant, "I suppose that such redress is not open to me. But you must leave this house at once, or I shall compel you to go, by personal violence."

"My God!" exclaimed Wiley. "You shock me. This is unendurable."

"It may be unendurable," said Grant, "but you must nevertheless go at once. What you began this morning you shall not complete this evening."

"This is horrible," cried Wiley; "it becomes a matter very different from your supposititious quarrel. This is to be weighed. Understand, sir, that in leaving this place, I go because the time has come for my doing so."

"So I think."

"Your threats have no effect upon my motives sir—none whatever. Peterkin! Peterkin!"

The footman came in, and shouldering the box of gold bore it to the carriage. Wiley, in silent wrath, followed. He was soon rolling away. As he cleared the old gate way, whose carved figure-heads, mutilated in features, looked down grimly, more like lemures than the better guardian spirits, his anger seemed to leave him. Even in so short a time his habitual caution had regained the mastery.

"I shall drop this business" he mused. "The compensation isn't worth the danger. What a devil of a person this deliberate, slow-talking youngster is, to be sure. Such enemies do harm, but no good. I must get upon an amicable footing with him."

Henry Grant rode away from Hackwood soon after the lawyer's departure. And he, in turn, had been but a little while gone, when Miles Gregory came back from the wretched visit to his son.

CHAPTER VII

The miser cross-questioned Jenkin concerning Wiley's absence. Jenkin could give him no satisfactory information. He presently locked himself into his room.

Sitting in his arm-chair, he pondered for a long time. Soon the annoyance, occasioned by Wiley's not awaiting his return, gave way to a train of absorbing thought. He had dared to reclaim the gift to his son, in defiance of his wild-tempered daughter, and of her former threats to rob him, because he had resolved to remove his hoards, and hide them away in a place of perfect safety. He had caught at this purpose, we have seen, as his hands were dipping into Wiley's gold. He had carried it with him as a stimulus to his resolution in the encounter with his daughter and son. He still retained it, in spite of Joan's changed manner, and the contrition with which she seemed to recall her threat; for the first impression had been sharply sunk into his suspicious, covetous, and fearful nature; and, in truth, he distrusted the genuineness of his daughter's present show of inactive, sluggish despair. He now meditated upon this removal of his boxes of money and other valuables.

"I must begin to-night," he mused. "The quarry pit will be the place. And then, then, when I am safe from the girl—why I shall do as I please."

Was the affection of a father for his children wholly gone? No: In all the scene at the house of his blind son, there had been an ache of the heart, under the cupidity and anger which he displayed. Perhaps this heartache, these pangs keen in the core of the miserable man, did, in their struggle with a cupidity too strong for them, cause the anger. When we are driven by any strong evil passion to measures of cruel wrong to those we love, we are very apt to be fierce in temper, and to lash out at others, in resentment of our own want of internal ease. Now that cupidity had gained its end, it might have slumbered, and the good principle might for a little time have come up from its profounds, and ruled over his meditations, suggesting plans of aid and protection to his children; but the cunning schemes for hiding his wealth abstracted him from such softer thoughts, and left them to visit the sombre solitude of some future hour.

As he sat, maturing his purpose, night drew on. About dusk, in the first mutterings of a rising storm, Joan came home. The gusty wind roared through the great door, as she entered the house; and the miser heard her well-known step on the stairs, and along the passages, as she sought her chamber. He fell into a nervous disorder. He had not expected her return so soon. She had said that a gulf was sunk between them—father and child—and that the fortunes of her blind brother were her own; and yet she had returned in a few hours to take her accustomed place in the household. The truth is that despair had dulled the reason of the poor girl, and she had come back from mere blind obedience to habit. The miser grew more and more nervous, as he reflected upon her return and presence on this night fixed for the removal of his moneys.

Dusk deepened into an intensely dark night. Soon the roll of distant thunder gave way to explosive peals near at hand, and almost incessant flames of lightning gleamed and burned over trees, buildings, and the coverts of the barrens. The windows of the miser's desolate room became oblongs of yellow flame. In his nervous disorder, weak in the solitude which was commonly his strength, there was something living and terrible in the dread voices, and lurid fires, which roared, pealed

and blazed without. The old author of one of the Elizabethan morali-
ties makes a monster of Thunder, and calls Lightning his red-winged
sister. Brother and sister—these furies of the elements—were wildly
alive on this stormy night.

The miser summoned Jenkin to bear him company. Jenkin made the
shutters close, and lighted a feeble candle. For several hours the storm
raged; it then passed away. The rain, which had fallen heavily, came
down with only a capricious patter upon the roofs; the peals of
thunder became more distant; the reopened shutters showed only
flashes in the east. It was like the dying away of a battle which has
become a rout; a feeble rally on the far hills, a flight into the valleys
beyond.

"I must strengthen myself with food," said the miser, as the storm
passed away. "It has been a long fast."

Jenkin brought from a closet cheese and hard bread. The owner of
many thousand acres looked carefully at the provision, to detect any
possible diminution of it since, like some old gray mouse, he last
nibbled at it.

"Very little is enough, if we are saving," he said, as he entered upon
his repast.

It was about midnight. The miser, who had gone to bed at his usual
hour, got up again, and puffing at some coals which, pleading the
dampness of the night, he had made Jenkin heap in the hearth and
cover with ashes, lighted a candle. He next left his room quietly,
and went to the room of his youngest daughter. Opening the door
stealthily, he looked in. Anne slept soundly. The watery moonbeams
touched a white shoulder which lay exposed to the old man's view.
The light of the candle, which he had brought with him, blended
feebly with these beams. He drew near to the little white bed and its
gentle tenant. How beautiful the child-like woman was—how low,
tranquil and soft was her breathing. Bending over this best-loved of his
children, the old man sighed; the girl stirred in her sleep, but only
moving an arm, which exposed still farther the white shoulder, resumed her tranquil breathing. The miser left the room as stealthily as
he had entered it.

He next turned his steps to the chamber of Joan. The door was ajar.
He looked in. Joan also slept. Her hands were locked, one in the other,
over her breast. Her face was in shadow. Her breathing was heavy; the
long and large limbs of the beautiful amazon, shaping the drapery
which concealed them, were motionless. It seemed to be a sluggish and

dull sleep that chained the senses of the unhappy girl. This bed, and its sleeper, the miser did not venture to approach. After listening for some time, he withdrew, leaving the door still ajar. As he passed back he heard something like a moan; it came from Jenkin who slept in a passage below. The old servant uttered some sounds, such as we hear from our hunting dogs when they dream on the hearth rug; but, starting from sleep, shook himself, and muttered, "the Lord have mercy on us."

The master, after waiting until Jenkin was again asleep, re-entered his room, leaving the door half open. Presently he unlocked the hiding place of his moneys, and, kneeling on the floor, leaned into the recess, until only his skirts and long thin legs were out of it. Then he brought out a box which he lifted with difficulty. As he placed it on the floor, another sound mingled with its dull thump, the sound of a soft foot-fall. Turning quickly, he saw Joan. With a swift shudder he made the opened panel fast again; and then, with the key clutched in the palm of his right hand, his back planted against the wainscotting and his body shrinking into a bend, fronted his daughter with the mingled courage and fear of a stag at bay.

The girl approached with singular motions and gestures. Her arms were lifted, and advanced with the palms of the hands downward; her chin was raised, and her mouth tightly compressed; her eyes were fixed as if on some far object; her body had the staggering motion of one wading in deep water, and beaten by counter currents. Presently, as she came quite near, the miser saw, by the candle-light a dead lustre in her blood-shot eyes, and his real fears gave way to mere nervous tremors. Joan had come, not as a robber, but as a somnambulist. She turned aside when her swaying and shaken steps had brought her almost to his feet, and said:

"Drowned—drowned; ah! no help—no help!"

The miser blew out his light and drew closer still to the wall. His eyes attempted then to follow his daughter in the dark. One might have seen an animal glow in the round staring balls. His heart beat with a dull, muffled sound. It was not fear of real danger, but nervous suspense, and perhaps the terrors with which the weird and unreal fill us, that oppressed him. As he watched his daughter's motions, he saw her leave the room. With a sense preternaturally quickened, he heard her slight footfall at every step, as she retraced her way to her chamber, and finally the sharp creak, and catch of the bolt, as she shut herself into it.

It was quite an hour before the old man recovered sufficiently from the shock of this interruption, to be able to resume his operations. Then, ignorant of the hour, and fearful that his inaction had continued too long, and that day might be near, he crept to a window and would have looked to the eastern horizon; but a moving light on the flat just beyond the little stream, at once fixed his attention. The light moved with a gliding motion just above the long grass; presently, it became stationary, and seemed to be poised, and to round itself into a perfect orb, burning with a pale light without lustre; then it resumed its motion, and went gliding away, at a sharp angle with its former course. It was a lamp of the marshes—a Will o' the wisp.

The old man, familiar with such lights, looked away from it to the stream; the brook, usually clear and slow in its current, had been greatly swollen by the recent rain, and ran now in a torrent, whose yellow and turbid surface the moon made quite visible. From this again he looked to the east. Day was not near. Then lighting his candle once more, he resumed his interrupted labours. The box which he had taken from the recess, he lifted and carried across the room. This proved its weight, which he found greater than he could readily manage. Casting about for an expedient, he hit upon one: he took a rope from the cheese closet, and fastening this to the handles of leather, at each end of the box, made a band to go over the head, and rest on the neck and shoulders. This would, of course, diminish the labour of the arms in carrying so great a weight.

Having completed these arrangements, he blew out his candle, took up the box, first placing the rope over his neck, and after a little delay at the door, which he quietly locked after him, stole down the creaking stairway. Jenkin, between sleeping and waking, had a vague consciousness that a tottering old man, bearing a burthen, passed him, and left the house by a back door. But when he had fully opened his eyes he saw nothing except the moonlight lying upon the great old stairway as yellow as gold, and cut, as it lay, into the quaint traceries of the arched window by which it had entered.

CHAPTER VIII

Day came. Sunshine and rain-drops made the face of nature flash and glitter. The martins filled the air aloft with their cries. The swallow chuckled as she hung about her nest, and saw her swift mate dart away to bring back provision from his market above the moorlands. Even the old peaked gables of Hackwood put on a grim smile as nature laughed through her tears.

Joan awoke with the consciousness of having been distressed by bad dreams. She remembered something of one of them. It was a dream of waters rising from valley to hill, from hill to mountain, and drowning the world by horrible degrees. Perhaps the material for such a dream had been furnished by the storm. She smiled bitterly, as now, awake and hardened by sorrow into indifference to life and death, she recalled her dreaming emotions of dread and hope.

The sun had been some time risen, when Jenkin went to the door of his master's room. He found it locked. He endeavored to make himself heard. He knocked repeatedly, and finally used his voice. No answer came, and the old servant, beginning to be alarmed, hobbled off to his young mistresses. Joan and Anne presently came to the fastened door and called loudly, but to no purpose.

"You must cut this door down," said Joan quickly. Finding that Jenkin hesitated, and that Anne seemed surprised, she added, "He may be dying—or *dead*."

"Ah! cut it down—cut it down!" cried the youngest girl infinitely alarmed; and then called—"Father—Father!" in so clear and ringing a voice, that the garrets echoed as if an Ariel had found his way into them.

Jenkin brought to his aid the two or three old servants of the establishment, and the door was forced. Miles Gregory was not in the room. This discovery at once removed the alarm of his daughters. They withdrew, supposing that he had gone out and would soon return.

But when several hours passed without his appearing, the household became again seriously alarmed. Search was made in every probable place. Sometimes a seeker would imagine the old quaint hat with its peaked top, which the miser commonly wore, in some fantastic form of the foliage of the neighboring coverts. Sometimes a sound like his stealthy step would make the eyes turn quickly, but it was always a sigh of the faint wind, or a noise of the brook, already much subsided, and regaining its clearness. When the evening drew on, quite a crowd had collected.

A boy, a little keen-faced fellow, at last found a trace of the missing man. On the narrow border of level ground, between the foot of the hill and the end of a log which made a bridge over the brook, were several impressions in the grassy soil. All of these were dull except one, which showed clearly the slip of a foot, and then a clear stamp where the foothold had been secured. Jenkin, brought to the spot, examined the footmark, and was sure that the patched shoe of his master had made it. A part of the crowd gathered about him. One of the number went upon the foot-bridge, holding, as he walked, by a rude hand-railing. About midway, an end of one of the laths of which this railing was made, sprung out under the pressure of his hand; the nail which had fastened it to an upright had given way.

"If the old gentleman tried to cross here in the night," said the man, when he had secured his balance, nearly lost by the yielding of the rail, "ten to one but he fell in. But this is a little branch to drown a man."

And saying this, the bridge-walker began to look into the water, and to feel the bottom with a long stick. He found the depth much greater than might have been supposed. It was quite six feet; the current had washed the brook here to an unusual depth. As the man felt about with his stick, he touched upon a substance which arrested the sweeping motions of his search; he pressed upon one spot—and lingered upon it.

"He is here—I think he is here," said the stout countryman in a low and grave voice.

And so indeed it proved. The body of Miles Gregory was drawn from the bottom of this brook—a stream so narrow, that a good hunter might ordinarily have cleared it at a leap. But the storm had swollen it, and then a fatal cause was at once seen in the manner in which a box, so heavy as to add greatly to the labour of drawing the dead man upon the bank, had been fastened to the neck of the body. One hand, however, retained a fast hold to a handle of this box, and the death-clutch could only be broken by wrenching at the fingers. This was the manner of the death of Miles Gregory of Hackwood.

What subtle connection there might be between the dream and the dead man's daughter, and this his unhappy end, I cannot say. Country gossips, on a no better basis, have often established a spiritual foreknowledge of events; and indeed the wisest, who see under the show of life its inexplicable mysteries, whilst not weakly credulous as to such things, are yet not apt to disbelieve as pragmatically as that long-eared formalist, the Broctophantasmist of the Faust; or to run logical tilts which can only result in catching a mist on their spearheads.

With the death of Miles Gregory, the distresses of debt, and obstructed love, which had pressed heavily upon his children, and which have made the staple of my story, were removed. He left no will. His large property passed, by inheritance, to his children. I have only, in conclusion, to give the reader some knowledge of the after fortunes of my characters.

Anne Gregory became the wife of Henry Grant, and mistress of Statton. Her dowry increased the means of her husband so materially that hereditary debts have been discharged; and the sweet girl, become now a gentle matron, lives in a cheerful and proposperous present, and looks with reasonable assurance to a happy future. Little boys and girls are beginning to perplex old Jenkin, who has a cabin at Statton, and basks under its western wall on sunny evenings. He has stories to tell them, and toy baskets to make for them. He is occasionally peremptory, but one little girl of the number always carries her end, when, stealing behind him, she puts her smooth arms about his neck.

Her father's death fell with a terrible effect upon Joan Gregory. The dark dread that her threats had caused it, preyed on her spirits for years. But time triumphed. The suffering woman regained the spring of her bold nature, and came to look upon life more hopefully, and with the courage of one who salves the past with the consciousness of good motives. She became the wife of an honorable and distinguished man, of great force of character, and lives now in a distant country.

Lewis Gregory has been partially cured of his blindness; but not sufficiently to return to his profession. He is now master of Hackwood, and has restored the house and its grounds. The barrens are made fertile; and the ash coverts have given way to waving grasses and grains. Grace, his wife, is still living. She has sought life in foreign travel. The airs of Montpelier, in the Lower Languedoc, have alleviated, if not removed, her malady. Perhaps happiness will perfect the work. It is surely a sweet medicine.

I trust that the reader has taken something more than a cold interest in the distressed, and subsequent prosperity of, "The Gregories of Hackwood."

The Crime of Andrew Blair

On a small lot of ground, fenced off from a corner of a large and valuable estate, stood many years ago, a mean log cabin. It fronted upon a
highway, which, like many others in Virginia, was a river of mud in
winter, and a strip transplanted from Sahara in summer. In this cabin
lived Molly Herries, an old witch of a woman, and Jack Herries her
son. The mother was hideously ugly, ill-natured and querulous. The
son was a heavy, round-shouldered fellow, with high cheek bones,
cunning black eyes, a dark oily skin, and damp-looking black hair. One
day—at that ripe season when the haze of the Indian summer obscures
our landscapes—Molly Herries and Jack conversed:
"Mother," said Jack, "I see the rich men go by on their snorting
horses: are they any better than I am? I see the rich ladies go by in
their grand carriages: when you go out it is on foot, with a stick in
your hand. God made all of us. There is a great injustice in some being
up so high, and others just as good being down so low."
"Work, you rascal—work," answered the old woman. This good
advice seemd to fall like a fagot upon the embers of Jack's meditations.
"Work!" he retorted—"it's very easy to say *work*. Words come
glib. But when I am straining my back, which is weakly because I have
been growing too fast, and when I lose my wind, which has never been
good since I was down with the measles, it's little comfort I get from
thinking of what's to be made by my working. I might work for thirty
years, and the best would be a coat of plaster, and a new stone chimney
to the old rat-trap of a cabin. Mother, I am a rascal—am I? Well, I'm
going out to seek my fortune."
"You are—are you?" said Molly Herries. "And what's to be done
with me?"
"That's your look out," answered the affectionate son. "When birds
get their wings, Mother, they fly away. The old hen shifts for herself."
"But Jack," said the mother, softening under the first growth of

alarm, "we can maybe fix things without your going away. It's not the bird that flies furthest that finds the greenest tree, or the fattest stubble to light in."

"Mr. Blair promised to inquire for an overseer's place for me," replied Jack. "I am going to see him. But if he can't do anything for me, I'm off. I'm very fond of you—I am positively. But every tub on its own bottom. Of course, in this country, which is so enlightened, nobody's going to burn you for a witch."

Molly Herries made a blow at the head of her son. He avoided it with a leap which put him outside of the cabin.

"Throw my coat out, Mother," he said coaxingly. "You don't suppose I was in earnest. You don't suppose I would leave my respected parent." Jack, at this effective stroke, put a knuckle into first one eye then the other. "Throw my coat out. I'll be back from the great man's in a little while. Throw my coat out, Mother."

The old woman slammed the door in his face; then, grimacing angrily, threw a shabby coat out at a little loop-hole of a window. Jack Herries put the garment on, smoothed down the cuffs, roached his hair with several applications of his beefy fingers and set off at a lazy gait. His destination was the house of Andrew Blair—the master of the estate, on a corner of which stood his mother's cabin. We must go before him to this house.

Andrew Blair, a man of wealth, talent, political training, and a fair degree of distinction, had built a palace on his patrimonial estate. It stood on the broad top of a towering hill—some foundling of mountain origin, put down far away among the lowlands. He called this residence, which his pride had established in place of the old rambling homestead of his father, by a fine name—Lindores.

Andrew Blair sat in a superb room, at dinner, with his neighbor, Colonel Arthur Pellew. As the wine does its work of development, you may perhaps read the two gentlemen. The host is a man of singularly quick senses. His eyes watch and discover everything. He hears a faint whisper at a remarkable distance. His mind is subtil and winds to its object. He is not dishonest, or even crafty, in the evil sense of the word. It is but the mind's constitution to do by graceful indirection, and with an intense enjoyment of its own dexterity, what a bold mind does better at a direct bound. His passions are swift and dangerous, but rather those of a woman than masculine. When he seems to be controlling them, he is only directing them: the calmness which looks like forbearance is only the cool search for the weak point of attack.

His guest is blunt, frank, and choleric.

As Jack Herries trudged up from the cabin to the palace, these gentlemen conversed over their dessert.

"You wronged me in that business," said Pellew, "and the more I think of it the less I am satisfied with it."

"Pellew," Blair answered, "I have more than once assured you that you misunderstood my agency in the affair. I explained to you in great detail, not a week ago—I thought at the time, quite to your satisfaction."

"So you did. You explained until devil the bit could I understand a simple matter. A dirty wall requires a great deal of white-washing."

Blair looked quickly to his guest, but answered with a smile:

"Pardon me; but the clearest truth, where facts are minute and crowded, is unintelligible if one has a very single impatient mind to bring to judge of it."

"I understand you," answered the choleric colonel. "You talk about my impatient mind. You mean my stupid mind. May be I am a jack ass. But by——you wronged me in the business, in spite of your fine excuses."

Blair answered with a paling cheek, and a low, clear tone:

"Excuses? excuses did you say?" But he checked himself, and added coldly—"Finish your wine, and let us go into the open air."

The gentlemen left the table and walked out. Pellew lived at no great distance, over some fields, beyond a skirt of woodland, at an old barracks of a place, which his bachelor life and bad temper made desolate enough. He had walked to Lindores, and now expressed his determination to go home. Andrew Blair quietly insisted upon walking a part of the way with him. One of the servants heard his master mutter—"A cut-throat evening it is, to be sure." Guest and host—the ox and the panther—walked away together.

The comment which Blair had made on the weather was well enough merited. It was abominable. The air was dry and hot. The sky was dull with a haze exaggerated, from a delicate veil to an oppressive blanket of smoke—or of something like smoke. The wind made melancholy sounds. No deciduous tree, except the white oak, retained its leaves; and these were as dead as the beauty and youth of the world of a thousand years ago. The sun looked as it does when seen through smoked glass—orbed, rayless, and blood-red. The Indian summer, when it just a little touches our country scenes, is good and welcome; but when it shrouds us, and melancholy winds rise, I know nothing in the ill looks of honest winter half so dismal.

Andrew Blair and Colonel Pellew had been sometime gone, when

Jack Herries reached the house. The negro is generally an affectionate creature, but he possesses very little generosity of sentiment, and deals hardly with his inferiors. Freeborn Jack Herries in such a coat, with black oily face, and vulgar manners, excited the positive indignation of a composed-looking old negro gentleman, in breeches and long hose, whose bushy grey hair spread to his shoulders like an ample and well-powdered wig. But Jack was not to be driven off until his questions were fully answered. When they were, he cocked his (substitute for a) beaver, clenched his fists in his pockets, and renewed his lazy gait in pursuit of the gentlemen, whom he could see drawing toward the skirt of woodland.

The next hour of that dismal day saw a fatal deed done.

Andrew Blair came home after night-fall. He was disordered in dress, and as wan as the messenger who pulled Priam's curtain.

Jack Herries about the same time got back to his cabin. He seemed, beneath his weight of thought, to forget the foolish quarrel with his mother. He entered, sat down without a word, and with elbows on his knees, and face between his hands, meditated under a volley of questions. At last, as if thought had done its work, and the inexorable will was armed—on foot—and ready to advance—he looked up firmly and said boldly:

"Mother, we must make a bon-fire of the old rat-trap. I have the great man in my power. The old witch shall have a coach for her crab stick yet. Money—money—makes all the difference between people, Mother."

CHAPTER II

The chapter just ended is but the prologue to my story. We must pass, at a bound, over a space of time greater than the interval which brought gentle Perdita from the wreck to the dance of the shepherds.

Five and twenty years have passed away. The rough bachelor's establishment, which once belonged to Colonel Arthur Pellew, has undergone great changes. A cupola surmounts the roof—so burnished a cupola that, in sunlight or moonlight, it blazes like a bale-fire. Pigeon-houses, imitated from the pagodas which we see on blue India china, pierce the foliage of willows, and shine with glossy birds that chase each other on the steep roofs, making war or love. The portico of an Athenian temple towers in front of the renovated edifice. Close, cramped avenues, walks edged with box, little gods and goddesses with cracked legs and weather-stained shoulders, tulip beds under forest trees, and numerous other evidences of the introduction of a very refined taste, confound, if they do not delight, the visitor.

The interior of the house, whose surroundings are so elaborate, is quite splendid. I can, however, be only particular enough to say that one apartment, the dining-room, is adorned with paintings, and prints of a singular character. Amongst the paintings, a series illustrates Hood's "Dream of Eugene Aram." The execution of these is, in general, bad enough, but the painter has seized a ghastly conception ably and the face of Aram, repeated in the different pictures, is something to haunt one. There are again some wild scenes, highly colored, and with a fantastic horror in their details, of man-killing on the Spanish main. Two Shakspeare prints—"The Death of Desdemona," and "The Murder of the Princes"—are amongst these proofs of a strange singleness of idea in the pictorial adornment of the room.

It was a sunny evening of late autumn. Along a cramped avenue—up to the Athenian portico—rolled a carriage. Out of it got a well-dressed man, of middle age, with black hair, dark skin, and shrewd eyes. He looked about him, and gave directions, with the manner of a master. Such, indeed, he was. Jack Herries had become John Herries, Esq., a man of influence and large possessions, and rode in the coach which even his old mother—now some years dead—had lived to be trundled grandly about in, in fulfilment of his bold promise. After him a lady, very small, very meek-looking, with a prim cap border visible under her bonnet, and a rich dress remarkable for a sort of tidy simplicity in its fashion, also descended from the carriage. It was clear, from the fact that Herries merely stood to one side, and turned his tobacco in his cheek, leaving her to get out or tumble out as might happen, that the lady was his wife. And she did bear to him this relation which seems to justify every sort of affectionate negligence. The poor boy, very soon after his escape from poverty to brighter hopes, had married this lady, then a comely and well-educated country girl, as much above him as her honest and simple tastes reduced her, in his false opinion, below his present grand position.

Man and wife were presently talking earnestly in the long dining-room hung with the pictures of murder. The conversation would seem to have been a continuation of one begun in the carriage.

"These schemes," said Herries, with a slow emphatic utterance, "whether honest or wicked, must at least now be perfected for our security. Our son must marry the niece of Andrew Blair. I have broached the subject to Blair."

"And how did he meet it?" the wife asked.

"That matters very little," Herries answered evasively. "Pride must bend in this world. You groan, and say that I have borne hard on this man. Now I tell you that those who come after him, if he should die without a safe conclusion of matters between us, would bear harder upon us—yes—ruin us utterly—even to the second generation. One day I found my hands on a round of the ladder of life. I have climbed well since that day, but always with a danger pulling at my hands and feet, and threatening to drag me suddenly from the extreme height if I should win it."

Herries strode to and fro, his face inclining toward his breast, his brow darker than the swart hues which anger produces could have rendered it; despondency had, for the moment, seized upon him.

"Husband," said the wife, "if we keep our truth and purity, the rest is but dreams."

"From the day—the day—which brought me up from the poverty which I may be dragged back to, I have used Andrew Blair," Herries continued as if talking to himself. "I began by borrowing a sum of money from him, which, coming so freshly out of poverty, I thought quite a fortune. The use of this money enlarged my ideas. I borrowed again—and again—and again—year after year. I bought lands, I speculated in many ways, losing and winning, and now what is the result? Against the property which I have got together is a monstrous debt. The man who has built up my fortunes holds my bonds to so great an amount, that the carpet I tread on would not be left to me if I were compelled to pay them. It was a weakness to *borrow* from him, when I might have compelled him to *give*. I wanted boldness to say *give*."

"Not so—I hope—not so: it was honor, and the sense of right that prevented you from saying *give*"—stole in the fine clear voice of the prim little wife.

Herries turned with a sudden step. His face assumed a resolute expression; but it was not because the good fairy of his household had strung his nature with better thoughts, for he said bluntly:

"The safe ending must now be this. Our son must marry this girl, who, besides my bonds, will bring him the fine Lindores property. Blair of course will give every thing to the girl. He *must*. This will be a safe and honest conclusion to my dealings with him: every way better than my original scheme, which was—keeping a keen watch on his health—to strike in at the earliest failing symptom, and extort a surrender of my bonds. Tom must marry the girl, or I must at once adopt this original plan. Do you know that Blair has lately had a very singular attack? He may die suddenly any day."

"When we begin to scheme," answered Mrs. Herries—clear-minded and unyielding—"we begin to make cares and troubles for ourselves."

"You must admit," said Herries impatiently, "that I have schemed into all that we possess—property, influence, and good position. Indeed you never would have been my wife but for those first steps of my scheming which brought me up to an equality with your family."

Mrs. Herries, being anything but one of those caustic wives who avail themselves of opportunities such as this to suggest the possibility that wedlock has proved a one-sided blessing, only said with honest energy:

"Our property is not really ours—your influence is but caused by the weakness of human nature which pays court to the appearance of wealth—and our position, not being natural to us, is not truly so comfortable as the middle station. An industrious perseverance would have brought you to the middle station. These things being true, in seeming to gain, what after all have you gained?"

"Nothing," says Herries, "unless I get rid of my bonds."

"Ah! even accomplish that end, and apart from the remorse which may afflict you for the use of bad means, you will inevitably find the emptiness of the human baubles which your schemings have secured to you."

"My dear Mrs. Herries," replied the husband, "you have very profound reflections. You have read your Bible until you are sufficiently impressed with the idea that the possession which follows human desire is vain and unsufficing. But if Solomon, my dear, declared this for an inexorable truth, you must remember that he nevertheless held on to his throne and power. I have played the game of life with some effect. I shall not, from any motive of that despairing wisdom, give up the game quite yet, and consent to be blown away like a dead leaf from a tree. However, we are wasting words. We must act, not preach. Some first steps must be taken. It was with this idea that I invited my friend Blair and his charming niece to dine with us tomorrow. There will be a mixed company to meet them—but we can do no better. We must have Tom polish himself a little."

I am afraid that a feature in the character of good Mrs. Herries was obstinacy. Instead of dropping the conversation here, she fastened a pair of very gentle grey eyes upon John Herries, and said:

"Husband, it is not often that you honor me by talking to me about your important concerns. I must say a few words now, because I may not have another opportunity until too late. If Minny Blair will marry our son from love, or liking, let them marry, and end your troubles. But if you have some secret knowledge of some dark deed of that unhappy man, her uncle—and I long ago suspected as much—and mean to use what you know to drive these great people to the match, why, in the name of God, do not continue in the project."

Herries looked to his wife with an expression of gloomy apathy. She continued:

"You borrowed sums of money. Well, honest men borrow sums of money. Let these debts remain debts, either to be paid or to be left unpaid as your means may or may not enable you to pay them. Let your concealment, of what you may know to the harm of poor Mr. Blair, be a friend's concealment of a friend's misdoings. I have not a heart to wish justice brought down where it brings misery. We can be happy if, losing our property, we keep our honesty. We must have a wretched old age; no cheerfulness, no self-respect, no peace in this world or hope of happiness hereafter, if we are dishonest, false, extortionate, and cruel, in order to keep together our riches."

The comeliness of Mrs. Herries became decided beauty, so warmly did her countenance express truth and honesty.

"The marriage will end all safely and well," said John Herries, with a nervous, but persuasive accent. "We need not take trouble on interest. Tom will make himself agreeable. Blair will aid us. We must use a little innocent adroitness—that is all. Minny will no doubt consent. We will all be happy—Tom will be supremely so. Wife, we will go down the hill of life, you and I, loving each other, hand in hand, without a care."

"It will be a proud, grand match for our boy," said the good mother, impressed, in spite of her cool reason, by the hopeful picture which her husband drew. Presently the maternal heart made her add:

"But Tom is kind-natured, and an honest lad, and, when he comes rid of his young nonsense, will make a good husband."

Shortly after this conversation between man and wife had come to such an end, Tom Herries, the son, came home from a visit to a neighbor. As he rode into the grounds near the house, the smooth broad road of a circle invited him to feats of horsemanship. He put his horse, a strong sorrel, with long flapping ears, and a heavy tail lying close to his quarters, into a quick gallop. Flap-ear, in making the round, shied from a statue of Mercury. The God held his caduceus, with its twining snakes, horizontally at arm's length. "When we come around again," thought Tom, "we'll try a jump at the little fellow's walking-stick."

At the next round, Tom rode his horse at Mercury, drove in the spurs, and succeeded quite badly: he carried away the God's wand, his winged cap, and the head under this latter, with Flap-ear's heels.

"What in the world are you doing, my son?" said Mrs. Herries from the portico.

Tom dismounted without answering, and gave his horse to a groom. As he came upon the portico, his gait was somewhat unsteady, and the expression of his eyes peculiar.

"Ah!" muttered the mother, "you are tipsy, my poor son. Come to your room. Your father is in one of his black humors."

Tom, a short, straight fellow, with aquiline nose, a receding fore-head, and prominent eyes, pinched as close together as the muzzles of a double-barrel, took his mother's arm, and entered the house, saying with a groan:

"I have a severe rheumatism in my heel, Mother, which accounts for my manner of walking."

CHAPTER III

John Herries gave a great dinner, and invited many persons to it. The principal of these were Andrew Blair and his niece. Five and twenty years had made Andrew Blair a ruin. A poor, sad, old man he looked now, with an expression of desolate distress in his eyes, and the pinch of pain in his sharp features. Mary Blair, his niece, called by every one Minny, was a girl of twenty—tall, well developed in person, and generally considered a commanding and superb beauty in spite of extremely light hair, and eyes of much too pale a blue. Her demeanor was reserved, her expression cold but observant. What wealth of thought and feeling lay, like a mine, under the unbetraying surface, even her friends could but guess. She was physically agile, and an accomplished horse-woman. Her uncle, left a widower, without children early in life, had never married again; and she, taken very young under his roof, was the heiress presumptive to his large fortune.

In addition to these two guests, a jolly old fox-hunter, one Major

Wright, came to the table of John Herries. There were many others, but they must make a mere cloud of heads in the back-ground of our picture.

It was with the coming on of the dessert, that Major Wright, avoiding wine, and drinking brandy and water out of a silver cup, became very genial and amusing.

"I hear, my young lady," said the Major to Miss Blair, "that you can carry your horse over a rough country, like an angel."

"I ride very well," said Minny.

"There are no such horses, or men, now as we had in old times," sighed Major Wright.

Tom Herries had an extraordinary reverence for the jolly fox-hunter: he was awed beyond putting in a defence of himself, or his sorrel Flap-ear. Minny Blair had no vanity, and said nothing of her noble mare Flight. One of the cloud of heads, however, opened its in-definite mouth, and contradicted the Major. The Major, the copper of whose face gleamed ferociously, put in a killing retort; the head disap-peared again in the cloud. The Major, quickened by this daring oppo-sition, entertained the company with a riding adventure which he had witnessed in his youth. His narrative, episodical as it may seem, must make a part of my history. The reader, in the end, will discover why.

"I never told you the story of Rattlesnake Bob Wormley's ride," said Major Wright, after applying to his silver cup. "That was a perform-ance to talk about. Rattlesnake Bob—the country called him so because Rattlesnake was the name of his place, and there were several other Bob Wormleys—was a tiptop housekeeper, a fine specimen of a coun-try-gentleman, never went abroad without a half dozen body servants at his back, and died at last with his debts twisted up in such a manner that he ruined his heirs, executors, and assigns—every mother's son of them—and every body that came within forty miles of Rattlesnake. I believe the Yankee that bought the estate gave out in the long run, and went by the universal board also. If so, it shows the liberalizing and humanizing effects of our climate, institutions, and society upon north-ern character.

"But I am growing philosophical. Rattlesnake Bob was one day full of wine—other drink, of course, must be taken into the count—when Jack Brooke, a very fine fellow, bragged a little of a recent perform-ance of his. 'I rode as the crow flies,' said Jack, 'from Hallowell's to the old Fort, taking the river as I went.' 'That was nothing,' said Rattle-snake Bob. 'You are not the man to do more,' said Jack. 'I'll ruin myself or do twice as much,' said Bob. 'You can get a chance at a bet,' said Jack. 'From Hallowell's to the Fort,' said Bob, 'is five miles. From here to the Fort is ten. The ground is pretty much the same for roughness. I can start from my door here, and ride, as the crow flies, to the sign-post at the old Fort. I'll go my estate on it.' 'I take that bet, and count acre against acre of better land,' said Jack Brooke. So the gentlemen bet their estates on the ride. One of the company, a little lawyer from the old Fort, a bit of a town, remonstrated; but we made him drunk in a few minutes, and had him as uproarious as the rest for the business.

"Well, the day was fixed for the ride, terms were settled on, judges were appointed, the county surveyor was employed to run a bee-line from Bob's front door to the coming out post. It was to be marked off with blazed posts a couple of hundred yards apart. Bob had ten feet on each side of the row of posts. If he went further out he lost. He was to have three horses. The surveyor went to work. Now what should happen? The line brought him plump up against old Toney Smith's new brick house.

"Here was a poser. A gentleman, of course, would have blown his house to the devil with a keg or two of gunpowder, under the exciting circumstances. But Toney was not a gentleman. The blackguard talked about appraisers, and all that. I gave him a bit of my mind. It had no effect on him whatever. At last it was agreed. For about the price of his house out and out, Toney consented to let a hole be cut through it, nine feet high and four feet wide.

"The young attorney from the Fort got particular on this head, as an infraction of an article in the bet which forbade the removal of 'fences, natural obstructions, &c.' I just inquired if he took a house to be a fence, or a natural obstruction; he refined a little, but was pretty strong on the '&c.' I told him that if he put his law books between gentlemen and their amusements, he and I should be obliged to call in a friend apiece to aid in clarifying the argument. He understood the suggestion, and found an authority to show that he had been altogether wrong about the '&c.' So the hole was cut in Toney's house."

Tom Herries, at this stage of Major Wright's narrative, gave symptoms of being both delighted and drunk. The Major, gratified by Tom's evident admiration, went on:

"The day fixed for the ride came. If any member of the grown male population, for thirty miles round, was absent on the exhilarating occasion, I am ignorant of the fact. A great many ladies, my dear Miss

Minny, also were present. The garden was a wild—till woman smiled. I give the tails of some lines which I forget, but which are as elegant as true. But you doubtless recall them, my dear young lady—I think they occur in Pope's Iliad. Rattlesnake Bob, inflamed by woman's eyes, and big with the magnitude of the job before him, looked red and heroic. His horses were wonderful creatures, perfect sons of thunder—except one which was an Alderman mare. Syphax was the name of the best of the horses. He was a tremendous red bay. He was steady and still always before starting—still as a cannon loaded to the muzzle, and just the beast to go off like one at the touch of the match. On this occasion his tail and mane were tied with ribands, and his coat looked like the most beautiful mahogany with the mottles and curls of the wood all brought out and polished.

" 'I'll make a side-bet,' said Bob, 'that I go the whole distance on Syphax.' A bet was made on that to a large amount. Bob mounted, and with a very gentlemanly waving of his cap to the spectators, moved away at a pretty gallop. I forgot to say that time was not an item in the bet; it was against the doing of the thing at all that Jack Brooke felt himself safe in betting; he didn't limit Bob as to time. As Syphax moved away, 'He's a horse in ten thousand,' said one—'and it's a man that rides him,' put in another; and then, Bob, having got a little clear of the crowd, there was a hurrah that made Syphax strike forward as if a whip had cracked at his haunches.

"We went on just promiscuously, some pulling down fences, some going over them, some already on foot screeching after their horses that ran away with stirrups striking, and heads and tails up. It was a great sight. Bob rode just through seven fences, for Syphax took the bit in his teeth and couldn't be gathered. Jack Brooke's judge, myself, and the umpire, went close after and had a clear way of it. At fence No. 8, Bob got a telling hold, and lifted the beast over. We took it behind him. Next we came to a gully eighteen feet across and as many deep. Syphax took it with three feet to spare. We economised inches, and also got over. When, after some as bad ground as I ever saw, we got to Toney Smith's, his wife—who was a well-bred woman to be married to a blackguard like Toney—had herself and her daughters dressed out and ready to do the honours. Bob stopped Syphax in the tunnel, which had been cut through the house, and which had been hung with cedar and lilac and hollyhocks; he took a cup to refresh him, kissed right and left, and complimented the ladies for ten minutes. 'I feel certain I shall get through,' said he to Mrs. Smith. 'I'll be proud to hear it,' said Mrs. Smith back again; 'and if you do, the hole in the house shall stay as it is just to keep such a grand performance in memory.'

"My dear Miss Minny, that heroic woman was an honour to her sex. It was not her fault that Toney afterwards built up the hole to keep out the nor-wester, and to save the walls. The family were down with rheumatism, and the roof was coming in, before she capitulated.

"From Toney's to the old Fort was a gullied country. Bob got over a dozen of the gullies, some of which invited us to go a little about. He came to number 13. 'If you clear that,' said I, 'Syphax beats the world. It's thirty feet if it's ten.' Bob drew up, and looked in and over. 'Give me a drink,' said he. Of course we had the conveniences. He took a strong pull, and then splashed a little into his horse's mouth. He rode back about a hundred yards, and then putting his teeth together, raised a gallop. He made it faster as he came on. His eyes looked wicked. It was beautiful to see how Syphax planted his feet from the strokes of the gallop, just on the edge, and let himself be lifted. Bob drove in the spurs. 'Go it,' we screeched. Go it he did, but the bank gave way under the hoofs. There was a struggle as if the beast had wings; but he went down to the bottom of the gully like a locomotive.

"We scrambled down on foot. Bob had a shoulder out of place. Syphax got up, holding out a foreleg, and puffing like a brewer groggy with the steam from his vats. You could see by the beast's countenance that the courage was knocked out of him. 'Pull my arm in,' said Bob, 'and then go back for the Alderman mare. Ride her in at the lower end of the gully, and get her here. I can ride her up that bank by taking a slant. We have twenty feet wide to do it in.' We pulled the arm in. The Alderman mare was brought. Bob mounted and tried the slant. It would have been no go, but we shouldered the mare up, and got her out. Jack Brooke's judge, a tiptop fellow, helped; his blood was up, and he had no idea of such a ride being stopped. Bob looked like Julius Caesar when he got out, except that he was a dirty image of that elegant Roman.

"Away he went with a yell, and by the time we came near him again, he was in a gentleman's garden, and trying to get out. It was a six-foot brick wall that was before him, but he had jumped it to get in, and why shouldn't he jump it to get out? We were obliged to leave our horses and climb over to see about matters. 'Brandy and fire will do it,' said the umpire. Bob took the brandy, and I tied a bundle of straw to a pea-stick. 'Back to the centre walk,' said I. Bob backed. The mare was already furious, and the blood spirting from one of her flanks. 'Put her head well to it—we'll spoil her looks, but we'll get her over.' I lit the straw with a match, and clapped the blaze to her tail. She went at the wall like a charge of shot. She made her leap too quick, and lit on the top, but she rolled to the other side instead of falling back.

"Bob never gave us a shout to show that his neck was safe, but we presently saw him get away with his mare strong under him. We went on after. A mile further we saw the old Fort on a hill over the river. Bob took to water, scrambling down a muddy bank; he got over with a straight swim, climbed the bank with his mare looking sleek in the legs, and whip-tailed, and rode straight to the sign-post. Most of the company, by fast riding and driving on the high roads, had already got there.

"Wasn't there a roar when Bob came out! The breaking of a mill-dam in a freshet is nothing to it. We got to the place as soon as possible. Bob was saying nothing. I found something was the matter, and got close to him. 'The roll out of the garden flattened me,' he said, in a weakly way, 'the mare rolled over me twice. I'm hurt inside.' This, my friends, is the story of a remarkable ride. I defy the present times to produce a Rattlesnake Bob or a Syphax. My opinion is that the breed has run out—I mean both as to men and horses."

Major Wright sighed, and drank brandy and water. As he did so several of the indefinites of the party said to each other:

"The Major bores us confoundedly. Not a soul has said a word for thirty minutes except himself."

Tom Herries, with a good deal of fervour, begged to know "if the whole-souled gentlemen, who rode so well, got over the inside hurt?"

"Yes," answered the Major.

"And won the bet?"

"Certainly. But, upon my word, he won a loss. Jack Brooke's estate, it naturally turned out, was covered with mortgages. Bob came near calling Jack out when he made the discovery; but reflecting that Rattle-snake had been in the same condition, and that he had acquired a great deal of glory by his performance, he forgave Jack, and left him to mortgages, lawyers, &c. They made a clean sweep of it. As for positive losses, Bob had to pay the bet that he made on riding no horse but Syphax; then he had to owe Toney Smith for damage to his house. I assure you the winner lost in the business."

"It was a great ride," said Tom; "what became of Rattlesnake Bob?"

"Tom, my boy, you seem to be interested," said the gracious Major.

"Bob went out of the world shabbily for a fine gentleman. At a convivial party, some bets passed as to the time one could stand on his head. Rattlesnake Bob, in the midst of the best society in Virginia, made a bet, and undertook to win it. He was to stand on his head twenty minutes. He was so unfortunate as to smother at the end of three."

Andrew Blair had listened to the narrative of the ride, with an inattention, which his host construed into a rebuke of the Major's coarseness. Minny had listened with a good deal of interest. Perfectly refined people are not so fastidious as those who are climbing into "society" are apt to imagine; and this fair girl, moreover, had a weakness on the subject of horses and bold horsemanship. Whilst Minny said a kindly word to the Major, Tom Herries, ignorant of the rebuke of his father's looks, drank a brimmer to the memory of Rattlesnake Bob. Then Tom mused. Presently he said in a loud voice, from a distance of several seats:

"Miss Minny, could you stand on your head twenty minutes?"

There was a dead silence. Minny slowly lifted her eyes, and, like Lady Clara Vere de Vere, would have killed him with a stare, if Tom had been capable of being killed. Andrew Blair, quickened out of some absorbing meditations, looked surprised and shocked. John Herries bit his lips and was about to speak, when his wife left her seat, and inviting Minny to accompany her, withdrew. Major Wright laughed enjoyingly. Tom, as soon as the ladies were gone, became quite boisterous. The Major humored him. Black looks are nothing, where full cups have done their work; those of John Herries were impotent. Tom got from his chair, and coming to a wall, attempted to stand on his head.

"I'll bet fifty I can do it—for twenty minutes—if the wall's allowed," said Tom Herries.

"Come—come—my fine lad," said the Major. "Do you think that nobody's drunk but yourself?"

"Take Tom to his room," said the host controlling his rage, which yet gave a hissing sound to his voice. The servants, going about this task quietly, succeeded. Tom lost his bet: but no one had taken it.

John Herries saw that a great shock had been given to his project of a marriage between his son and the niece of his guest. Andrew Blair's countenance displayed this clearly enough. It was time to resort to a remedy. He called a servant.

"Give me that middle picture," he said quietly.

The servant brought it. It was one of the series illustrative of the

Dream of Eugene Aram. Aram, with the ghastly face, which I have spoken of already in noticing these paintings, bore on his back a dead man. A few drops of blood on the hair of the corpse, were so naturally painted that they seemed to be in reality drops of blood.

"The obscure artist who imagined that face," said Herries, holding the picture before Andrew Blair, "must indeed have been full of genius, and yet he died without the least fame."

"Terrible—terrible"—muttered Blair with a growing pallor.

"And this," said Herries, with words as clearly toned as they were deadly in their purpose, "this must positively be blood. Let us see."

Slowly he drew from a pocket a long knife, of an old fashion. He opened with deliberation the single blade—rubbed at some spots which seemed to have been rusted into it near the haft—and began scraping at the blood drops on the picture. The eyes of Andrew Blair protruded. They were no longer fixed on Eugene Aram and the dead man. They saw nothing but the knife. Presently their lids quivered, some faint streaks ran in zig-zags between them and the blanched cheeks, and the old man sank in his chair.

"I have gone too far," muttered Herries, springing from his seat.

CHAPTER IV

The Greeks believed that their Achaian temple, dedicated to the "dread Eumenides," could try, by some influence of its cold walls or sombre airs, the purity of those who entered it. If a man entered it with a crime lying secret at his heart, he betrayed himself by bodily tremors and the loss of reason. The house of John Herries, with its murder-pictures, and its thronging reminiscences of a former master, had been such a temple of the Furies to Andrew Blair.

He continued for many days in a state of mental imbecility and bodily prostration. During this time Herries hung about the sick man, with a misery and dread in his looks which excited the remark of all who saw him. When, at last, he learned, watching in a room adjoining the chamber in which Andrew Blair lay, that the unhappy man had awaked from a long sleep better in body, and with a restored intelligence, he placed a hand upon his brows, and drew a breath so long and so loud, that one might have fancied he had been fished up from a lake of brimstone just at the last gasp. And indeed the catching at hope, of which that hard-drawn inspiration was the outward sign, was the catching at life. When he spoke it was but to say—"Now we will do well again."

"Yes," replied Dr. Gaunt, the physician in attendance, an old gentleman of much simplicity, who saw a great deal of sweet affection and sympathy in the emotion of Herries—"yes; he will do well now. These attacks are peculiar. Indeed I may say that my patient is already fully himself again."

And, in confirmation of Dr. Gaunt's decisive opinion, Andrew Blair immediately prepared to return to his own house. Persuasion against his doing so too suddenly only threw him into nervous agitation, and Herries willingly saw him depart. The old man went away in his carriage, with Minny at his side. Erect, pale, with feeble hands clutching for a support, and the resolution of his features making all the sadder their strange expression of distress, the uncle deeply moved the heart of the niece on this melancholy return to Lindores. Minny had learned a profound lesson of devotion.

As soon as he could safely do so, Herries went to Lindores to arrange his important affairs. He chose for his visit one of those miraculous mornings, of glorious sunshine and cheering airs, which we sometimes find in the budget of December—like a leaf of Ariosto misplaced into Young's Night Thoughts. Andrew Blair sat by an open window, which, facing the south, caught obliquely a gentle south-west wind. The rays of the sun, coming also obliquely from the morning quarter, began to touch him. A pair of blue birds interchanged merry speeches, in a lilac clump, the buds of which were bursting. About a dwarfed cedar, misshapen and crouching, and looking like a Caliban among the straight brotherhood of lindens and beeches, some jays were engaged in a battle. The din was prodigious, and occasionally a pinch of feathers was whisked away, and scattered on the air. The jay is irritable and punctilious, and prefers war to peace, in any weather. Far away, down the slopes of the great hill, cattle browsed, or economised the unseasonable sunshine in motionless attitudes. At times, the shadow of a soaring hawk fell upon the grass, still green, below the open window, and silenced for a moment the pugnacious jays, leaving the blue-birds—those little winged violets which peep from under the fringes of winter, and are safe in their humility—to prate away as if not a care hovered in the skies above them. Refreshed by the scene—enjoying the southwind—cheered by the sunshine—Andrew Blair had not for a long time escaped so far from unhappiness. But suddenly the jays retreated from the cedar; the blue-birds passed twittering round a corner of the house; the calm currents beginning to keep even tone at the old man's ruined heart became again troubled. The arrival of John Herries made the change.

Herries, entering, greeted his host with politeness, and apparently with kindness. He congratulated him, pressing his hand at the same time, upon appearances of improved health. After a time he approached the point, and said:

"I have come, sir, to renew a business which your unfortunate illness interrupted."

Andrew Blair waved his hands and became troubled in countenance.

"I think we understand each other," continued Herries; "and I shall touch the subject now without cutting to the quick. I content myself with repeating that my son is a suitor for the hand of your niece. I presume that you will use your influence in his behalf?"

Herries paused upon this last sentence, which, worded so as to express a fact taken for granted, was yet sounded as a question.

"This is a sad proposition," said Andrew Blair feebly.

"How a sad proposition?" Herries became sinister in his looks. "You think it a degradation to mingle the common blood of my family with the pure blood of your own. Such is your thought, is it not?"

"I have no thought. I am incapable of thought, my good Herries," Blair replied. "Give me rest, Herries—give me rest."

"Willingly would I do so," said Herries, with a show of feeling too natural for hypocrisy; "but rest to you will be fatal to me."

"I do not understand you, Herries. Why are you bent upon this marriage? How can it affect you so deeply?"

Herries drew his chair close to his listener. "Hear me," said he, "and do not be unmanned by a fear that I shall tear open old wounds. I have a great object in view. I attain it by this marriage. It is unnecessary to enter into details. We *must* bring about this marriage."

"Then bring it about, Herries. I am shaken by disease and cares, and can aid very little in these struggles."

"Why should there be struggles?"

"Surely you cannot believe," said Andrew Blair, "that poor Minny will become willingly the wife of your son?"

"Why should I not believe so?" Herries replied, with bended brows. "You make a mistake. You have seen the surface of this wild boy of mine. Perhaps it is ridiculous. But I tell you that we—you, sir, and I—have nothing so good or so great in us as this apparent simpleton possesses under his absurd appearances."

"He may be worthy enough—and yet, Herries, he scarcely seems to be a match for my niece."

"Here is again your prejudice of blood," said Herries. "Blood—blood—when it flows under the lancet we see no difference between the currents of the high and of the low; when it spirts out under the knife, and boils into the ground, it cries with the same voice to God, whether the arteries from which it springs belong to a gentleman or to the poorest devil that ever dug for his bread."

"You are killing me," moaned Andrew Blair.

Herries paused. "I forget my resolution," he muttered, and held his peace for some minutes. The sunshine, the light wind, the glitter of the grassy slopes, restored the old man as certain remedies restore the patient who sinks under the knife of the surgeon. "We must deal gently," said Herries, and then in a louder tone spoke on:

"My friend, there is a secret between us. Be firm, I beg of you; let us forever drown the recollection of it. Let us bury it in a community of interests—in a fatherly affection centering on the same objects. My son once the husband of your niece, we will stand together, united, with no room for doubts, suspicions, *betrayals*, between us. Urge your niece —even give her a glimpse of the danger of your position, if you fail to move her by other means. You understand me when I say *the danger of your position;* and truly these are not empty words. Your disgrace —your destruction—will be the result of your failure; for I shall be desperate, and *will speak.* I temper my words to your weakness. You take their meaning fully, however. Now decide: will you or will you not urge the girl to this marriage?"

The lips of Andrew Blair moved, but no language came from them. Presently he succeeded, with a feeble struggle of his thin hands, in opening a case attached to his chair. He took from it a small bottle, and a wine-glass. He drank, with tremulous haste, a black looking draught.

"Send Minny to me," he said, "and wait below until I can give you an answer."

Herries, with a quick step, left the room. In a few moments Miss Blair entered it.

"You have sent for me, uncle," said Minny, as she drew a chair to the old man's side.

"Yes, my child; but give me a little time to collect my poor old intellects."

"How pleasant the wind is, uncle."

"Yes—yes—pleasant."

"This balmy weather brings up the violets; here is a bunch of them.

You see how I have tied them up with berries of the strawberry tree. It makes something quite pretty. The little blue flowers are relieved by the scarlet wax of the berries."

"My child," said the old man—beginning to assume an energetic expression, which perhaps his recourse to the bottle with the dark-coloured liquid had something to do in producing—"my child, what we shall have to say may prove a bitter sequel to this pretty nonsense of yours."

"I listen, sir."

"To come to the point then. Mr. John Herries has this morning proposed for your hand in the name of his son."

Minny stared.

"Is it so?"

"Even so," said Andrew Blair.

Minny threw her head back and laughed. It was a vibrating, metallic laugh, that. The ceilings pealed it back as though her white pulsing throat had been like that of Arcite, which Dryden tells us was "a trumpet with a silver sound." She presently controlled her merriment and said:

"And what answer did you make to this proposal which flatters me excessively?"

The old man seemed to be pained by the levity of his niece. It was with a manner of nervous irritation that he said:

"Be graver. If you reject the young gentleman, do it with a decent composure. Regard his feelings."

"Ah, sir," Minny answered, no longer laughing,—"he will find me grave and gentle when, face to face, I deny him. Do I wound human hearts wantonly? But you rebuke me for a slight fault as if there was more in this thing than you discover to me." As she spoke her glances became quick and apprehensive.

The old man answered:

"There is indeed a stern necessity that you should give to this proposal a serious consideration; indeed that you should school your inclinations, and give even a favorable answer."

"Uncle—uncle!" cried Minny Blair, with eyes round with their wonder, and her mouth contracted to a ruby ring. "Do you say that I must become the wife of silly Tom Herries? You are in one of your dreams."

The uncle shook his head. Presently he replied: "Minny, this young person is quite respectable,—honest and kind-hearted, I think,—and not ill-looking. His property will be considerable—and although I shall make your own considerable enough to render this argument of no great force, perhaps you will attach some importance to it."

"None whatever, uncle. Hear me sir. You seem to be serious. I hardly understand that you can be so. But I must be so. I am then with a solemn face to answer *yes* or *no* to this singular proposal. Well I answer *no*—a thousand times *no*."

There was spirit enough in this answer to rouse the old man to a peevish and direct assault.

"My dear," he said, "our preface has been long enough. You must marry this Tom Herries."

The girl rose in strange amazement—paused a moment—then putting the palm of a soft hand on each of her uncle's shallow cheeks, brought her lips near to his, and replied:

"No—inexorably no."

And she kissed his lips many times to prevent his answer. Perhaps she imagined that dull, ill-omened, denying monosyllable—a wave of the Dead Sea to draggle and drown poor Cupid at any time—made an end of the matter. But the answer, delayed by her gentle arts, came at last.

"Then, my child, you to whom I have looked for happiness in this miserable world will betray me to ruin, disgrace, perhaps *death*."

"You are dreaming uncle!"

"Dreaming? not so. This decision of yours will surely destroy me."

"Explain sir—make your meaning clear to me."

"No—there can be no explanation. But I speak the truth." He presently added "Know this much: years—many miserable years ago —I lost the great game of life in the temptations of one awful hour. I committed a terrible crime. There was a witness to it. I am the slave of that witness."

The girl stood speechless. As she stared, the eyes of her uncle seemed to protrude from their sockets, his hair to rise with electric life, and moisture gathered upon his forehead and upper lip in distinct drops.

"The vision is coming," the old man murmured. But the pale and nervous girl cast her arms about his neck, drew his cheek to her warm maiden bosom and said:

"Then there is a terrible truth, uncle. It is remorse, and not merely a disordered imagination that has shaken you for years. Poor uncle! Do you think that your Minny could love you less? You have fed me— loved me—saved me from the world that has but a cold heart for poor little parentless children. I have grown up to be of some importance.

How proud I am! Uncle, I am to save you. Worse than this absurd marriage would be possible to my love for you. I do not say 'I consent' —that would be rash. It may be avoided with safety to you. We must see. Man yourself. There is nothing to frighten us. We are here in the blessed sunshine. These are Minny's arms that you feel on your neck."

"Our hearts must break"—said the old man in tones infinitely mournful—for his spiritual terrors had subsided into mere grief. "Our hearts must break. How often high natures come to despair! Ah, we are creatures of fire when we are young; it is quicksilver that courses in our veins then. We are proud and swift, and do many unwise things. Well, we cure the unwise deeds with after wisdom. In our youth too we break dear ties, estrange those that love us; for we are self-sufficient, and say we are strong, able, chosen lords of the world, made in God's image; and the fires which we kindle within us for self-worship, we think should dazzle our fellows also and bring them to bow down. Even of this, age tames us. Time sweeps the nature bare of its vain glory. We heal the wounded self-love of others; we reunite the broken ties; we win back the lost friendship. Our errors break under us and are trampled into dust as we pass on. The road of life may glitter darkly with them under the onward feet—and yet the bright goal may be won. But crime—crime—ah! that is fatal. When in our swift pride we *strike*—when we shed the blood of man upon the betraying ground— then is there no cure—no cure. We pass then, living, the inexorable gates, with the fiery blazon 'hope passes not here.' We are given over to the fire that is not quenched, and the worm that never dieth."

"Uncle," said Minny, when these wild laudanum-kindled sentences had blazed to an end, "there is always hope. Our Saviour died that he might win that touching title. Let us pray to him."

The old man bowed his head; he did not answer the invitation to prayer. He presently spoke on:

"I am a poor old man—worn, weary and desolate. I have been sinful. Have I not been punished enough—punished enough? And yet around my closing years, in accumulation upon these dreadful sufferings, are crowding real dangers. Child, did you never discover that I was a—*coward*. Yes—men—the very brutes—have always quelled me. I have been subtle, never bold. Minny, if the true temper of a courageous nature which I have seen flash out from your girl's face had been mine I would have been to-day on the summits of man's ambition, re- nowned, able, and iron-braced. I did not possess it. I quailed—took life like a crouching beast that springs on a sure prey—and have grown old, remorseful and trembling. I quake now with real fears. Forgive me, brave little child, I am a *coward*."

Minny Blair answered:

"Uncle, I grope in the dark. I will not ask you to enlighten me. I catch, perhaps, a true guidance from the wild gleams which you have thrown on my path. I fear to have more light. We speak no more of your deeds, or of the inexplicable power which another seems to possess over you, and over my poor self. Just now I told you that I should postpone my consent to the proposed marriage until I discovered that it could not be avoided. Your manner and words drive me on. Perhaps I err; but for life or death, happiness or misery, I choose my lot promptly. I consent to the marriage which, a little while ago, I abhorred. Truly I am changed; I no longer abhor it."

Hope struggled with surprise in the weak visage of the old man.

"Say you so, my dear child? But you will again abhor it, when you fall from your higher feelings, and then you will renounce this decision."

"Uncle, I have come to a resolution, I will remain constant in it. Send for this gentleman who comes to us as a messenger. I will presently answer him."

The old man drew his niece to his bosom; no female emotion disturbed her; a smile more like the quivering gleam of blue steel, than any more cheerful radiance flitted over her cheerless face. She kissed him with hard lips, so strictly were they compressed, and said:

"Who knows, uncle, but we may be a very happy couple. A good heart does much to make a home happy."

Presently the elder Herries was summoned.

"My niece assents to the proposal with which she has been honored," said Andrew Blair with a slight haughtiness in his manner.

"I willingly consent to become the wife of your son," Minny added.

Herries answered these supremely pleasant words with mute action. Pressing Minny's white hand, he bowed very low.

The scene was at an end.

The stately girl, with head a little drooped, and a step as noiseless as the fall of snow on a winter lake, passed to the door, and disappeared.

CHAPTER V

"Wife, wife," said John Herries, "we have triumphed, and now life really begins to us. I feel like a Caesar fresh from a Pharsalia. That magnificent swindler you know, Mrs. Herries, extricated himself very honorably from his debts by that success. Now I may say that the past is purified, and future secured."

"We should thank God, and not be too presumptuous in our anticipations," answered the wife.

"There it is," said Herries. "You and I never seem to hope together. Put your hand into the bend of my arm. Now look up. Don't we look very much like a candlestick and its extinguisher? Madam, your are my extinguisher. But to-day my blaze is too strong for you. Dropping figures, Mrs. Herries, you are a conceited little person; you imagine yourself to be temperate, calm, and very wise. The truth is you are only not ardent, your frigidity has sometimes seen dull results which, in my sanguine temper I would not see; the consequence is you fancy your frigidity to be infallibility. You are conceited—more, you are wrong. Even if you were infallible it would be one of those cursed gifts which make life barren. What the deuce would life be without its delusions? Are you happy now, looking into the future as you do—like a little plain statue, cut out of cold gray marble, looking out over a waste tract, with two fixed frigid eyes? Madam, you take a great deal of trouble to make yourself disagreeable to me."

"I have no enthusiasm, my dear husband. But am I really disagreeable to you? I thought, if this grand match was made, we were to go down the hill of life happily together. I think you said that."

"If we have a partnership in happiness, you must contribute to the common fund. And yet after all, wife, I think I have enough for both. You are a good kind creature. God bless you with your demure airs. I feel like a lad of twenty. Positively I have not a care on earth."

"When will we have the wedding?" asked the wife, with a smile which discovered something of the hopeful cheerfulness of the husband.

"I did not forget that. Time defeats us too often to trust over much. A month from to-day the wedding will take place. What a lucky dog Tom is, to be sure. Thank you, my little fairy of the primp cap, for this son who secures so much to us. We must send for Georgiana. She must come from school to her brother's wedding."

With such talk Herries cheered himself after his successful visit to Lindores. His cares seemed to have been broken up and blown away, like a bank of cloud which a March wind assails, and lashes, huddling, beyond the horizon. His welkin was blue again, and flooded with a sunstream.

Meantime, as the days flew by, Minny Blair became less and less braced for the sacrifice, to which, in a moment of extreme emotion, she had devoted herself. The first visit of poor Tom Herries gave a beginning to this unnerving process. She spent a wretched night after enduring the interview with her intended bridegroom, whose misfortune it was to conceal many genuine qualities, of which the reader will become cognizant, under a mask of awkward folly. What an end did this marriage seem to those beautiful dreams which the imaginative girl had treasured, and which the young and pure of her sex, even where the instinct of love is yet objectless, "the maiden meditation fancy free," always pour upon the future!

Poor Minny concealed, as well as could be, the despondency into which she sank deeper and deeper. Her nature had an unusual degree of force, and those controlling grasps with which the strong of soul hold down their feelings and hide their sufferings were possible to her; she could put self down, and cheer the old man who had devoted her to wretchedness, with a brave ease and quite a genuine appearance of contentment with her fate. But this noble hypocrisy, exacting so much of her, was a stifling mask which might be assumed for a time, not worn constantly. She found her best escape from it in those out-of-door exercises to which she had always been accustomed, wandering walks to the woodlands, or gallops over the breezy slopes.

The beautiful weather of which I have spoken continued, with only some temporary interruptions. On a day as bright as that which saw her consent yielded to the approaching marriage, Minny Blair rode her swift mare Flight at a restrained gallop over a firm road at the foot of the Lindores' Hill. A servant followed her at a short distance. She rode to a rendezvous. Our friend, Major Wright, and his daughters, two magnificent young monsters of a family of Centaurs, had given her an invitation to a fox chase; an invitation which, making an experiment with the "*atra cura post equitem*," she readily accepted. Animated by the exercise, and gathering that confidence in self which the swift but controlled motion of a free horse creates in the rider, Minny came in a resolute humor to the rendezvous.

Major Wright, his daughters and a number of other persons were assembled in an open field when Miss Blair arrived. Dogs were howling, whining and yelping, horses were snorting and pawing, young gentlemen were laughing, elderly gentlemen were directing and swearing.

"My dear young lady," cried Major Wright, who had come to the ground in a sulky, and seemed, by ridding himself of a superfluous coat, to be preparing to get on horseback—"my dear young lady, you are quite an acquisition, and I appoint myself your servant in the ride. But here comes that blackguard Tom Herries, to deprive me of the greatest pleasure in the world. Tom, you rascal, what are you doing in that extraordinary toggery? Do you think that you cut a creditable figure?"

"Whatever mistake there is, Major, Jerry Maddox the tailor made. But attend to your own business."

Major Wright, without deigning an answer to Tom's rebellious request, brought his long whip over his right shoulder, and then into contact with a particular portion of the body of a small boy who, doubled up behind him on the bars of the sulky, held a saddled horse by the bridle. The manoeuvre displayed practice; the tip of the thong came down with precision; the little knot of a boy unrolled himself as a matter of course, got down and led the horse forward. The dogs, meantime, had been turned off into a swampy thicket near at hand; as the Major mounted they broke suddenly into full cry. Almost at the same instant a member of the party gave the view halloo. The fox had waited to be *flushed* like a woodcock, and now made a gallant dash forward at his best pace, with the pack thundering after him, all in a body, over open ground.

"He'll never get clear. They'll have him down at the first fence. We must give up all hopes of a run," sighed a rosy old gentleman, as the well-disciplined party awaited with drawn reins the moment for dashing on after fox and hounds.

"He's over. That snap of Black Bell's just missed him," cried Major Wright. "Set forward—slowly."

Thirty good horses went forward with one will. Tom Herries rode at Minny Blair's side, Flap-ear keeping an even stride with Flight. Poor Tom, generally an ardent fox-hunter, looked moody. A minor trouble had grown out of Major Wright's critical remarks upon his coat. His tailor, perhaps a runaway English apprentice, had made it after a subdued and correct English fashion; Nimrod might have approved of it—Major Wright did not. Tom was enflamed with disgust for it.

"But," he resolved, "I will carry it with the foremost, and a tumble or two will make it plain and common enough. However, if I live, I shall beat Jerry Maddox."

But this minor annoyance was only one trivial cause of his moodiness.

The party presently came to a strong fence with a single panel half down. All took it, in turn, at the gap—all except Tom Herries. He diverged and selected a high and strong panel; he touched Flap-ear with the spurs, lifted him and went handsomely over.

"A good, and bold horseman," mused Minny Blair.

A word from the lady showed Tom that her criticism had been favorable; and this word chained him all the more surely to her side. As they rode on, Minny was forced to perceive that her lover was many times on the point of speaking, and that the subject which occupied him was quite too engrossing for his enjoyment of the chase.

"You have something to say to me, Mr. Herries," she said kindly.

"Yes," Tom answered; "but how did you know it, Miss Minny? It is kind of you to give me a chance of speaking what I have to say. I could never find courage to speak out on my legs; but on horseback it is different. I feel myself more of a man when I have a fast horse under me."

"Speak, Mr. Herries—I am listening."

"Miss Minny, the old folks have arranged that we are to be married. If any man in the world says that any man in the world—you see I hitch in what I had to say already; but I mean no man in the world ever loved a person more than I love you. Do you see the cabin there—to your left? I would give the best part of my life if you were a poor girl living there, that I might show how dearly I love you, by lifting you up to be my wife. Pardon me, Miss Minny, if I am too bold."

"We are to be man and wife, Mr. Herries," replied Minny coldly, "and, of course, you are not over-bold in saying that you love me."

"Thank you," sighed poor Tom, "but you talk so coldly, and look so sad, that I am afraid the old folks are forcing you to marry me. If so, say the word; I think I can manage the matter."

"How would you manage it, Mr. Herries?"

"By breaking my neck in this ride."

"He possesses generosity and courage," mused Minny. She smiled kindly, but gave no answer in words.

Riding side by side, the unmatched lovers took every obstacle with equal strides; the chase had kept a direct line; only Major Wright and his elder daughter, Miss Boadicea, were well up with them. The crowd came in long-drawn array behind. The chase had continued an hour at a quick pace. Miss Araminta Wright, who surely would otherwise have been with the first, loitered with a lover—a young townsman who thought a gallop a dreadfully fast gait, and was by no means comfortable in a pair of close-fitting buck-skin breeches, which the same innovating Jerry Maddox had made for him.

Major Wright, observing Tom Herries and Minny Blair, said to himself:

"I never before thought 'em matched."

Then he shouted to them. They were fifty yards before him, but his voice was sharp and practised, and they heard him very well.

"Turn to the right—bear down."

Tom and the lady made no answer, but galloped straight on.

"Bear to the right," shouted the Major again. "The Deep Cut is half a mile ahead—just before you."

"I know that very well," Tom shouted back. "I think I shall go over it, Major. Remember Rattlesnake Bob."

"Hold up—hold up," cried the old fox-hunter. "It is a real gulf—thirty feet across, and fifty feet deep. Turn you fool—turn to the right."

"Rattlesnake Bob rode at a gully thirty feet wide," answered Tom, without turning in his saddle.

"I exaggerated," screamed the Major. "Besides, he fell in. Stop—stop —for God's sake."

As he said this, Tom and Minny Blair, galloping over descending ground, came within view of the gully. It was indeed more than enough to justify Major Wright's remonstrance. The gathered waters of a wide extent of sloping country, contributed in rills, made a torrent here after every dashing rain, and had ploughed out not a mere gully but a frightful chasm.

"Do you mean to try that leap?" said Minny calmly, as she saw the gulf full in front, at a distance of some four hundred yards.

"Answer me one question," Tom Herries replied with fire in his eyes. "Do you love me, Miss Minny, or am I to marry and break our hearts?" Tom reduced his speed as he spoke.

"Do not try the leap," said Minny. "I warn you."

"Yes or no." Tom raised his reins; the fire of his eyes burned brighter.

The mind will sometimes take in at a glance the full picture of life, condense thoughts and passions into the throb of a moment. Minny Blair, as Tom Herries spoke, sounded the present, and despaired of the future. Then a resolution, as swift as that with which Bianca Capello halved the poisoned cake and ate with her husband, took possession of her.

"Perhaps you are wise," she said. "Death is nothing."

Tom Herries saw the purpose of the gallant girl; a sudden appreciation of this sole fellowship of which she could assure him, made him furious with joy.

Major Wright, thundering on, screamed with a cracked voice: "Stop—stop—you d—d fool."

Tom, now within a hundred yards of the chasm, answered:

"Good-bye, Major. Your fine story gave me this glorious idea."

"Be wary," almost whispered Minny Blair, with a sudden return to love of life. "It is possible to get over."

Flight and Flap-ear were within ten yards of the brink. The sharp whip of the lady stung the shoulder of the gallant mare. Flap-ear felt the grinding rowels tear his flanks. Then both bounded. Major Wright dashed a hand over his eyes to clear their vision. He saw the mare clinging to the opposite brink of the chasm, Minny bending forward in the saddle to aid her. His heart was in his mouth. But in another moment he found words. "Thank God," he said;—for he saw Flight rise with a struggle, which broke away several feet of the bank, and escape with her burthen. Tom Herries was not visible.

CHAPTER VI

Major Wright, by a circuitous course, reached the bottom of the Deep Cut. He hurried to the spot which must have received the falling man and horse. He came near it; he gave that first eager look which we give with beating hearts, when we dash on to learn if life has become death. The horse was lying on his back, with his neck bent beneath him, and the foaming mouth *turned up* near the saddle. There could be no life with such a posture. At the distance of several feet from the dead horse lay the rider. Major Wright bent over him.

"Tom—Tom—my boy"—cried the old gentleman—"if there's any life in you, for God's sake inform me of the fact."

Tom Herries made no answer. Major Wright called to his daughter, whose large-featured face, surrounded with superb red curls, he saw thrust forward beyond the brink above.

"Gallop down and head the crowd; bring Gaunt; you'll find him amongst the foremost; ride fast, you jade, ride fast."

As he spoke a shadow fell on the ground near him; he was kneeling with the head of Tom Herries on his arm; as he looked up from this posture he saw Minny Blair coming to join him. The red face of the immense gully was in most parts nearly precipitous, but Minny had chosen her path well, and the nimbled-footed girl was presently at the bottom.

"If the boy is dead," said Major Wright, "a good rider, and a bold fellow has gone to his account."

"And a generous and true-hearted man"—added Minny Blair, with white lips, as she sought with tremulous fingers for the pulses of life.

"See how this arm falls," said the Major; "and here is a bloody cut on the head. Look at his neck. It is as white as your own, and as round as a column. And his breast here—what muscle the boy shows!"

Minny searched the wound on the head, cleansed it of the clay, and bound it up with the kerchief from her neck. Then with no feminine fastidiousness she placed her fingers upon the natural surface above poor Tom's heart.

Meanwhile Miss Boadicea, with fast riding, had overtaken Dr. Gaunt. Long, slim, sallow, high-cheeked, with hat aslant from the stress of the wind, and skirts puffed wide, loose-riding and enthusiastic, the good Doctor took his fences and snuff alternately and with equal precipitation. He reminded one, in some points, of Punch's imagination of Lord Brougham hunting the wild boar at his French chateau. Miss Boadicea, overtaking, laid violent hands on him.

"You must come, Doctor. Mr. Herries is hurt. Father sends for you."

"In five minutes—the fox will be down in four," remonstrated Dr. Gaunt.

Miss Boadicea, with a "gentle force," wrenched the old gentleman's hand from its hold on the reins, drew these over his horse's ears, and led him at a canter to a place of descent into Deep Cut. Dr. Gaunt took snuff out of his waistcoat pocket, like Napoleon.

When the Doctor had examined Tom Herries in silence, for a minute, he said:

"Life is still in him."

Major Wright snorting like one of his horses, blew off a thousand motes of trouble. But he quickly asked:

"Will life stay in him?"

"Get him up," answered Dr. Gaunt; "get him up without a rub. We may save him."

"Thank God," escaped Minny's lips, with a subdued sob.

News of the fall into the Deep Cut had reached the hunting party at various stages of the chase. Some were already at hand to aid in getting Tom Herries up. When this had been accomplished, Dr. Gaunt plied his art with judgment. In a short time plain signs of returning animation appeared. At last the lips moved, and the eyes opened.

"The left arm is broken, and the cut on the head has let out a great deal of blood," said the Doctor. "But the bleeding has saved the brain. If there is no serious internal damage, we will make him all right again. Go some of you to the next cabin and bring the door and a bed. What an escape to be sure! He must have been terribly stunned," concluded the old gentleman as he looked over, and down, into Deep Cut.

"If the boy is alive this day month," said Major Wright with a fine energy, "I'll give him such a dinner as will put the county under the table; and, Gaunt, we'll drink his health before a tip-top appreciating company as a fine, dashing, dare-devil fellow. We will. I have made up my mind. After that," added Major Wright, "never say die."

"We must bring him through," said the Doctor enthusiastically.

"And this dear young lady," the Major continued, "has positively succeeded in doing what this stout young fellow showed a glorious spirit in only attempting. The mare beats the world at a level leap. We must meet here shortly to measure the distance accurately. We must also look about for some expert writer to put the young lady and her mare into a spirited description. Gaunt—if it wouldn't disturb Tom, I should like very much to make myself comfortable with a shout or two."

By this time a door and bed had been procured; Tom, placed on these, was borne homeward. Minny Blair remained with Miss Boadicea, whilst a servant went after Flight, who browsed beyond the gully. As they waited, Miss Araminta approached with her lover. They came on, now swiftly, now cautiously—cantering and walking by turns—like the measure of Mr. Poe's Ulalume. The young gentleman from town was in a gay humor. The pair had heard nothing of the misadventure —love is so engrossing. When the owner of the uncomfortable buckskins was enlightened, and looked, craning, into the depths of Deep Cut, his whiskers stood on end, and his boots rattled in the stirrups.

Miss Blair, once more in the saddle, bade the young ladies adieu, and turned Flight's head.

"Won't you ride home with us?" suggested Miss Araminta politely.

"You must excuse me," answered the poor girl, only slowly recovering a firm tone. "I ride after Mr. Herries."

The young ladies stared.

"Well, I thought Miss Minny detested Tom Herries!" said Miss Boadicea.

"They are lovers. Love—love!" sighed Miss Araminta, looking affectionately upon the young gentleman from town.

"Do your ladies," inquired this latter, who had conceived, from her unimpressed demeanor, that Miss Blair appreciated himself too lightly —"do your ladies ride off, in this way, after their sweethearts, as a general thing? But a person who could bring herself to take such a jump as this, over such a terribly deep place, is capable of the most extravagant actions."

Minny Blair, unconscious of this censure, galloped away, saying: "To-day has made a great change in my views."

Some hundred yards before her Dr. Gaunt and Major Wright rode, one on each side of Tom Herries.

"What are you thinking of, Gaunt?" said the Major. "Does the boy's case look worse?"

"No—he does well enough," replied Dr. Gaunt. He added after a sigh—"We lost the best end of the run. What became of the fox, gentlemen?"

CHAPTER VII

Two weeks passed away, and the day appointed for the marriage of Tom Herries and Miss Blair came. It found the bride-groom in wretched condition. A violent fever had seized upon him soon after the dreadful fall; it had abated, leaving him very feeble and not out of danger. So the rising sun of the wedding-day brought no peace or joy to John Herries. He had labored with a stern energy to have the marriage accomplished without delay. He would have given Minny a dying husband; but his son would not permit this extreme measure. Tom retained something of the singular purpose which had urged him into the Deep Cut. On the morning of the wedding-day he mused to the following effect:

"If I die now it will be all the better. If this life is worth any thing, it is only so when we can be happy in it. We like to live because we like to enjoy ourselves; if we find it impossible to enjoy ourselves at any time, ever in the future, the best motive for living is gone. Men often come in this way to be disgusted with life, and yet are afraid of death. It scares them back; it does not scare me. But all this is only one selfish view of the case; I am to front death because I cannot be a happy man. There is the other and greatest reason why I should die; Miss Minny will be very much relieved by my death. Fever, burn on."

And supplied with the fuel of such despairing reflections the fever did burn up anew. Tom Herries became delirious then, and raved for several days and nights. On one of these terrible days, the elder Herries and his wife were in a distant apartment, to which only the shrillest of the wild cries penetrated.

"We are ruined—lost—overwhelmed—I am one of the damned," groaned the black-browed father.

"It is a grievous trial to lose this my only son; but, husband, your despair is a more dreadful blow to me than the death of my first-born child."

"Wife, these cold-blooded Blairs have crushed us. That girl led the boy to his death. May the curse of Almighty God—"

A low tap at the door arrested the blind malediction of the thwarted and despairing man. The door opened, and Minny Blair entered. At the same time also entered one of those doleful cries of delirium which wandered about the passages, and galleries, and recoiling from the closed doors, rose to the ceilings and even to the hollows of the great roof above.

Herries shuddered; the cry went to his heart like a dagger. In the face of his wife was that dry anguish which craves tears, and sometimes becomes madness for want of them. Minny Blair was calm, resolute, but very pale.

Herries advanced to meet her, saying with an impetuous manner:

"You are here! You are as cold as a pillar of salt. Are these howls, which are two-edged swords to us, nothing to you? Come." He took the girl by the hand with a rude force and led her from the room, along the gloomy passages straight to the chamber of his delirious son.

"Death is nothing," Tom Herries repeated as they came into his chamber. His mind had wandered back to the moments passed in that restrained gallop up to the verge of the Deep Cut, and words then spoken were now on his lips, broken, wanting in continuity, but full of meaning to the pale girl who stood above him.

"Death is nothing," repeated Tom. "Don't take the leap; we may get over. The white queen with a yellow crown round her head condescends to ride with me. Her hair is like long willows. Lord! how it streams in my face. It blinds me. Death is nothing. Whip—spur—here we thunder. Screech, Major." And Tom Herries yelled. The wild

Jager, who is said to traverse the German forests by night, might utter such a yell, in the closing rush of his moonlit chase.

An old servant, looking like some old noble physician of Carthage or Utica, so striking was the fine antique dignity of his face, held poor Tom upon his bed. Dr. Gaunt slept in a chair in a corner of the chamber; the cries of his patient did not rouse him.

"How deep her eyes are!" The speech of Tom Herries went wandering on. "They are like two blue wells, with a little star glimmering in the bottom of one of them and a horned moon in the other. Take away your eyes—they are distressing because they are so sad. And so you will ride with me, beautiful lady? Flight rushes like an eagle. An eagle has a singular scream; don't you think so? I saw one, a short time ago, come down from the mountains on his way to the sea. As the wind struck him he yelled. I must let you hear how he yelled." Again Tom uttered a cry, as shrill and defiant as the osprey's.

A mind all a-glow with the wild fires of fever is often raised to be of kindred with that of the rapt poet; the "vision" seems to be as palpable, and "the faculty divine" as vigorous: only as a fatal drawback, the vision of delirium goes flitting, shifting, now some bright face, presently a fanged mouth, alternately something angelic and something demoniac; and the faculty divine of delirium, instead of persevering into fair creations, mars its work into the same incongruities of the vision—for instance, when it would finish a delicate hand to its idea of an angel, or beautiful woman, it is taken captive by a fantasy, and makes the arm stream off like a horse-tail, or end with a serpent's open mouth.

Tom Herries was a-glow in this way; and his stimulated wits were busy upon such wild work. He had not been sufficiently trained in speech, or fed with the thoughts of others, to talk the delirious eloquence of a mad scholar, but his speech was yet in its way brilliant, and ran into metaphor and simile; the fever-blaze had even brought out upon the tablets of his memory, as heat brings out characters traced in sympathetic ink, certain odds and ends of old verse. Tom certainly, in his ordinary condition of wholesome dullness, could never have recalled them.

I cannot venture to tax the reader with the whole of the wandering talk of this cheerless scene. I must hurry to the end of it. After much of a like kind, Tom said—still recurring to the desperate ride:

"We got upon fast horses. The sun was shining and the ground was all in a white blaze and singing like silver under the clack of the horse-shoes. Lord! what a gait we went at!

> 'He mounted himself on a coal-black steed,
>   And her on a freckled grey—
> With a bugalet horn hung at his side—
>   And roundly they rode away.'

So—so. She rides like a queen of the Tartars when she hears her king's horn. She is strait as a poplar. How her curls fly! I thought one of them was a yellow snake, and snapped at me as the wind whipped it out. But it was not so. The beautiful lady has a delicious mouth with scarlet lips, and eyes cut out of blue jewels. Father, give me some wine. There is a little stream coming down a hill—what a fresh, cool stream!—bring me near it, and put my mouth to it. How careless! You have let me fall to a great depth just as I meant to drink. The fall stuns me, and I cannot look up. Ah, now I can. Reach out a hand, Miss Minny; Lord! what an arm she puts out—long, and white as the wood of a peeled maple. But it lifts me—up—up—up—to life again. You draw me up—you make me live—your merciful eyes give me unspeakable happiness."

The last sentence was spoken calmly; the eyes of the speaker were directed full to the face of Miss Blair; the deeply-moved girl answered it as though it had been the utterance of a sane man.

"Would that I could draw you up—would that I could make you live."

"What price would you pay for his safety?" the elder Herries asked with a manner of harsh scrutiny.

"My life, if necessary. You have misjudged me, sir. I am not cold and indifferent to the condition of your son."

Miss Blair passed to the chair of Dr. Gaunt, and shook him with so much force that he presently looked up with a pair of very red eyes, and said—"Bless me, I must have fallen into a doze."

"Doctor—are you quite awake? Is there no means of curing this terrible delirium?"

"The delirium will go off," replied Dr. Gaunt, rubbing his eyes with the corners of his handkerchief;—"but how it will leave him is another question." Then the old gentleman blew his nose explosively; and having done so, proceeded to charge it again with an immense grasp of snuff—not a pinch.

"Now that you are quite awake, promise me this, Doctor; stay faithfully here, and when the delirium is about to subside send a fast rider for me. Whatever the hour may be, night or day, through any weather I will come at once. I have a remedy which I wish to try as soon as your patient can receive it."

So saying, Miss Blair came again to the bed—removed the elf-locks from the forehead of poor Tom Herries—looked sadly upon his face whilst her lips moved with unuttered words—and then, turning, left the room. John Herries followed; as she sped along a passage he called to her; looking back she saw him come up slowly and with a meditative countenance. He presently said:

"I have entertained hard, and now I am sure, unjust thoughts of you. Pardon my rudeness—forgive my evil thoughts."

"I do so, Mr. Herries, without reservation."

"We are overwhelmed by this domestic affliction."

"Let us hope, sir."

John Herries fixed a forgiving and even a tender regard upon Minny Blair; the community of feeling avowed in her brief "let *us* hope sir," swept his mind clear of all lingering doubts, and of much of its fear. This gentle and generous girl, partaking his griefs, was not an enemy to darken his future, when the power to do so should pass, by the death of her uncle, into her hands; moreover, a finer chord than this selfish one was touched.

"I confide in you," he said, "for I begin now to know your noble nature. We turn over a bright leaf, Miss Blair, when we discover a true and self-sacrificing friend—and all the brighter when we find the friendship where we looked for a scornful want of sympathy. God bless you."

Minny Blair's eyes became suffused with tears. The gentleness of a stern man is always effective.

Minny sat by her uncle's side, at Lindores, one stormy morning a few days after the visit, some scenes of which I have just given to the reader. The old man quietly enjoyed her presence and discourse. He did not perceive a frequent lapse, from the topic which seemed to engage her, into momentary silence, and thoughts of other things; for the devoted girl would quickly fly back from these broodings, and re-enter with hurried animation upon her suspended task of amusing.

Breaking in upon her feverish discourse, came a summons; Dr. Gaunt had despatched the fast rider to say that Tom Herries had recovered his reason. Minny, faithful to her promise, encountered a severe storm, and was soon at the bed-side of her lover. Tom, whose face had

become very much like a hatchet, held her hand placidly and welcomed her with intelligence, but without excitement. His cheeks were
of an ashy white; his eyes were all the more prominent for the falling
away in the adjacent parts, but they were redeemed by a soft and
gentle expression; his chin and upper lip had sprouted a neglected
beard, crisp, short, and of an auburn colour. This Aenobarbus with the
hatchet face was certainly not very winning in his looks, but the eye of
pity and generous appreciation which beamed upon him seemed to take
no note of his extraordinary want of comeliness.

"You perceive," said Tom lowly, "that I am nearly gone. Have a
little patience; I will be out of your way before long."

Minny stooped until her breath stole like a faint south wind over the
stubble of Tom's chin, and replied:

"I perceive no such thing. You are strong and will live now. Do you
know that you must *live for me?*"

"Live for you?"

"Certainly. We are to be married—are we not?"

Tom sighed, and looked up sadly and wistfully.

"Why do you sigh?"

"I must not have a wife so much above me. Of course you must
always despise me, and be incessantly wretched yourself."

"You are generous, and devoted," the beautiful girl said in low tones,
and with a tremor in them which is always of gentle omen. "But you
want a just and manly self-appreciation. I think so nobly of you that,
upon my word, I am unwilling to forego"—here Minny checked
herself with a smile. She presently said—"Will you keep my hand,
which you hold now, if I give it to you willingly?"

Tom seemed very much surprised.

"I perceive," said Minny, "that you are incorrigible with your
humble and delicate fancies; you are a singular lover. But if you are
resolved not to speak, I must be so unfeminine as to do so. Mr. Herries,
will you remain faithful to your engagement, and permit me to be your
wife?"

The truth dawned upon Tom Herries. After a long silence, during
which his countenance betrayed many varying emotions, he said:

"You are not a human creature—but one of God's beautiful angels."

"Thank you. You are very much mistaken, however; you must
perceive that my hand, which you have nearly broken, is substantial.
You must also perceive that I have no wings." To prove this last
assertion the tall and lithe girl turned her person until the graceful

sweep of her shoulders became visible to Tom Herries. There were no celestial pinions, but only such shoulders as the quiver of Diana the huntress doubtless rested upon.

Her modest lover, retaining her hand, answered the speech and the pretty gesture which accompanied it:

"Your hand is substantial and warm, and you have no wings, but you are at least as good and beautiful as if you were an angel. Miss Minny—Miss Minny—do not conceal anything from me. Speak truly, from the bottom of your heart. You are perhaps pretending that you love me, in order to save my good-for-nothing life."

"I said just now, Mr. Herries, that you were incorrigible. How often do you mean to compel me to tell you that I love you? Recollect that you have not once said that you loved me. Do you wish me to explain why it is that I am willing to become your wife? Well, fellowship in high sentiment produces love; and did we not, Mr. Herries, you and I, unite ourselves in gallant fellowship, when we galloped down to that frightful gulf? I felt it possible to become your wife in that swift moment; it was because I did so that I flew back to the hope of life, and used my best means—then when the speed of our horses, on the very verge as we were, could not be restrained—to preserve it. You heard me, in that last moment, call to you to be wary."

"Speak on; your voice is so musical. What a brave heart you must have! Speak on."

"I have positively very little to say, Mr. Herries. It is not often that we find inviolable truth, generosity, extreme devotion of self for the ease of others, courage, tenderness, united in one human being. I think that I have found them in you. Whatever drawbacks you may possess with them, you will, doubtless, cure in time. Your worst faults have sprung from a want of self-respect; there can be little dignity of character where a modest but manly self-respect is wanting. Is not this a strange, grave mode of speaking to you? I repeat that I love you—if you take any pleasure in the avowal. You still hold my hand; it shall be yours forever, when you are well enough to receive it."

"Well enough to receive it? That I will be without much delay," said Tom Herries. "I have entirely given up the idea of dying. God bless you—good—beautiful—generous—lady! Do not go yet. Leave your hand in mine. So you are to be my wife? This hand—how soft, and white, and warm it is!—is to be mine forever?"

Tom drew the hand to his lips. Almost at the same moment he

caught a glimpse of himself in a glass across the room. He heaved an immense sigh, and muttered:

"There never was any one so miserably ugly as I am."

Minny Blair laughed, and said:

"You are certainly not very handsome; but sick people are not generally handsome. You must be well very soon, and then you will be better looking."

Adding quickly, "I seal our contract," she stooped and kissed his cheek.

When Dr. Gaunt came back to the chamber from which Miss Blair had for an hour banished him, he found his patient in so hopeful a state that he began to entertain sanguine expectations of the fulfilment of Major Wright's promise. This promise, the reader will recollect, was to celebrate the recovery of Tom Herries with a dinner to the "picked gentlemen" of the country; at which dinner the hospitable Major was under an obligation to toast Tom as "a fine, dare-devil, dashing fellow."

"We will get on now, I think," said Dr. Gaunt. "If there is no change for the worse by to-morrow, Wright must have notice."

And Tom Herries shook disease off. Azrael has little to do with bold, hopeful hearts. Minny Blair had poured oil into his flickering and failing lamp; it began, with the moment in which she did so, to burn up anew, and soon regained a clear and strong lustre.

CHAPTER VIII

When I began this history it was with the purpose of developing the progress of a nature in some respects well-gifted, from a single crime to which unrestrained passions in an evil hour propelled it, to remorse and eventual ruin. I found myself very early beguiled into a love-story, and thrown quite out from my original design. I must now leave the more pleasant theme, which should have been subordinate, to give in a final scene some necessary explanations, and an appearance of connection between the beginning and ending of my work.

In hastening on to this final scene, I pass over the details of a great event—the marriage of Tom Herries with the beautiful Minny Blair; a lady whose worth, inasmuch as it was infinite—I trust the reader has long ago discovered this—could receive no increase from the splendid dowry which the love of Andrew Blair bestowed with her. It was a brave wedding; and its results have been fortunate. An unequal match can scarcely remain unequal very long, except where mutual dislike exists as a repellent, and prevents assimilation. The coarse and common must yield to the high and refined, or the converse must happen. There must be a lifting up or a pulling down.

In the case before us the better result has followed. It will be remembered that the follies which Tom Herries committed in an early part of this history were after-dinner follies; he has since become somewhat marked for a gentlemanly moderation in his cups. His intelligence is not remarkable; but his manners are sufficiently subdued, leaving a fresh, entertaining and natural gayety without coarseness; indeed I find this excellent gentleman a very agreeable companion, in the long evenings which I occasionally spend with him. When we recollect, moreover, how honorable, courageous and devoted he certainly is, we can scarcely pity his magnificent wife for the union, or deem her aristocratic hand and true heart, more than his due. Now let us pass on to a conclusion.

It was a summer evening, six months after the wedding. Death was descending upon the old and weary master of Lindores. His intellect, enfeebled but not clouded, measured the pace of its approach.

The windows of the chamber, in which he lay dying, were raised; their curtains, hanging before them, shut out a flood of moonlight, but let in the warm breath of an August breeze. The trees, whose long boughs rustled against the walls and eaves of the house, were alive with the sharp cries of katydids and numberless other little musicians of the summer night. Now and then a bat flitted in, as a curtain streamed with the entering breeze, and circled about the ceiling until a succeeding swell of the wind reopened a way for egress. Continually several large beetles droned in their harsh flight, beating the white walls with horny wings. Lights were burning dimly in the chamber.

At the bed-side stood Minny Blair, now Mrs. Herries, and a tall gentleman in the black dress of a clergyman. As we join this group Andrew Blair begins to speak decisively.

"Minny, the time has come for acquainting you with the dreadful secret of my life," he said with a transient energy.

"Any extraordinary communication will move you, sir, and may injure you."

"Go to the walnut cabinet; press the carving at the extreme corner next the window; you will find a drawer—it fastens with a spring. You will see a single paper—bring it to me."

His niece followed these directions—discovered and opened the secret drawer of the cabinet, and presently came back with the paper. It was folded like a law-paper, and labelled simply, "The statement of A. B."

"Bring the lights nearer; and you, Mr. Gibson, read aloud what I have there written. Minny, remain and hear."

Presently Mr. Gibson, the clergyman, putting on his spectacles and arranging the lights, opened the paper and read aloud.

"I ask pardon of Almighty God for a grievous crime which I, Andrew Blair, have committed. I fear to make appeal for forgiveness to the less merciful tribunal of man; for my crime man and his laws will not pardon. I make this confession to be read by my representatives when death shall have removed me from fears of earthly justice. Why do I make it? I know not, except that my secret struggles incessantly to escape, and I imagine that some peace may be gained by providing even for its eventual release. A secret of blood ravages the heart that would utterly confine it.

"On the 20th day of November, in the year 18—, Col. Arthur Pellew, my neighbor, came to my house. I received him kindly, and induced him to remain and dine with me. Some months before, a portion of his lands had been sold under my agency; I had been made trustee in a deed of trust to secure payment of debts due from Pellew to certain persons living at a distance. The debts had slept for several years; demand of payment happened unfortunately to be made shortly after a change in Pellew's political relations with me, and upon the heel of something like a quarrel which his failure to support me in a closely contested election had produced between us. At a time subsequent to the sale of his lands I yielded so far to my desire to appease him, and regain a lost friend, as to explain fully all facts in connection with my trusteeship. He seemed then to yield up his harsh opinion that *I had brought his creditors suddenly upon him, and pressed the sale of his lands, in vindictive return for his political desertion of my cause.* I fancied that I had convinced him of the truth, i.e. that his creditors had made the demand of their own accord, and had even compelled me against my earnest remonstrances to make the sale.

"On the occasion of the visit to me I continued for several hours to believe that my guest had been quite satisfied by my explanations; as we dined together, however, I perceived that I had been mistaken. His complaints were renewed, and in exceedingly offensive terms. I endured them with a show of equanimity, but with an intense rage under it. He left my house; I could not remain behind; with a half-formed purpose of vengeance I joined him. My manner continued to be moderate—I uttered certain formulas of regret that my neighbor and old friend should misunderstand and so deeply wrong me. His answer was a direct charge of falsehood, and double-dealing, accompanied by an oath, and a look not only of anger but of contempt. Then the measure was filled to overflowing.

"Would to God that my nature had been of the common sort which resents wrong or outrage on the spot, and when reflection comes, has no pang but for the passionate blow which laws and the best wisdom of man half excuse. *Ira brevis furor est.* But the very moderation which I could seem to assume, and which was commonly considered proof of a poised intellect and tutored nature was my terrible curse. Why should I not admit the truth? The moderation of manner under offence which I had always practised was only the result of *cowardice.* The red blaze of anger in my fellow man paled me into timidity; it was only an art of manner that made the timidity appear a temperate and wise forbearance. I was in fact a craven, with a vile and vindictive temper—more unrestrainable after its subtil sort than the more ordinary passion of a rash choleric man.

"I continued to walk with Col. Pellew, but now in silence; he gave me, at first, a look of contemptuous surprise, when he found that his insults had not driven me off; then he walked on as if he had been quite alone. I determined to take venegeance for his insults—direct, terrible insults, such as no man had ever before put upon me. What measure or kind of vengeance? If a spark of manly courage had quickened my nature, the course would have been clear and the task easy. What easier than to say in the fields—'Turn sir; you have grossly insulted me; give me satisfaction?' But I was a coward; I could not dare so extremely; the choleric giant would have turned upon me as the Bull of the Alpujaras meets the Toreador.

"I yielded to a wild anger and a base cowardice; I was sold to the evil genius; I yielded to the subtil devil within me; I determined to strike my adversary at advantage—*to murder him.* When this purpose was matured I found temperate words to utter; if Pellew had shown the least return to kindly feeling my purpose might have been even then suddenly relinquished. But he strode on in sullen silence. We came to the line of the estates—a skirt of woodland lies on this side of it. A disused well was near us; the foundation walls of an old farm-house, and some straggling fruit trees of a great age will guide those who may search for this well, although it has long since been filled up quite to the grassy level.

"As we came within a few steps of the well I drew a sharp and long knife; I stood one step behind my victim; I struck. I repeated the blow —I struck many times—for there was a confounding and desperate struggle. But death came at last; the giant was quite dead at my feet. More in obedience to a predetermination than from any present prompting, I drew with a great effort the body to the edge of the well, and permitted it to fall heavily in. The depth was inconsiderable; I gathered heaps of the dried grass and weeds and threw them in upon the corpse. As I was engaged in this labor a man came running to the spot. I remember in a dull and ghostly way his looks of horror as he caught my arm. I spoke to him—what, I do not recollect. We left the field of blood at last.

"The name of this man I will not give. If he has committed an offence it has been merely one of concealment—concealment of my crime. And yet he has not dealt in all things gently by me. I forgive; I have so much to be forgiven.

"The witness of my crime came to me one terrible night—the second night after the fatal evening—and said that men should have burial, and not be cast into pits like dead brutes. How awful was his proposition. It was that the dead body should be taken up and buried in consecrated ground. He seemed to pity me—and if his views have since proved selfish, I am sure that his pity was then genuine. He seemed to be full of superstitious horror—I have no doubt he felt it—at the idea of the brutal neglect of the remains of a fellow man.

"I gave in to his proposition; I could do no otherwise. The deserted Baptist burial-ground, by the old church in the hills, a mile from the spot of the murder, was chosen as the place of sepulture. We went to work that very night. A horse, snorting under the horrible burthen, bore the corpse. We opened an old grave where the dead tenant had returned to dust, and placed Arthur Pellew in his place. Some forest leaves and a dead thorn tree covered the marks of the fresh burial; there now lie the remains of the murdered man.

"Col. Pellew had no connections in this country. His disappearance excited surprise only until it was discovered that his fortunes were hopelessly involved. Then it was easily conjectured that he had collected his available means, and left the country.

"I ask pardon of Almighty God for my terrible crime. I have

besought His pardon for years. I do not despair of it; for His mercy is infinite; and indeed I have suffered the tortures of hell here on earth. In consideration of my poor human weakness; in consideration of endured agonies, and a ruined earthly peace; but above all, upon the blessed basis of the Good Saviour's atonement, I beseech the divine pardon."

This lamentable paper was written in a broken hand; it was also marred and confused, in a part of it, with repetitions, as if the writer dreaded to approach the principal fact. Most of the repetitions I have suppressed; I have suppressed also here and there an interjectional comment, into which feeling seems to have forced him, upon the enormity of his offence. The original narrative is frequently inter-rupted with such "cries of anguish."

As the good clergyman ended his task of reading, he heard a husky "Amen—Lord pardon me." It came from the lips, and the profound heart of the dying man. Then, as the exclamation reached him, the minister knelt gently by the bed-side, and prayed. His prayers, accom-panied by the sobs of woman, and the feeble echoes of his words from the dying, became fervent and eloquent.

It was ended. There was a lull. The breath of Andrew Blair became obstructed. It might scarcely be heard for the wind that filled the chamber with the fresh odours of the summer world out beyond it; for the music of the insects housed in the rustling foliage; for the very beating of the two good hearts so near him. Finally it could not at all be heard. Andrew Blair was dead.

*　*　*　*　*

Perhaps the reader will expect a few concluding words concerning the families of Herries and Wright. Major Wright still lives, and has not lost his relish for the chase, or his power of undergoing its fatigues. He has married his daughter with the name of the British queen—a name which I was quite clear upon when I formerly gave it to the reader, but which I have since forgotten from some trick of a bad memory—to a ruddy young fox-hunter with a good property. Miss Araminta Wright is still in a condition of enforced celibacy—her father having dismissed "the young gentleman from town" as too bad a horseman to marry into his family.

John Herries, soon after the death of Andrew Blair, made a bonfire upon a small scale. The pictures of his dining-room were consumed. In the ashes left in the hearth after this conflagration, a servant afterwards found the metallic skeleton of a long-bladed knife, which, as its temper was gone, he threw away, with some ordinary comment to his fellow-servants. This knife had in its time pierced human vitals. The plough has doubtless buried it long since in the fruitful soil, over which springs and summers, as they pass, make the hiding wheat wave in its green, and droop in its russet. The life of John Herries, clouded by doubtful practices but fortunately not stained by crime, became and continues serene. Prosperity has proved wholesome to him. His meek wife is a picture of sedate cheerfulness. Her daughter Georgiana, a sweet girl whom we have too much lost sight of among the crowding forms of this history, is her gentle and affectionate companion. She looks too with pride and love to Tom Herries and his beautiful wife, and is a great deal with them at Lindores.

I bid the reader adieu. Perhaps at some future time I will again impose upon his good will and courtesy.

Joseph Jenkins' Researches into Antiquity: Erisicthon *

Ovid gives an entirely incorrect account of Erisicthon and his daughter Metra; and as I happen to be better acquainted with their singular story, I am able to put an end to the currency of that fabling poet's counterfeit narrative.

Erisicthon was a country gentleman, and lived a mile or two from the foot of Mount Olympus. He was a man of importance in his neighborhood, and supposed to be very comfortable in his circumstances. He had been chosen as soon as eligible, to represent the Olympic district in the Thessalian Senate, and was for a long time, a Justice of the Peace, and, by virtue of his office, Judge of the county court of Olympus. He spent his winters in Thebes, and when his daughter was grown a great girl, she turned out in that metropolis, and became very much pursued and courted. Metra was, to be sure, an interesting and lovely young person; but I have no leisure just now to be particular in the description of her charms.

One evening Metra left her father's house near Mount Olympus, and rode down to the sea-side to enjoy the pleasant Aegean airs. She rode a donkey with ears of the slimmest and most charming shape, and quite a yard and six inches in length. The waves were rolling like carded wool upon a beach of blue sand, and two arms of green forest-land, reaching into the sea, made a cove within the semi-circle of their embrace. As Metra came upon some inconsiderable hills near this cove, a singular murmur, as indistinct as the sigh of the waters, but nevertheless sounding like the conversation of ladies after champagne, only muffled and deadened in some strange way, made her give her little pearly ears, in imitation of the long ones of her dappled donkey, a sea-ward inclination.

Imagine her amazement when presently, seeking with eyes and ears

* [An entry in the second edition of the *Dictionary of the Noted Names in Fiction,* by William A. Wheeler, suggests the probable inspiration for Cooke's use of the fictional pseudonym. It reads, in part: "Jenkins. A cant name for any snobbish penny-a-liner. It was first given, in 'Punch,' to a writer for the London 'Morning Post,'—said to have been originally a footman, ..."—Editor]

an explanation of the sounds, she beheld an elderly gentleman about eighty feet long, dressed in a sea-green sack, pantaloons of an extraordinarily indeterminate colour, a shirt with a milk-white ruffle at least twenty-five feet in length, and an unexceptionable summer cravat of sea-grass linen, lying comfortably along the waves of the cove, and as naturally as if upon a sofa. He was smoking a cigar, about the size of the chimney of a steamboat. Metra had seen this cigar first, and taken for granted that the steam packet from Lesbos was coming in. It was only on looking lower to discover the hull, that the elderly gentleman, coloured very much like the waters, and yielding to their comfortable undulations, grew defined to her sight.

Metra, of course, was very much astonished, but not more so than her donkey. The wretch Dapple stood a moment—with the very fire of alarm in his eyes; and then, without a forewarning, planted his nose to the sand, and, kicking up desperately, made the long old gentleman a present of poor Metra. The long old gentleman picked her from the water into which she had been soused, and after an ogle from a pair of distinguished green eyes, replaced her quietly on shore. Metra was in wretched case. Her hair hung as lank as her riding skirt, and a driblet of sea-water ran along her nose until it made a little cataract from the end of it. The old gentleman laughed; Metra added the brine of her tears to the brine of the sea-water. The old gentleman softened.

"My dear," he said, "I am Neptune. You seem to be very uncomfortable in your wet clothes. Glauconome, and Clymene, who are talking under us here, shall bring you some dry ones. You must be drenched quite to your skin."

"O Neptune!" said Metra, "give me vengeance upon Dapple."

"My child," replied the good-natured god, "pull a leaf of the sheep-sorrel you see growing there behind you, and chew it."

Metra plucked the sheep-sorrel, and bruised it between her white teeth. She had scarcely done so when she leaned forward, bending her pretty bust, and seemed feeling for the earth with her fine hands. A rapid change took place in her shape; her hair parted by the back of her neck and falling along her cheeks, in a few moments shortened into the silken ears of a spaniel. Her human nose, so recently coursed by tears and sea-water, grew in length, and, slim and delicate, projected over a canine muzzle. Something mysterious agitated the lingering skirt of her riding habit; and presently, flirting loose from it, curled a jaunty canine tail. With a cry of distress and astonishment, which became in spite of her teeth a musical bark, she gave a bound, cleared her skirts effectually, and ran about a spotted spaniel. It was clear to Neptune, from some of the dog's gestures, and tones, that it made entreaty to him. The pretty creature crouched on the margin of the sea, put its slim nose between its paws and whined movingly.

"My dear," said Neptune, "you seem to be distressed. You have no reason in the world to be alarmed. You can amuse yourself by snapping at Dapple's heels, and punish the rogue to your heart's content. When you want to regain your former shape, you have only to chew a rose. Doubtless your papa has an abundance of them in his garden. If you find it agreeable, or convenient, to change your form at any time hereafter, eat of the sorrel, and you will take any shape you have previously wished. The rose will always make you a woman again."

Metra barked her thanks, and forgetting to take vengeance on Dapple, ran homeward to find the rose. A great many surly dogs, with tails making awful curls over their bristling backs, attempted to arrest her course with inquisitive courtesy, as she went. But at last she dashed into her own fair garden, and, dodging a blow from the spade of the gardener, which broke seven lights of a hot bed, plunged into the midst of a microfella. This beautiful rose had been procured at extraordinary cost from Mr. Prince, a Floriculturist of the Peloponessus, and the dragon of a gardener trembled with indignation as the spaniel, snapping several of the blooms off, broke through its prickly stems, and ran behind a hedge of Persian lilacs. He pursued like the genius of wrath. He made a circuit of the hedge, and lo! his young mistress, screaming, and skulking, and diving into the screen of green leaves, human again, but in a sad predicament! That was a great mistake, Metra. You should have taken care to be within reach of your wardrobe, before resuming your natural shape. But her female servants have wrapped her in a counterpane, worked in humming-bird patterns, and the adventure has terminated "as well as could be expected."

The day after all this happened, Erisicthon walked out to see after the concerns of his farm. He was in an exceedingly bad humor. Wheat had fallen a sixpence, by the latest price-current, and his miller having made an over advance on the last crop, refused under the circumstances to let him have money enough to meet the summer expenses of a trip over the Aegean, to a watering-place on the Scamander. As he walked on, condemning the miller, and low prices, and perhaps his own eyes, he saw just before him a grove, reputed to be one of the favorite residences of Ceres. He had, of course, often seen the grove before, for it was on a corner of his own farm. But now it occurred to him that the timber of the grove would sell for as much money as he wanted: "Besides," said he, "I shall get a famous crop of potatoes, and small grain from the ground, after clearing it." And, so, he set his men to work upon the groaning trees of the sacred wood, and crash after crash, they fell down before the axe.

One evening, soon after the destruction of the grove, Erisicthon was riding along a road which led in the direction of Mount Olympus. He saw, at a little distance before him, a cart drawn by two brindled oxen, and driven by a hearty thick-waisted countrywoman. The woman rode the near ox, and held a pitchfork in her right hand and over her right shoulder. In her left hand she held an apple, of which she ate as she rode. Erisicthon rode up, and was passing on, when this countrywoman called out to him to stop. "Erisicthon," she said, masticating her apple, "I am Ceres. I understand that you have cut down my grove."

"Madam," said Erisicthon, "I was under the impression that the grove was mine."

"You are a scurvy fellow," said the Goddess, becoming very angry. "The grove belonged to me, before the old rascal, Triops, your father, set his foot upon it."

"My father, Madam, was not an old rascal, and came by the property honestly. He bought it from the sheriff, for arrears of taxes. You had your equity of redemption, but did not redeem in time, and cannot now. I have a right to cut down my own trees."

"Stupid ass!" said Ceres, "you have no idea of any tree but a cornstalk. I am the mistress of the full horn, but I abhor one of your water-blooded utilitarians. You were a beast to destroy that grove, allowing your title to it to be good. But the property, I say, was mine, and I punish you with the curse of everlasting hunger for cutting down my trees."

Ceres turned angrily away, and, smiting about her with the pitch-fork, put her oxen into a gallop, and disappeared in a cloud of dust towards the divine mountain.

Erisicthon reined his horse to a stand-still. He had begun to have a twinge at the stomach, with the close of the Goddess' speech, and now he felt the positive gnawings of hunger.

"Metra put away a cold leg of lamb," he presently said; "and I think I shall return and take a few slices of it with oil and celery."

And, so saying, he turned and rode homeward. In five minutes he reached the house, and, in five more, become too wild with hunger for the pleasant trifling of the salad, held the leg of lamb in his hands and devoured it, by pounds, from the bone.

Ovid, whom I, Joseph Jenkins, am undertaking, with that true modesty of genius for which I am remarkable, to correct in his history of Erisicthon, gives a true account of what occurred immediately after this voracious beginning with the leg of lamb. Erisicthon in a short time, devoured his flocks, consumed his bacon, desolated his poultry-yard; and then, having done all this, converted his farm into food, and ate himself out of house and home.

"My daughter," said a thin-visaged old man, to a beautiful girl who walked at his side, on a dusty highway, "you told me that Neptune had bestowed a rare power upon you. I have a project in my head. We are approaching a great city. I entreat of you to take the shape of some valuable animal, whilst we are yet alone on the way. I will lead you in your new shape to the rich dealers of the city, and sell you for money. I can imagine no better way of raising the wind. You can change forms again, and join me, and all will be well. An ox is a valuable animal. Become an ox and I will wind a halter of grass and lead you to the market."

"Father," replied the maiden, "if I become an ox, the citizens may give me no chance of finding a rose, but presently eat me."

"I forgot that, my dear," said the hungry old gentleman; "we must think of something else."

Just then a falcon, milk-white and of extraordinary size, flew very near their heads, and hovered within reach of Erisicthon's staff, screaming as if glad of the meeting with human beings. Erisicthon designed the bird's death, and, suddenly swaying his staff, struck her upon the wing and brought her down. A fox does not pluck and devour a goose more swiftly than the hungry man plucked and devoured the falcon. The wind dispersed the white feathers, and father and daughter moved on. They had gone but a little distance when a horseman came on the way to meet them. He was dressed in close-fitting leathern breeches, and a green coat with brass buttons. He rode, at a fast rack, on a pony with the front of a little giraffe.

"My good man," said the horseman, "have you seen a white hawk as you came on your road?"

"Nay," answered Erisicthon. "I heard the flutter of birds, in a wood, many miles away. The falcon may have been warring upon them. But I know not the truth, and cannot answer you to your satisfaction."

"A great man has lost his hawk," said the horseman. "He offers an immense reward for her. I must get on to the wood."

As the stranger rode away, Erisicthon and Metra conversed for a time, and then passed away into a thicket near at hand. It was not long before Erisicthon came forth to the road, and renewed his journey with a white falcon on his arm. He spoke to the bird, as he went on, as if he found a companion in it.

"My dear," he said, "this sheep-sorrel is a plant of wonderful virtues. I think the great man will not find a feather unlike in our counterfeit. I will claim the reward, and live in pleasant abundance again."

And Metra, metamorphosed into a falcon, smoothed her neck against the cheek of her father, and looked affectionately into his eyes.

"I have brought the white falcon and claim the reward," said Erisicthon, standing at the door of a marble-fronted house in the city. The rich man hurried out from a banquet which he was holding, the wine red and generous on his lips. He was very happy to find the bird, beautiful in her glossy mail, staring him in the face. Erisicthon received a check on a banking-house, and the front door flew to in his face.

The great man bore his falcon—that is to say Metra—upon his fist, and re-entered the room in which he had been enjoying his dinner with a pleasant party of his friends.

"I have had the greatest imaginable good fortune," said he. "I have recovered my bird. My friends, congratulate me."

And the great man's friends at once congratulated him with all their stomachs. There was one young gentleman of the party who went through the ceremony with less ardor than the others. His name was Menon, and he was of so distinguished a beauty that Metra fixed her bright eyes, a little moist with the distress of her singular lot, upon his face and scarcely withdrew them to eat languidly of the food which her master offered to her jetty beak. The young person, so honored by her stare, seemed to observe something in the eyes so fixed upon him, and presently extended his hand saying—"a beautiful bird, kinsman." And he would have caressed the glossy white mails of the falcon. But Metra lifted her wide wings, and leaving her master, perched on the extended hand.

"There is positively something human in the eyes of the bird," said Menon.

"Ah, you gadabout!" said the ruby-nosed host. "You refuse my polite attentions. I am tempted to wring your neck."

Metra put her head close to the cheek of Menon. Her soft breathing affected him strangely. He positively felt himself enamored of a white falcon.

"Gentlemen," said the host, after the wine had gone round many times, "this is the first of September. Thirty days hath September— April, June and November. We are getting on rapidly to the lawful hunting season. In thirty days we shall have a little amusement. I propose that on the first day of October we go down to my country-seat and fly our hawks. My steward writes me word that blue-wings are making their appearance, and that partridges are plenty."

"We will go with all the pleasure in the world," said the party, and then poured out a great many bumpers, and drank to the issue of the sporting enterprise.

On the first day of October, about noon, a white falcon sailed over a wood, in a pleasant country of farm-houses, forests, and cultivated fields. "Metra—Metra!" shouted some one from the wood; and the bird descended rapidly, with the motion of a kite dropping upon a thrush in a tree-top, and was then hidden by the boughs.

"Bless my soul, daughter," said the person who had shouted; "I had almost given you out. I have brought a good horse, which I found by a stream, where the rider was dismounted and asleep; and I have, besides, taken care to bring a rose, and some very nice clothes for you. We had better lose no time."

"My dear father," said Metra, "how do you do?"

"Hungry," answered Erisicthon.

In a short time Erisicthon, who had gone a little way into the wood, that Metra might resume her natural shape and dress, mounted a fleet horse, drew his daughter up behind him and rode off at a dashing gallop.

"And how did you manage to get away from the great man?" said Erisicthon.

"I saw you," Metra answered, "by the way-side; and soon after, when my master threw me off at a blue drake I canceliered and then came off to seek you. But how did it happen that you came prepared with the rose and the dress, which really fits me quite nicely?"

"I heard of the hawking party and, before following it, provided both, so that if we met, as I hoped we should, you might, at once, resume your shape. I wanted to see you very much. Besides, I have eaten up the great man's reward."

And, so conversing, father and daughter rode on through, and out of the wood, at a swift pace.

That evening Erisicthon sold the horse which he had taken from the person asleep by the stream. Two days after, he had eaten up the price. Father and daughter were again on foot, toiling through the dust of a highway.

"Metra," said Erisicthon, "it is quite impossible that I can endure this singular gnawing at the stomach. I am sometimes disposed to believe that Ceres has put a tiger into me. If I am not eternally throwing food to him, he begins to munch at his cage. Unless I devour I shall be devoured."

"I am ready, my dear father," said Metra, "to assume any form you choose and to take a master that you may not want food."

"The horse fed me two days," said Erisicthon. "I am so hungry that I have no imagination. Take that shape now, and hereafter we may imagine some other forms. I see a clump of sheep-sorrel. I declare to you, my daughter, that my hunger is excessive."

As he ended Erisicthon plucked some leaves of the sheep-sorrel. Metra looked towards Olympus, the blue top of which was just visible in the distance, shining with the golden gleam which the presence of the gods bestowed upon it, and said:

"Mighty Ceres! if it be thy will that Erisicthon shall continue to wander, overcome by canine hunger, I bow myself, and will devote my life, and all that is seemly in maidenhood, to lighten thy curse to him. But, mighty mother of the teeming soils! be merciful. Forgive this old man."

No answer came from Olympus, and Metra, taking the sorrel leaves, chewed them resolutely, but at the same time, with tears of distress in her large and expressive eyes. In a short time Erisicthon continued his journey, leading a beautiful horse by a rope of grass. He came to a village. A fat landlord stood in the door-way of his inn.

"My good fellow," quoth he, "you have an uncommonly fine horse. One of my customers lost his hunter a day or two ago, and will buy yours—no doubt. Wait a little until his dinner is over."

"I will sell the horse," said Erisicthon, in a paroxysm at the mention of dinner.

The gentleman came out. It was the young Menon of the rich man's banquet—the same, moreover, from whom, whilst sleeping by the stream, Erisicthon had taken the fleet hunter. Menon bought Metra in the guise of a horse, and Erisicthon again fed abundantly. Metra uttered a neigh of delight, when she found herself the property of the youth, Menon.

Menon lived in a fine old house in a grove of white-oaks, a little way from the village. An hour before the setting of the sun, he put his foot into the stirrup, and threw himself gallantly upon his newly purchased hunter. At the very outset, sanguineous with several tumblers of punch, he applied his spurs. He felt the glossy and tender flank shrink and quiver under his heel. Metra moved swiftly, but with a saddened heart, under her burthen; the cruelty of the spur augured badly of the new lot to which filial piety had devoted her. But Menon, finding how noble and swift the animal, on which he sate, was, instead of urging, used restraint and caresses. Metra felt his hand upon her neck, lifting her mane, and smoothing the proud curve beneath it.

She replied by a grateful neigh, which must yet have been an affirmative, for she increased the speed and ease of her gaits. And so horseman and horse came to the old house in the grove of oaks. Menon left Metra at the rack and went in to pay his respects to his mother—a very distinguished old lady, with the kindest heart in the world, and perfectly devoted to her son. Presently he returned and walked by Metra's side to the stables. He saw her put into a comfortable stall, with a good supper of oats, in a clean trough, and a rack full of sweet hay, newly mown from his meadows. He patted her yielding sides, left her for the night and locked the stable door.

It was about midnight. Metra, in her horse-shape and with horse-appetites, had been chewing the sweet hay in the rack. Her eyes were half closed, in fact she was dozing. What makes her start so suddenly from her half somnolence? She has eaten a rose which, blooming on the meadow, has been cut down with the grass. That start was Metra's last equine performance. Her mane became presently the lovely dark hair natural to the maiden—growing until it hung almost to the ground. Her white shoulders, plump and round, gleamed out from its parted darkness; her curved body gave undulations to it. Only the face and the arms, lifted to the brow in confusion, and parts of the pure lower limbs were clearly discernible; so long and dense was the screen of her magnificent hair.

What shall she do? The stable is locked. She cannot escape. Where shall she find a leaf of sheep-sorrel? She rummaged the rack, feeling and then putting to her lips everything that seemed, in the dark, at all like the plant. It was to no purpose. In her despair—for in a few hours Menon would come again to the stable—she went to work, with flying fingers, to make a garment out of the long grasses of the mow. It occurs to me that I have, somewhere, seen it remarked that perseverance overcomes all things. I am not certain. Perhaps this remark is one of my own powerful original reflections. Be this as it may, the truth of the observation was exemplified in the instance before us. Perseverance enabled Metra to make, in a short time, a mantle—rude in its texture, and perhaps unsafe in the tenacity of its parts, but answering the purpose tolerably.

Wrapping this mantle around her, under the natural mantle of her hair, and spreading this last in concealing disarray about her person, she awaited the end. Her heart and lips throbbed and quivered, to be sure, and she might have wept, but that her late sad life had deepened the well of tears. Apollo came up gladly over the autumnal hills. Metra saw the streaks of his light upon the walls and floor of her prison. One of them traversed her body, resting its golden point upon the arch of her white instep. She moved more into the shadow. A noise of birds twittering about the stable-eaves, and singing blithely on the wing above them, came to the matutinal bidding. One, a purple-glossed swallow, darted through a crevice in the wall, whirled past the maiden's head, made a skilful course of the stalls, returned to whirl past it again, and then, as if perfectly informed of the reality of the wonder, passed out, by the same crevice, to give an account of his extraordinary discovery and adventures to the crowd of his companions.

"Apollo!" said Metra, clasping her hands, and falling upon her knees, "Apollo—beautiful and generous! rescue me, a poor child, from the horrors of this condition. Thou knowest that I am not unworthy— being a pure maiden—of thy kindly care. Rescue me. The autumnal wood is daedal under the splendor of thy flashing locks. Bear me to its wildest recesses, that my maiden purity may not meet the jeering eyes of men. Apollo—beautiful and generous—be kind to me."

This prayer exposes the simple and relying piety of the maiden. If she had been skeptically acquainted with the character of Apollo she would have hesitated to make so singular a request of him. She had, doubtless, been kept ignorant of his adventures with Daphne, Cyrene, and a great many others.

A low twanging, as of a harp string, came from the rafters above her head, and Metra, assured of the god's protection, folded her arms upon her bosom, and awaited the end. Presently some notes of natural music reached her ears. It was the melodious whistling of Menon. He came to look after his horse. The key turned in the lock—a kick which did not drive the door open, another that did, and—he entered. "By Pluto!" said Menon, who saw nothing of his horse. He stepped three steps on.

Some tresses of Metra's hair caught his eye. He advanced and stood within a step of her. Within one step of her he stood, but then he at once increased the step to half a dozen. It is not a common thing to see a beautiful woman, veiled with hair, in the stall of a horse. Metra, finding the youth utterly astounded, spoke.

"Menon," she said, with tones of resigned sadness, "you are amazed to find me here. My story will increase your amazement. But provide me with garments befitting a maiden; you shall then hear my unhappy history."

The voice and gentle words reassured Menon. His eyes dwelt upon the charming speaker. Metra marked the close scanning of the youth, and, blushing to her temples, said:

"If you have a mother, I beseech you to bring her speedily hither. It is not seemly that I should remain here; and—alas!—your own eyes already note me as common, and of little value." And Metra aided the sweetness of her tongue with tears.

Menon, abashed out of his scrutiny, blushed a little, and, placing his hand on his heart, promised that he would instantly acquaint his mother with the maiden's presence and wish. And, so doing and saying, he left the stable in a great hurry, and went to fulfil his promise.

A stately old dame, with a cap four feet high, and spectacles upon nose, came at a slow pace towards the stable and Metra.

"Madam," said Metra, calmly, when the dame was drawn near, "you find me in distress. That will plead with your kind heart to give me present relief. I can convince you, at a better time, that I am innocent as well as unhappy."

The mother of Menon, touched by the distress and beauty of the fair stranger, made haste to clothe her beauty in more becoming and reputable habiliments. Servants ran about, and it was not long before Metra stepped into the sunshine surrounded by a troop of waiting women, and looking as beautiful as Aurora—only with the sad eyes of of the earthly-weak Merope. It is said, and I am unable to contradict it, that the music of a sweet instrument sounded in the air, or under the earth, or from some unascertained quarter which the inclining ears of the waiting-women were pricked to discover, as the train passed from the stables. The music had a sweet effect upon Metra. Her red lips murmured "Apollo"—and her eyes acquired the lustre of a divine hope. Crossing her arms upon her bosom, she moved with the stately step of one assured of the loving protection of the gods. And so the train entered the house of Menon.

The story of Metra was presently told, without a particle of concealment. If you had been near you would have seen that the youth, Menon, listened with his heart as well as his ears.

A week passed away. Under the serene umbrage of a dell, in the wide-spreading grove, Menon and Metra walked and talked as lovers.

"I cannot conceal from you, Menon," said Metra, in answer to some warm urgency of the youth's passion, "that your kindness wins daily upon me. But I am devoted by Fate and filial affection to the fortune of my father, Erisicthon. The curse of Ceres still clings to him, and his canine hunger is unappeasable. Let us, in the purity of our youth, journey with sweet instruments of music to the foot of Olympus, and offer up sacrifices and prayers to the great goddess. She may relent; then, happy in the happiness of my father, and in the satisfied love of my own heart, which, in my candor, I do not conceal from you, the days will pass gladly with me, Menon."

And Metra, full of the joyous hope, melted Menon with the glory of her eyes.

Then it was arranged that the propitiatory pilgrimage and sacrifices should be made.

On a fair autumn day, with a cool breeze to chide the over-warmth of the sun and the tinted shades of the gorgeous boughs of forests mellowing the natural light of a thousand lovely scenes, the pilgrims set forth on the way to Olympus. Menon and Metra marched first, the one with the heat of passion on his cheek, the other calm with a serene and consoling confidence in the mercy of Ceres. A sow, with her farrow, was led in the midst of the crowd that came after. The sow grunted; her offspring also remonstrated. It was to no purpose. Lofty music drowned the remonstrances. And so the train swept on, gathering way-farers as it went, and came, at last, to the foot of Olympus. After the sacrifice had been offered, and the loudest peal of the blended music had gone up with a glorious swell, and come down with a wandering and fitful cadence (what goes up must come down), a stout country-woman, who had joined the train by the way-side, stepped out of the crowd, and, walking to where Menon and Metra stood, awaiting some divine utterance or gleam of light, addressed herself to the latter.

"Metra," she said, "your father committed a great outrage upon me; and all the polite attentions yourself and this good-looking young gentleman can shew me, shall not change my opinion of him. But, nevertheless, I am willing to wipe out old scores, for your sake—my dear."

Menon and Metra, of course, stared very much.

"You are a little perplexed, my young friends," said the stout country-woman; "you probably do not recognize me. I am Ceres."

With the words, three hundred knees—there being just one half so many persons in the company—were bent to the ground, and a prayer which sounded like the shouts of an army storming a city, made the leaves on Olympus quake.

"That will do," said Ceres, blushing under the extraordinary civility. "I accept the sacrifice. Erisicthon shall return to a slender, natural appetite. Go, my young friends and marry as soon as you will. But stop —I am just now at leisure. I will be very busy after to-day. I should like very much to be at your wedding, and insist that you invite me to witness the ceremony to-night."

Metra blushed—Menon looked delighted and as soft-eyed as an amorous falcon.

"Go back," said Ceres, "and make the wedding-feast ready. I will be punctual"—and saying this she drew her skirts a little up and walked away over the ascending slope of Olympus.

The feast was made ready at the old house in the oak grove. The clergyman had just arrived in a barouche, holding, in addition to himself, his wife and eleven small children, drawn by a meek old horse, with the agitations of a springhalt in his gait. The venerable horse was moving slowly from the door. "Make way for my lady's chariot," was heard above the grinding sound of rapidly approaching wheels. It was a bravely adorned woman, with a majestic presence, that descended from the chariot and entered. All knew Ceres. She led a miserable man by the hand who, amazed at what he saw, blinked his feeble eyes in the wedding lights.

"I bring Erisicthon," said Ceres. "I will that, from this moment, he be as he was, before stricken by care and hunger."

Erisicthon became, in a moment, a hale and portly country-gentleman.

"You will return to your house to-morrow," whispered Ceres to him. "I shall have the present owner ousted to night. You shall be reinstated where my curse found you; but bear in mind hereafter that the lovely trees of the earth are living things, suffering and rejoicing, after their kind and in their degree."

The wedding rite was over. Ceres took a hand of Menon and a hand of Metra, and, with a divine aureola encircling her majestic head, bestowed her blessing upon them—saying: "Metra, your filial piety and sweet resignation to an unhappy fortune—Menon, your truth and gentle kindness have made you, joined now in hands and love, and one household, my peculiar care. So it has been that I have forgiven this old man; so it is that I bestow my blessing upon you; so it will be that sorrow shall never darken your doors. Farewell. I am obliged to leave you now on very important business."

Plenty ever after filled the garners of Erisicthon. Love and happiness took up their abode with Menon and Metra.

Having thus vindicated the truth of history, I retire from the admiring gaze of an appreciating public, with that prompt grace for which my friends declare me to be remarkable.

JOSEPH JENKINS.

The Turkey-hunter in His Closet

I have formed a resolution, this morning, to amuse myself by occasionally writing down my experiences, random thoughts, and so forth, in all matters relating to land and water sports, in a plain way.

It is not the quantity of game killed in a day's hunting or shooting, or the quantity of fish caught in a day's fishing, that makes the record of the day pleasant reading to the world. If it was, the slaughters of a battle, with the numerical list of the killed, would make more pleasant reading than any sprightly adventures of a single sportsman, where he happened to come in with an empty game-bag.

Now, I think the most pleasant shooting record I ever read is that of the "Thrush hunting" in the Italian tour of Alexander Dumas; and yet the thrush hunter in that record follows a thrush from the centre of Piedmont very nearly to Naples, putting up at night always in the town nearest the grove or thicket in which he had roosted it, borrowing the dogs of landlords to nose it out—one of which dogs, with a singular gesticulation of the hind leg, committed a remarkable indignity upon the thrush-hunter's gaiter, in contemptuous depreciation of him after an ineffectual shot at the bird, and instantly trotted off to his owner—and, after all, does not succeed in bagging the thrush. Besides, in regard to fishing, who cares in reading gentle Izaak Walton—that venerable *Kingfisher*—how many or how few pounds of trout the moralizing old gentleman caught on any morning?

The man who kills no game, or catches no fish, may have a more entertaining story for you, of his adventures, of observations, than one who, if your larder depended on him, would better supply your physical appetite. I do not mean to say either that I have been an unsuccessful sportsman, or that I have a pleasant story to tell. I have killed a great deal of game, of one sort and another, in my time; and as for a story, I fear, after all, that, like Canning's knife-grinder, I have "none to tell"—pleasant, or unpleasant.

What purpose did I set out with? I recollect now. I expressed my resolution to put down my experiences, and random thoughts on sporting subjects, as the whim might seize me. I mean by "experiences" such points of knowledge as I have picked up, of the best ways of taking game where I have happened to hunt it, of its habits, of shifting beauties of the woods and fields, connected here and there, perhaps, with recollections of particular adventures, or sporting excursions.

I live near the western foot of the Blue Ridge, in the Valley of Virginia. The game in my neighbourhood is not very abundant. It consists chiefly, however, of good kinds—turkeys, mallards, blue-wing, and some other tolerably good ducks, pheasants and partridges. I call the last two by their familiar names here. I have a distaste for dandy shooting-jackets, and dandy particularities in the nomenclature of birds and beasts. There was a controversy, some time ago, as to whether our partridge was *coturnix* or *perdrix*—quail or partridge. In such controversies it is indifferent to me whether Punch strangles the devil, or the devil flies away with Punch. I suppose, however, they are necessary to the settlement of questions in natural history. Frank Forester calls our pheasant "ruffed grouse." I have no objection. But leave all niceties of nomenclature to natural history, and call things, on ordinary occasions, by their common names, or you will be as fastidious and interesting as an instrument of legal conveyance, or a physician's prescription. I wish, never so long as I live, to bag either Coturnix Virginiana, or Perdrix Virginiana—yet I go to some trouble in preparing for the fall campaign against Virginia partridges. I premise then that where, hereafter, I use the word "partridge," Frank Forester, or any other northern stickler for the proprieties, must understand me to mean quail, and, where I speak of pheasants, to mean ruffed grouse.

The Wild Turkey is the most respectable game bird I know, and I shall begin my experiences with it. By the way, the question seems never to have been settled, whether the Turkey is exclusively American in its origin. The persons who argue that it existed in Europe, or Asia, before the date of American discovery, say that Pliny described a bird answering in several respects to a description of the Turkey—that the name "Turkey" is proof that the bird existed in the country of that name—and, finally, that Smith in the history of his Virginia voyage and discoveries, speaks of the bird only in a casual way, as if it was already known to his European readers. I do not care anything about the question. But nevertheless, I think the Rhinoceros as much of a Unicorn as the Turkey is Pliny's bird—probably a bustard; that the strutting gobler is grand and grave enough with the pomposity of his red wattles swelling about his head, to have led our first voyagers, who were full of the ancient notions about the stately and turbaned Turk, to select the name for him; and finally that Smith mentioned the bird in a casual way because he gave his book to the world in 1629, nearly a century and a half after the discovery of the American world, and perhaps nearly as long after the discovery of the American bird—certainly after it had been introduced into the armorial bearings of one of King James' Baronets; and after Shakespeare had spoken of it in his plays—e.g.

"Here he comes swelling like a Turkey-cock."

Let me notice here that a Mr. Micajah Cock, (what a name to be sure!) who wrote a book on poultry some short time ago, takes occasion after calling the gobler "Turkey-cock" (as of course he had a right to do) to pronounce "gobler" *vulgar*. I have no doubt Mr. C. is a gander, and only calls himself cock on this same principle of refinement. Perhaps he uses "vulgar" in its ancient signification "common." There is a word differing in the same way in its ancient and modern significations—I mean "impertinent;" I think it very applicable to all such refinements. But Micajah, let me do him the justice to say, has written a very good book, upon the "setting of hens" and the pathology of chicken diseases.

My passion for, and all the skill I possess in, Turkey hunting, grew out of my association with two gentlemen nearly of my own age, and closely related to me in blood. One of these is so inveterate a hunter of this particular game that his friends call him "Turkey-foot." I shall call him Turkey-foot, or Adam Hunter, hereafter, as my humor happens to be grave or jocular. The latter name is not very far from his real one. My other friend rejoiced when we were at college in the nick-name of "Tom Beef"—and this name I will adopt for him now. After the separations which generally take place at the period when men marry, form new friendships, and diverge into the regular pursuits of life, it happened that we returned still very young men, into an association as congenial and intimate as ever, and became—like

"The reverend Ichabod Beresford,
    That mighty hunter before the lord"—

famous for the passion, and successes, of hunting. At the time that circumstances led me back into this close association with my former friends, I was reckoned an excellent quick shot, an untiring walker, and in every respect good material for making a Turkey hunter out of; but I had only killed one Turkey in all my shooting. In the rambling licence I have given myself, I will go back to the age of fourteen, and tell how I killed that Turkey—a famous gobler.

I had gone into the country to a wedding. One evening during the festivities, from which I and a younger brother of Tom Beef, were somewhat debarred, as rather too young to participate in them, a tall bony fellow from the pine-hills, named Jem Waters, found opportunity to let us know that it would be a beautiful night for finding and shooting Turkeys on their roosts, and that we might go with him on a hunt of that kind, if we chose. Our elders had quite cast us into the shade in the gentler and more gallant occupations of the occasion, and we were ripe for such an adventure. Ned Beef and I went to bed in an out-house, which had been converted, for the time, into a magazine of beds for boys and supernumerary bachelors. We did not sleep a wink —how could we under the circumstances?—but lay awaiting "the rising of the Waters" as impatiently as a steam-boat captain on a sand-bar. At last the Waters (Jem) rose, and being notified of this important fact by a tap at a window, we huddled on such clothes as we had taken off, seized our rifles and pouches and issued out into the brightest October night that a Hare—

> "Scarce making more sound, with his delicate feet,
> Than your heart will make in its faintest beat"—

ever flirted his white tail, or bounced along a frosty path in. There was just that shining rime of frost on every thing, that puts, by its reflection, a steady gleam on the front sight of a rifle, and makes night shooting, where the object is large, a matter of little uncertainty or difficulty. As we walked off with our hunter, we went through the pantomime of aiming at poultry on the plum trees, and fences, and discovered, with great satisfaction, that the bead could be drawn in the moonlight.

How our young fingers itched to convert the experimental aim into the experimental shot! I as the eldest boy—Ned Beef being my junior by a month—was to have the *first shot* with the best of the two rifles; Ned was to take it after such first shot, and return it to me for the third —and so on, by a process of alternations, which, after strangling each other for an hour in bed, and a terrible contest of legs and elbows, we had finally settled on as the order of procedure.

Half an hour's walk brought us to an extensive range of wooded hills. The growth for the most part was of oak and pine. Every squirrel's nest in the crotches of the trees underwent a close inspection;

the wart or knot of a tree often set our imaginations to work until we saw a Turkey in it—head—neck—tail—all perfect. But squirrels' nests and knots were all we found. We had not, at the peep of day, so much as seen one turkey, roosting, or flying from its roost.

Just at the peep of day we came to the cabin of an old negro man named Vincent. This old man Vincent had been a house-servant—a much higher class than the "serfs of the glebe"—and at the death of his master had been exonerated from farther service, and established in a snug cabin just where a descending ravine came down at right angles upon a regular little valley, with a brook in it. There the old man cultivated a little garden, raised rose-combed chickens, and made brooms and mats. Old Vincent was up, and stirring, when we drew near his cabin. In answer to an inquiry about the Turkeys, he said that, the morning before, about thirty, with two very large goblers amongst them, had come down from the cross-ravine, passed the run, and gone over to a corn-field two or three hundred yards behind his cabin—and that, in the *evening*, the two goblers had returned without the flock, and gone up the ravine again to roost.

Ned and I immediately parted from Waters, whom we did not see afterward, and went up the cross-ravine. We had followed it nearly to its head when we found that it forked. I took one fork, and he the other. By this time the sky was of the deepest red-rose colour, full of beautiful mottles, from north-east to south-east, and so near, in altitude —I mean this flush was—to the zenith, that the upper boughs of the trees a little before me as I walked toward the east, were relieved against it. I do not recollect to have since seen so singularly beautiful a sky. I had gone some fifty yards up the fork, when I saw one of the goblers perched, with his bearded breast to me, on a horizontal limb of an oak, within close shot. As I stopped to set and cock my rifle, he rose and turned on his perch; but before he could get away I pulled trigger, and down he tumbled. Ned came up.

"You have done a thing," said he, with a manner of great solemnity, "that people will talk about"—

"To the remotest future ages," chimed in I.

"But do you know," continued he, "that it was rascally in you to put me up that fork where the Turkey *wasn't?*"—and here there was some danger of a renewal of a controversy of the night before.

I had shot the gobler in the thin of the flank as he stood with his tail to me, and my bullet had gone out through his back bone between the shoulders, and then passed, following its length a little way, through his neck. We tied his legs together with a handkerchief, at the spurs, and, slipping a rifle through, carried him in, dragging the ground with his venerable head. He weighed, when cleaned, unless a boyish exaggeration fastened itself on my mind, and came at last to pass for truth even with myself, twenty-three pounds and a half.

With what magnificence of gait and manner I walked into the breakfast room with the mighty trophy dangling at my heels! What laconic brevity there was in Ned's account of my achievement, and the hunt! How fully I compensated for his brevity in my own ample narrative!

A turkey-killing mania raged amongst the crowd at once. Guns were brought out and loaded, horses and *carriages* ordered; in the midst of the preparations Ned and I despatched a rapid breakfast and hurried out to make an assault upon the flock of which old Vincent had told us. Our adventures after it were unsuccessful, and not deserving of a record, but we saw one rare sight, and, I assure you, we laughed, behind a corn shock where we lay perdu, considerably at it. Along the edge of the corn-field ran a fine smooth state road. On this road the most stylish of our senior cousins—a young six-footer, of twenty, with gold spectacles, a moustache, and a turkey-breasted coat with rounded collars spread out over his shoulders—went it in his little carriage, with his bay bob-tails hitched tandem fashion, at the rate of sixteen miles an hour. He sat beautifully squared on his seat, only with a little projection forward of one shoulder, and cheered his trotters with a sharp and stylish "ha-a-a-h you dogs." Behind him, "devouring the way in his haste"—for he rode far forward in the saddle, and with his mouth open, came a servant, forcing his horse into that rollicking gallop which must grow, now and then, into a run to keep at the heels of fast trotters. The servant carried his master's gun directly transverse the mane of his horse, and bird-bag, flask, and pouch kept up a constant alternating assault upon his ears and hips. "That's Turkey hunting; I wonder how many he'll kill"—said Ned.

I must return from this digression to my more matured experiences with my two older friends.

But let me stop here for the present.

What signature shall I adopt? Shall it be, with an eye to the nature of the task I am about,

T. HUNTER—

leaving the reader to enlarge the initial T into Theodore, Thomas, or Turkey, as he chooses? That name does not come sharply enough off.

It was Scathelock, that keen-shooting forester of Robin Hood's band, who wrote his name (Friar Tuck may have done it for him, as the better clerk) on a scroll, fastened it in the fringe of his arrow, and then shot shaft, and scroll, into the crowd of Carlisle. I think I will let my arrow fly with the same label—

SCATHELOCK.

III ESSAYS AND LETTERS

A   Foreword   267

B   Essays

    English Poetry [Excerpts from Chapter II]   269

    Old Books and New Authors   271

    Dante   275

    Living Novelists—I   279

    Living Novelists—II   284

    Living Novelists—III   290

    Edgar A. Poe   297

C   Letters

    Cooke to Poe, Sept. 16, 1839   301

    Poe to Cooke, Sept. 21, 1839   303

    Cooke to Poe, Dec. 19, 1839   305

    Cooke to Poe, Aug. 4, 1846   306

    Poe to Cooke, Aug. 9, 1846   308

    Cooke to Nathaniel Beverley Tucker, March 29, 1847   310

    Passages of letters from Cooke to John R. Cooke:

    Dec. 29, 1840   313

    Sept. 20, Nov. 28, 1842   316, 318

    Feb. 1, April 26, Oct. 13, 1843   319, 320, 321

    Jan. 8, July 6, 1844   323, 324

    Feb. 4, 1847   325

    Nov. 29, 1849   327

Foreword

The three-part *English Poetry*, published in the *Messenger* in 1835–36 and the first of eight essay-like contributions to that periodical, is more than a "compilation which any one might compile," a term evidently used by Nathaniel Beverley Tucker in conversation with the editor and resentfully quoted by Cooke in a letter to the former. For a nineteen-year-old, it displays exceptionally extensive knowledge of what was currently known regarding the history of English poetry from its beginnings down through the Romantics. Much of it, however, consists of quotation; little of the commentary seems fresh; and expression is marred by mannerisms that in the mature prose of Cooke rarely occur. A few passages, however, have been selected to represent his early bent.

"Leaves from My Scrap Book" and "A Leaf from My Scrap Book," also contemporary with the early poetry, display a flair for contriving slight though somewhat amusing compositions in the tradition that had led to Lamb. Like the early poetry, and like *English Poetry*, their main value lay in exercising Cooke's pen. "The Feudal Armies of France and England," published twelve years later, is a much more finished piece of criticism. Strictly speaking, however, it is not literary criticism. Cooke evidently became interested in the subject through reading *Froissart's Chronicles;* that his interest was keen, his short fictional story of a freebooter, "Captain Guy; or the Unpardonable Sin," which was also published in 1848, will amply testify. It is omitted, however, from this collection.

In considering the five essays represented in the following pages, the reader should remember that he views them only in much reduced form. As did most contemporary critics, Cooke liked to quote often and at length from the text or from favorite and perhaps relevant authors. Moreover, since a gentleman could not ask for pay, and since *Messenger* editors were slow to offer it, prolixity perhaps seemed to him a not unjustified license in lieu of more material reward. The redactions below contain few quotations and little secondary matter;

but the passages retained should fairly represent the range and quality of the mind of Cooke as critic. That they remotely reflect Cooke's reading in such journals as *The Edinburgh Review* may well be the case. That they contain no profound contribution to aesthetic theory is hardly debatable. But except for *English Poetry*, they seem impressive as the cogent observations of a discerning mind, independently arrived at and conveyed clearly and forcefully in admirable prose—a prose which reflects the views expressed in Cooke's comment on the style of Bulwer-Lytton's novels.

Cooke wrote many letters after 1840, notably to his father; and a few passages from the latter were used in the Introduction. Others, also greatly excised, are included below, chiefly because they help to round out the image of Cooke as artist but also because they add details regarding the man. Extant correspondence between Cooke and Poe and portions of a letter to Tucker are for the same reasons included.

An asterisk in text indicates a note by Cooke. As before, spellings and punctuation marks are his.

Essays

ENGLISH POETRY

. . . In a tale, the more vivid the picture drawn, the more interesting the tale. To be minute and particular in description, is to beget a vivid picture: and this is the secret of Chaucer's popularity. He writes as if he were taking an inventory of, rather than describing, things around him. Ages after, when this same talent for descending skilfully into particulars, was used in the description of natural scenery and of the workings of the human breast, it gave Spenser's Pastorals, and the tragedies of Shakespeare and poor Shelley, a beauty which in the first two, men have long ago learned to appreciate, and which in the course of time, will place the last on the seat to which he is entitled. The whole secret of Chaucer's charm is, as I have said, particularity. If he had used this talent in describing the many workings of the human heart, he would probably have failed—for no man can describe that of which he is ignorant.* If he had turned his attention to pastoral poetry, he *might* have succeeded; and indeed, in the descriptions of nature scattered throughout his various poems, he has succeeded admirably. But some thing more is wanting than this power of description, in the song of a shepherd. From his wild and unrestrained life among the hills of a legendary country—surrounded as he is, by "kids and lambs, and blithe birds," we not only look for minuteness of description, but affecting plaintiveness and imaginative embodyings. This last is one great aid to Spenser's pastoral poetry. But I am anticipating my subject.

* * * *

Comparisons have been instituted between Milton and Dante; but however excellent the Florentine may be, he had not the grasp, nor the soaring power of the English poet. The images of Dante, pass by like

---

* Chaucer has the reputation of being a great "painter of characters;" but he excels in describing manner, bearing, dress, &c.—not in picturing the workings of the "human heart." [When Cooke wrote this he obviously had read little of Chaucer.—Editor]

the phantasma on a wall, clear indeed, and picturesque; but although true in a great measure to fact, wanting in reality. They have complexion and shape, but not flesh or blood. Milton's earthly creatures have the flush of living beauty upon them, and shew the changes of human infirmity. They inhale the odors of the garden of Paradise, and wander at will over lawns and flowers: they listen to God; they talk to angels; they love, and are tempted, and fall! and with all this there is a living principle about them, and (although Milton's faculty was by no means generally dramatic,) they are brought before the reader, and made, not the shadows of what once existed, but present probable truths. His fiercer creations possess the grandeur of dreams, but they have vitality within them also, and in character and substance are as solid as the rock.

*   *   *   *   *

. . . As a didactic writer, Pope stands conspicuous among the philosophic poets, not only of England, but of the world. Neither Virgil nor Lucretius can in this, boast superiority. And Akenside, Armstrong, and even Boileau, fall far beneath. I have remarked, that Logic suited no order of poetry, except the satirical: I do not contradict myself here. . . . In brief, sprightly carelessness of restraint, and *want of method*, render Pope's "Essay on Criticism," and the "De rerum natura" of Lucretius more agreeable to the reader than the best of Virgil's Georgics. In satire, Pope was superior to Dryden, chiefly I presume, in consequence of the latter's want of leisure to perfect the reasoning which enters so importantly into that species of composition. . . .

Pope perfected the music and elegance of the English verse. Drawn out of chaos by old Chaucer; softened by Spenser; twisted into pliancy by Surrey; subtilized by Cowley; smoothed by Waller; strongly and beautifully modelled by Dryden;—it still wanted the finishing touch, and this, Pope gave. But he was more than an accomplished linguist. A skillful satirist, a touching eulogist, a philosophic tutor, . . .

(*SLM*, June 1835)

OLD BOOKS AND NEW AUTHORS

Fairly, or unfairly, every new writer makes extensive use of old books. The "first author"—if there ever was a first author, for, like Buchannan's Kings of Scotland, they go back in a line that seems only to end because it fades out of view in the distance—must have found it difficult enough to accomplish his labors of pure creation. It must be always difficult for a man to do a first thing, in the fullest sense of the word "first"—to do, of his own God-given power, what no man ever did before him. The first Poet created his art, as well as his poem. The double creation—if his poem was any thing better than the measured howl of a savage—must have been a stern and scourging labor. But it would be still more difficult for any present author to produce a work strictly original—a work purely out of his own mind. He is so much at disadvantage with the primitive author, in such a labor, that he has to work, not upon virgin tablets, but upon a surface already crowded with the lines and impressions of others. He must erase all of these, every faint trace of their existence, and then burnish the palimpsest tablet back into its perfect glare and purity, before he can stand, in the rivalry of unaided creation, on the same level of advantage with his primitive competitor.

* * * * *

A short time ago a poem appeared, in Graham's Magazine, in which were the verses—

> "The dappled fawns upon the plains,
> The birds that love the upper sky,
> Live not in lovelier liberty."

These lines, Mr. Poe (a poet and critic of high powers) said were "imitative" of the "Know no such Liberty" of the Althea of Lovelace. If they are so, the imitation is one of the unconscious appropriations I have spoken of; I pronounce it so, on the highest authority, as the letter-writers say, for I wrote the verses myself.

In Mr. Poe's poem, "Israfel"—in the recent Wiley and Putnam edition of his poems—is this verse—

"None sing so wildly well."

In a fine and well known passage of the Bride of Abydos, is the verse—

"He sings so wild and well."

Of course this was, as in my own case, an unconscious appropriation —or, if conscious, still perfectly innocent. The man who goes out of his way to *avoid* such trivial imitations, is over dainty to do manly work.

To return;—the poet who writes to-day, is necessarily—and if so, of course, innocently—an imitator *in every portion of his labor*. His choice of a subject, of a form of stanza, or other poetic construction, of a measure—the thought, the very phraseology, often the very incitement to composition are (to use a phrase of the critics) "tinctured with imitation." His only trust must be, that, like the ancient painter, who borrowed a feature here, and a feature there and blended them into one face, unlike other faces because full of *mutually correcting resemblances*, he has produced a work, original in its combination of unoriginal parts.

Notwithstanding all this, which is so true, that I almost feel guilty of having elaborated a truism, our American poets, who, in most instances, are liable to the charge only of this species of inevitable imitation, and of no weaker sort, have been, more than once, recently condemned, in the mass, as unoriginal. . . .

*　*　*　*　*

I think such criticism overlooks the fact of our peculiar history. We sprung into existence like Minerva. We never had an infancy in this land of the occident. We must look for that infancy, or boyhood, to which the minds of individuals and nations, alike recur for poetic material and fervid impressions, abroad from our new homes to the old home, England. Shakespeare is as much an American poet's ancestor, as he is an English poet's; and surely the sequence of blood, and the common reverence for the common ancestry of bright-minded and immortal men, are not things to be affected by changes in political institutions, or by geographical distances. The beautiful and noble spirits, who have made the elder English literature renowned to all ages, were poets of our language and *our nation*. We are no more disfranchised of our rights in the inheritance of mind and its works, by the changes of locality and institutions, than the English sailor trading amongst the antipodal isles of Polynesia, or spreading his sails in reach of the "Sabean odours" off Mozambique, forfeits a property inheritance in Bristol.

In the course of time, I suppose, subdivisions of nationality will be brought to bear upon critical judgments. The New Englander will be deterred from the literary preserves of the Virginian or Carolinian; and he, in turn, must stick sacredly to "the burning slope that looks toward the line"—as his representative in Congress calls his country. There will be an interdict against the mutual aid of interchanged thought, the common building of a noble art; those who lend themselves to any thing of the kind, will lose the favors of the patriotic criticism which reprobates it as a mean spirit of surrender to foreign control, as unworthy the independent spirit of a "free citizen," who should feel himself constrained, by every high and refined sectional consideration, to support as something *sui generis*, the literature, and so forth, of that particular region,—better of course than all others,—to which he happens to belong. . . .

*   *   *   *   *

I will close this paper with an instance of plagiarism in prose, which will better illustrate the distinctive separations I have made, than any general argumentation could do. It occurs in one of the most brilliant books in the whole range of prose fiction—Vivian Grey. The stolen passage is pilfered from the Religio Medici of Sir Thomas Browne—a work now made common by republications, but little known to general readers when D'Israeli wrote Vivian Grey. I place the passages in opposing columns. The worst feature in the plagiarism is the concealing care visible in the changes made by the pilferer.

"Darkness and light divide the course of time, and oblivion shares with memory a great part even of our living being—we slightly remember our felicities, and the smartest strokes of affliction leave but short smart upon us. Sense endureth no extremities, and sorrows destroy us or themselves. To weep into stones are fables. Afflictions induce callosities—miseries are slippery, or fall like snow upon us, which, notwithstanding, is no unhappy stupidity. To be ignorant of evils to come, and forgetful of evils past, is a merciful provision in nature, whereby we digest the mixture of our few and evil days, and our delivered senses not relapsing into cutting remembrances, our sorrows are not kept raw by the edge of repetitions."

Sir T. Browne

"Oblivion and sorrow share our being in much the same manner as darkness and light divide the course of time. It is not in human nature to endure extremities, and sorrows soon destroy either us or themselves. Perhaps the fate of Nioba is no fable, but a type of the callousness of our nature. There is a time in human suffering, when succeeding sorrows are but like snow falling on an iceberg. It is true, that it is horrible to think that our peace of mind should arise not from a retrospection of the past, but from a forgetfulness of it; but, though this peace of mind is produced, at the best, by a mental laudanum, it is not valueless; and oblivion, after all, is a just judge."

Vivian Grey

I consider this a decided and remarkable specimen of plagiarism.
(*SLM*, April 1846)

DANTE

* * * * *

Those poets who immediately preceded Dante make a curious study to critics of the mediaeval literature. Only amidst the harlequinades of a chivalry become fantastic, could such a wonder as the power of the Troubadours—extending itself greatly beyond mere letters—have grown up or continued. The admiration of the lords and ladies of Southern Europe was not of the kind which crowns the poet, and then becomes secondary, or forgotten, in the homelier affairs of life; but . . . established a despotism which regulated all points of intersexual deportment, made honesty rustic, sublimated honor into an impossible and cloudy code, and imprisoned the universal reason and conscience in meshes of fine-drawn sophistries. No doubt the power of the Troubadours was, to some extent, the *result* of the diseased condition of the social mind; subtleties as foolish, follies as perplexed, as any of those in which a large part of Europe ran riot, had already been shown in the scholastic disputations on the graver subjects of theology and law, which a little before were greatly in fashion. But to some extent a result, it acted also as a cause, and made more folly than created it. The admiring submission of lords and ladies to the new sway in poetry, love, and morals, at first a mere matter of taste and will, became in time compulsory. Tribunals called Courts of Love were established, which, if they wanted the temporal power to send a gentleman guilty of a homely virtue to the galleys, could yet send him to Coventry, a punishment quite as terrible and as exacting of obedience. . . .

* * * * *

In illustration of the code of morals inculcated by the Troubadours, and common in society, we remember the case of Jean Raban and Edme Montone. Jean Raban discovered an amour between his wife and Edme Montone. The abused husband slew the lover and imprisoned the wife. A domestic tragedy of this nature at once took firm hold of the poetic sympathies of the Troubadours. It became the subject of several touching poems, and of inquiry, before the Courts of Love. Poets and judges united in eulogy and pity of the dead, in tears of sentiment for the imprisoned, and directed the wrath of all noble souls against the brutal and infamous husband who had rudely severed two youthful and loving hearts.

*   *   *   *   *

Of the works of the Troubadours, of which many specimens remain, it has been said with point and truth that "they can give pleasure only to those of so uncommon a taste as to relish love without passion, and poetry without nature." One decisive service they did render to the cause of European letters; their works written in the mixed dialect, called the language of Oc, were a means, by their popularity, of overthrowing the monkish Latin, in which it had been the fashion to write books.

Whilst poets . . . were dispensing their follies, and society not only receiving, but adding to them—until the rebound had, it seemed, occasioned an inextricable confusion of morals and mind—appeared Dante Alighieri. It was amongst the fantastic palaces of the Troubadours— "too toppling," as Petrarch has said of them, "to bear the weight of a stork of Aquileia,"—that the Florentine planted his foundations deeper than architect ever delved, and hung his mighty dome in the heavens.

We have dwelt on the condition of the literature, fore-running and cotemporary, which beset and involved Dante—for the clearer appreciation of his admirable genius. The poet who, in the midst of the darkness or frivolities of letters, overbears all hostile influences, enters into new fields, and produces immortal poems, is entitled to that grand isolation of praise and honor which the world justly yields to a discoverer of new lands, or of secrets in nature, or the arts—bestowing an inferior and common honor on his followers, who may even surpass him in extent of discovery.

And such a Poet was Dante—entitled to such honors. We are of course aware, that he professes to have drawn his inspiration from the ancient poetry of Rome, chiefly from his master, Virgil. That he did so detracts little from the peculiar praise we speak of. He none the less took a novel and bold course, leading to the loftiest summits of his art —he is none the less entitled to be remembered as the man who did what none in the generations of a thousand years before him had possessed the ability and earnest passion to do—he none the less enkindles a new world-wide light—say, a rekindling of ancient light, still little less miraculous, after the long obscuration, than Homer's first ignition of the mighty torch—he is none the less entitled to an isolation of honor above the great poets of many nations, who soon followed him, working in his light, quickened and instigated to their labors by the sudden commotion of mind produced by *his* triumph of noble thought and art.

If Dante took aid from the ancients, it was no greater aid than the pre-imagination of the ancient Atlantis, or the tradition of floating lands, seen to come and go on the horizon westward from the Fortunate Isles—shadowy apparitions beckoning the mariner into adventurous quest of new worlds—afforded to the restless mind of the "world-seeking Genoese." Over the obscured depths—the darkness of ten centuries—came no more distinct or reliable guidance to the Florentine Poet, than the great navigator won from that dream of antiquity and tradition of floating shores.

We have a theory that no man can write a great book until age and the rubs of a worldly warfare have matured his powers, and given him the stores of a worldly experience. We have no high appreciation of the books which young poets send out from the windows of their closets, to flash in an atmosphere higher than the level of human heads. They would do better generally to throw squibs into the streets. Their fiery projectiles may blaze like the arrow of Alcestis, but too often like that famed shaft, they fly to no mark. Shakespeare, Milton, Bacon, Scott, are examples fortifying our theory—and Dante is one more. . . .

* * * * *

An able review, in an old number of the *Edinburgh*, pronounces Milton "Lord of the *Ideal*" and Dante, by way of antithesis, "Lord of the *Actual*." We dissent from the opinion, elaborately as the reviewer has fortified it. We think Dante more remarkable for ideality than Milton, and quite as much so as any poet that ever lived unless we except Chaucer, pronounced by the same review the most earth-seeking of the actual minds in poetry. The imaginations of Dante are frequently homely, or grotesque—sometimes disgusting. He seems to follow his subject, not adorn it; and often the pages of the *Inferno* read more like an inventory of Hell—its tortures and tortured—than the collected imaginations of a poet. There is much of the sound of the actual and coarsely true about it. But ideality is not necessarily a cloud-cleaving power, delighting in the contemplation of objects beyond an ordinary human recognition, or beyond the homelier sympathies of men. The mind that imagines glowingly and vividly possesses ideality, whether its imaginations surpass nature or cling to her commonest levels and deal with her coarsest objects. We give our opinion broadly that the Poet is most highly endowed with ideality who, in his account of things not perceived by the senses, but only imaged or pictured to the imagination, can make the picture most distinct to the comprehension of others. . . .

*   *   *   *   *

Cary, in his critical observations on the *Divine Comedy*, says "the poem seizes on the heart by its two great holds, terror and pity." . . . We think that the very distinctness of portraiture, which we have pronounced proof of a high ideality in the poet, detracts from his terrors. Things are seen too clearly and fully to excite the highest degree or kind of terror. The most alarming tale of diablerie we know of is Horace Walpole's "Castle of Otranto." The gigantic leg and boot . . . always struck us in our boyhood as the summit of the terrible. A *pair* of great legs, with a giant body to them, and the grisliest head that Jack, the exterminator of such personages, ever cut off with his sword of sharpness, would have been nothing to that mysterious one leg with its huge boot. Our imagination went to work upon it—we could make nothing clear of it—the upshot was our hairs bristled. . . .

*   *   *   *   *

So we think it always must be; the greatly terrible must move in shadows: we must have no front to front communion with it,—fortified for the encounter by a cold reason and hearts made firm by the broad light; its effect is in great part lost when its form is seen *distinctly*. But such terror as a man feels at beholding extraordinary human suffering, and extraordinary engines for producing it, the *Inferno* abounds with.

*   *   *   *

(*SLM*, September 1846)

LIVING NOVELISTS—I

We propose to give our opinions upon some of the most prominent of the numerous living writers of fiction. What we have to say may do some service: the utterance of honest opinion generally does; but we write more for our own pleasure than from any ambitious purpose of purifying the public taste, or obtaining just popular verdicts against certain gaudy names in literature.

Bulwer, with whom we begin, created at once upon the publication of his first novel, *Pelham*, an extraordinary sensation. No such flood tide of literary enthusiasm had occurred amongst young readers, liable to extremes of admiration, since the era of the ardent misanthropies of Byron. And as the old Byronic enthusiasm had put Scott's verse out of fashion, so did the new threaten to dispose of his immortal prose romances. It is somewhat humiliating to know that the author of *Pelham* came very near supplanting, with a large class of readers, the author of *Ivanhoe*. Time and truth, however, have adjusted positions; the divine Sir Walter holds the throne and pinnacle: Bulwer has receded, and holds a position far beneath him.

* * * * *

In the first place, then, [Bulwer's] writings strike us as singularly undramatic. His characters talk very elegantly, and often deliver themselves of beautiful paragraphs, which read wonderfully well; but of natural dialogue, such as living men and women talk, there is next to nothing. And, chiefly a consequence of this, his characters want that distinctness and individuality which we so often meet with in those greatly dramatic authors who make their dramatis personae develop themselves in natural dialogue. . . .

* * * * *

We return from this digression. . . . We were contending that Bulwer's writings were singularly undramatic. In Devereux we have a great deal of sparkling conversation, and the reader might be deceived by it into a first impression that it sprung from a great dramatic power, refined and taught by experiences drawn from the courtly life of Salons, and gay *noctes* of wits and men of fashion. But the truth is, the larger and most brilliant part of that sparkling talk in the French capitol, where the bowl of wit is rolled from Count to Abbe, dice-rattling Baron to ribald Priest, is no more than a *refaciamento* well got up from the recorded bon-mots of that French society, and the epigrammatic dialogue of the elder French comedy. The art that enabled the novelist to put these things together and make brilliant chapters, is occasionally a good substitute for the dramatic power—but it is very far from being the power itself.

Again, in the Last Days of Pompeii, we have gay, easy table-talk enough; but where the chapters devoted to it become most witty, they seem to be amassed thefts from the same French sources, served up after pretty much the same recipe. . . . A common trick of the dialogue makers is also frequently visible in this book. A person has a calling or a passion, and he never speaks that his talk is not colored by it. One is a gambler and his illustrations are taken from games of chance, or he, at every issue in conversation, draws his dice-box from his bosom, and proposes to decide the difference by a cast of the die. Another is superintendent of the amphitheatre and its popular spectacles; his talk is of the saw-dust and blood of the arena: of pleasant reminiscences of dying gladiators or Christians disembowelled by wild beasts. Another is a gourmand and parvenu who prefers a wide and gaudy fringe to his napkin; and he talks in an unctuous mouth-watering way of British oysters and Falernian wine, whilst he waves the magnificent fringe of his napkin in the eyes of his table companions. . . .

*   *   *   *   *

These characters in [*The Last of the Barons*] do not talk like man the individual, but like man the representative of a class. Acres of such writing might be written *currente calamo* by any free writer without a spark of dramatic power in him; and after plodding over such acres, we would find ourselves without a particle of the sort of acquaintance we form with man the individual.

*   *   *   *   *

The only form of the dramatic in which Bulwer excels is the melodramatic. His natural tendency to it is strong, and where he writes rapidly and without caution, he always lapses into it. His refined skill and literary art, make him in all elaborated work subdue it within reasonable bounds, but, we repeat, wherever he writes from the natural impulse, he becomes inevitably melodramatic. . . . It is no doubt owing to the elaboration requisite in play-writing, that Bulwer, who shows everywhere in his elaborate work, by avoiding the taint of melodrama, that he is conscious of his natural bad tendency in this respect, has written dramas less marked by melodramatic faults than many of his novels.

* * * * *

A great want that we find in Bulwer is that he has not the least idea how to make men individuals, or armies fight. He manages the warlike, like a cross between a stage subordinate in a tin helmet, and a sentimental haberdasher. Read this description of the encounter of Glaucus and Arbaces in the Last Days of Pompeii.

" 'Ha!' muttered Arbaces, 'what fury hath sent ye hither?' 'Ate,' answered Glaucus; and he closed at once with the Egyptian. There is, perhaps, nothing on earth so terrible as the naked and unarmed contest of animal strength, no weapon but those which nature supplies to rage. Both the antagonists were now locked in each other's grasp—the hand of each seeking the throat of the other—the face drawn back—the fierce eyes flashing—the muscles strained—the veins swelled—the lips apart—the teeth set; both were strong beyond the ordinary power of men, both animated by relentless wrath; they coiled, they wound around each other; they rocked to and fro—they swayed from end to end of their confined arena; they uttered cries of ire and revenge; they were now before the altar—now at the base of the column where the struggle commenced; they drew back for breath—Arbaces leaning against the column—Glaucus a few paces apart."

We certainly never read anywhere else of so much fighting and so little execution done. How does this scramble compare with those buffets exchanged between Richard and Friar Tuck? If Glaucus, instead of "locking" his enemy in his "grasp"—"coiling and winding" around him—"rocking to and fro" with "cries of ire and revenge"—had struck the Egyptian scoundrel one honest blow between the eyes, or on the bridge of the nose, he might have saved himself trouble, and certainly would have risen greatly in our estimation.

* * * * *

We must give a few words to Bulwer's *style*. There are some singular notions current just now in regard to style. It was a theory of Dr. Channing's and to some extent a theory reduced to practice in his admirable writings, that the expression of thought gained dignity and impressiveness by being a little obscured. Willis, in a gay letter to a young friend, advises him to daily habits of trial-composition, and recommends to him a preservation and cultivation of the "foibles" turned up in this constant upheaval of the mental fallow, as a means of securing individuality as a writer. His own practice squints so singularly in the direction of this odd system of training, that we take the counsel to be serious in spite of its oddity. For ourselves, we think that good thought requires no trick in its expression; and that bad thought cannot be made good by an artful envelopment in musical, fantastic, passionate, or any other language. There are certain laws of good writing which we hold to be immutable and inexorable. Fashion may, for a time, put them aside, as it sometimes does the homely virtues in human character. But the recovering good sense of the world inevitably returns to them. Write clearly, go by the nearest way to your meaning, use words of distinct, well understood signification, abjure ornament as a separate quality, but where it comes as a natural grace make it welcome: if you follow these good old recognized laws, and your thoughts are sterling, you will write well.

Having these views, we consider Bulwer's style a false, bad one. It is painfully ornate, ambitious (a fatal fault of style), full of musical circumlocution introduced evidently for the sake of the music, and where natural often slovenly. John Bunyan, the tinker, writing in the language and idioms of the English hearth-sides, and never dreaming of style at all, has a better style than Bulwer, word-weighing and keen in pursuit of ornament as the latter so often is. . . .

* * * * *

We have prejudices against all style-mongers, but the worst of them all, we think, is the author who writes as if he feared the ink-soil upon his fingers; who writes as if an inelegance was one of the deadly sins; who writes as if the good homely words of plain life, short, perhaps rude, always strong and direct, were too coarse, too inharmonious an utterance for him, and precisely this fastidious, over-nice person we take Bulwer to be.

We are trespassing on the patience of our readers, and must hasten to a close. A man of brilliant genius Bulwer certainly is; nothing we have said contradicts, or seeks to contradict this fact. Faults we find in his mind and books, but they are not faults which stamp the author as a man of feeble genius. We never have stupidity, never the barrenness of the plain mind, which, ignorant of the vernal blossoms and summer foliage of the imagination, exhibits its thought as naked as winter. Creative power, inventiveness, a quick perception of the beautiful, a rare knowledge of certain classes of human passions, and emotions, together with a singular skill in their display, great melody of phraseology, which at times is exquisite enough to make the most stubborn critic forget his censure, these and some other gifts and marks of a genius great and accomplished, he certainly does very often exhibit.

*   *   *   *   *

(*SLM*, June 1847)

In certain ages of English letters not very remote, the writing of a book was a remarkable labor which, whether well done or ill done, made the writer famous. The fertility that produced two or three books was apt to be regarded as a phenomenon, or with a suspicion that work so hastily and irreverently accomplished could not be altogether solid. With this reverent awe on the part of the public, and its mistrust of prolific labors, authors became, naturally enough, very profoundly impressed with the dignity of authorship, and very deliberate and fastidious in their habits of writing. Most of them were men of one book, and expended the flower of their years in composing, correcting, writing and re-writing it.

An exception indeed to the popular respect, and this proud deliberation of authorship, was in the case of the dramatists. The poor devils who wrote those immortal dramas, which are the best wealth of English literature, were regarded by their contemporaries as a species of harlequin. Why men, who were in fact august poets, were slighted by a criticism so liberal to duller brains is easily understood. Their works were too numerous for their slow-paced judges; they were, moreover, creations of original genius, cast in novel moulds, and possessed no points of resemblance to the ancient classic drama to give a foundation for that kind of stately eulogy which expresses itself in the Plutarchian parallel. Of Amatory, pastoral, or allegorical poetry from a date which we may fix, with Bishop Corbet's verse,

"Since died our bold Elizabeth,
And learned James came in,"

to the middle of the last century, a very little was sufficient to make a reputation; for the balancing criticism of the times could parallel the bard of love and wine with Anacreon, the pastoral poet with Theocritus or Virgil, whilst allegory, having its excuse in the Greek tragedy, had become a principal element in the medieval literature of the cloisters and taken great hold on the mind of western Europe. Otway's crust shows the fate of the dramatist, whilst the Lucasta of the amatory poet, Lovelace, made him the rose of love and lamp of honor to ladies, kings and cavaliers—to all, indeed, but that stern critic Cromwell.

*   *   *   *   *

The state of things which we have been shadowing forth is now entirely changed. The sluices have been opened and stagnation has given way to currents which confound sky, air and earth with their spray and their roar. We are overwhelmed with books, we are bewildered by the crowd of authors, we can remember no contemporary name in letters unless we have constant repetitions of it ushering in new pages of new matter to interest us for a day. . . .

An author can no longer be slow-paced—no longer rest upon his laurels—no longer believe the eyes of the world to be fastened upon him, and wrap himself up in a proud composure to abide the admiring inspection. If he is deliberate at his labors, or stops between his labors, he is gone. In such a state of things he cannot be fastidious. Besides why should he be fastidious? The public, instead of nibbling at sentences, swallows chapters—swallows volumes.

In the new state of things it was natural enough to find authors quickened into astonishing labors; but it remained for the genius of M. Dumas (to whom we have at last come after an uncommonly long exordium), to discover and establish a mode of book-making of the most admirable convenience, and suited in every respect to the new necessities of authorship. Dumas has put into operation a kind of literary manufactory. He employs a number of clever young writers, who fill his hotel in town, and go with him on literary pleasure parties to his chateau in the country. . . . How much of the actual writing of his books is done by Dumas we can only guess at.

When an author of great reputation writes a book in conjunction with one less known, and the book proves unequal, we are apt to father the good upon the famous author, and the bad upon the humble one. In this, we no doubt often err. For instance Pope, whilst a mere boy and unknown, wrote some pages and made corrections in a work of Wycherley which, if we remember aright, made an otherwise dull and silly book quite respectable. The shadow of the name of Dumas may be hiding in the crowd of his journeymen some great and masterly mind, which, one of these days, will break out into splendid prominence, and have recorded in its "*ana*" the fact that we owe some of the best work of the Dumas establishment to it. But we are bound to believe against such a chance that Dumas, if he writes at all, writes the best of his books, or the best chapters of them. . . . But it is idle to refer, by name, to the books which Dumas has made, or procured to be made. His mighty list is longer already than that of Lope de Vega, and a mere titular enumeration would consume more space than we shall devote to the author.

Dumas has many and rare merits as a novelist. He is remarkable for a curt and rapid management of details, which leaves no feature of his pictures wanting or blurred; and yet with all his particularity he is never tedious. He really consumes less space in his minute and full narratives than most authors consume in that style of general description which pretends to dash off scenes with a few bold strokes.

Again he possesses indomitable good sense as rudder and ballast to his genius. His dramatis personae are natural and true to real life: acting in just proportion to motives, and deducing opinions from reasons which, if not sound, are as sound as most that men build opinion and faith upon. He is an admirable painter of man such as nature and circumstances have made him, and seems to have no notion of the fine creatures of porcelain which novelists generally delight to exhibit—fine creatures that neither talk with reason nor act with motive. His good sense shows itself constantly. It limits his tragedy and qualifies his comedy, and sometimes blends the two as we really see them blended so often out of books, but as no contemporary of Dumas at all knows how to blend them in books. It is worldly acumen—a shrewd and just knowledge of men—that dashes misery with the salt of fun, or places a profound melancholy under the superficies of humor. It is to such natural blendings of sad and gay, as much, perhaps, as to anything else, that such books as *Gil Blas* owe their enduring popularity with all classes, from statesmen to mechanics. . . .

*   *   *   *

Of the sententious conclusions in morals, philosophy, and manners, in which most of the French novelists of the day abound, and with which the universal mind is becoming, to use a phrase of D'Israeli, pretty well *guanoed*, Dumas has fewer than most of his cotemporaries. His books are chiefly narrative and descriptive—the dialogue being generally no more than a means of conducting the story. But where he does stop for such things he is generally brilliant and bold. His terse conclusions seem inherent to the subject—something natural and inevitable—they are the explosions that must occur when the match has burned to a certain point. This is rather an unusual merit. Such things are generally patched upon their pages by novelists, who as generally steal them.

*   *   *   *   *

We must pardon much to Dumas for haste—a haste which must also be pardoned because the exactions of the public make it necessary to the author. It is haste that renders many of his books, especially his stories from French history, rather collections of striking tableaux than well-arranged and connected works. Pearls are strung upon hempen strings—rubies are set in lead. Wealth of material we have in abundance, and it is finely worked up wherever the effort is made to work it up; but the result of haste of which we complain, but which we are obliged to pardon, is that the effort is too seldom made to work it up. Perhaps, too, as we have suggested, Dumas is to be credited with the striking scenes, whilst the labor of connecting them is accomplished by his young scribes.

*   *   *   *   *

The mind of Dumas is more of a fountain than a cistern, and has sustained the extraordinary drain upon it not only well but almost miraculously; he nevertheless occasionally diverts a driblet from the fountain of another to swell his own—or, as Coleridge says, "taps another man's tank." For instance, in the book just referred to, "The Planter," etc., the death of Laiza is clearly a copy of the death of Uncas in the "Last of the Mohicans." And in a chapter of the same book, the narrative of an experiment which George, the hero, makes to test his own courage, is taken *sentence by sentence* from an old article in one of the London monthlies. We pass from Dumas, whom we heartily recommend to our readers . . . to the author who, in the extent of literary production, most nearly approaches him—G. P. R. James.

James has written as many books as any one, working with only his own brain and fingers, could have well contrived to write in the same space of time. An author cropping his mind so incessantly and so closely, is entitled, as we have just contended in the case of Dumas, to be dealt with forgivingly. . . . But his defects are too many and of too serious a nature to be entirely forgiven by the blindest charity. They are defects inherent to the man, and do not grow from haste or multiplicity of labors.

In the first place his characters are never striking or impressive. He has dealt with more of the great names in history than any author that ever lived, and yet what more do we know of them for his labors? From the Captal de Buch to Henry of Navarre, not one of them is at all more distinct in his lineaments than history had already made him. Where among his kings do we find a Coeur de Lion, among his nobles a Dunois, or Leicester or Claverhouse, among his outlaws a Locksley or Rob Roy? The same poverty is visible in his conception and delineation of original characters. Here, untrammelled by history, left to the very license of liberty, he should certainly have given us something to remember. The eternal failure of James to make us know his characters intimately, and carry away lasting impressions of them, is proof of more than the exhaustion of over-cropped powers; it is proof of original sterility. This defect, which we have placed first on our list, is in the very base work of the novelist's art.

Again he is never bold or nervous in his thought. We have no stormy bursts of passionate thought; no "tumultuous throngings of the mind's children to the portal of speech;" not even charming irregularities. He is everlastingly respectable. He seldom trails below, and never soars above a very moderately elevated horizontal plane. His mind is a champaign, not a mountainous country. This is certainly not a defect to be excused on the ground of haste and multiplied labors.

* * * * *

It is no more than simple justice to pardon meagreness and sameness of plot in the fiftieth book of an author. We must, consequently, hold back the censure to which James provokes us on this head. It is right hard to forgive, however, a fault which he has carried to such excess. A lost heir turning up to confound the villain of the book, who has hold of his estate, and to delight an amiable old gentleman who was the friend of his father, and has a marriageable daughter with a charming face, warm heart and large dowry—this is the story, in outline, of some-where about the last twelve of his quarterly volumes.

* * * * *

As for style, James has that curse of facility which seems to mark all trained writers of tame genius. His words are good enough, and run naturally, and gracefully enough, into phrases and sentences; but it would be a relief to see something rougher—the perpetual facility wearies us. The man seems to be a machine turning out sentences, like calico, yard after yard, all of one pattern, and miserably correct. . . .

These are some of the defects, radical and minor, pardonable and unpardonable, of this popular author. We find much to redeem them in his books. He has the art to interest you in his narratives. He has the genuine talent of the *raconteur*. This is a talent of the first necessity to a writer of fiction. Imagination, fancy, clear sense, aided by all learning, and made facile in operation by long practice, are not enough without it. Lockhart's *Valerius*—a book full of learning, fine thought and refined taste, and not deficient in plot—is proof of what we say. Lockhart has none of this rare talent, and his book is utterly uninteresting. The peculiar gift, of which we speak, is not inventiveness, for which it might be taken, but rather something which manages, blends, conducts, and adroitly makes the most of, inventions. It is indeed a talent to itself, and by itself—of rare occurrence—above attainment where not native—not necessarily united to great mental powers, but of absolute necessity to a greatly successful novelist. James possesses it in a remarkable degree. . . .

*   *   *   *   *

(*SLM*, September 1847)

LIVING NOVELISTS—III

* * * * *

The most prominent—not the greatest—of D'Israeli's characteristics, is his perfect mastery of the English language. He cannot be said to have a style at all. He is singularly free from mannerisms. You never recognize him as you do the style-mongers. You discover him, not from his peculiarities, but from his power. Cobbett, whose pages are chopped up into monosyllables, has no purer Saxon than makes the strong staple of his sentences. The poets of the Elizabethan age, who infused the melodious words of Tasso, Petrarch and Ariosto, into their plainer language, possessed no richer music than he ascends to, when his thought kindles and rises to the poetic pitch. He has the Spaniards' *boca de oro*. Of kindred with the elevated music borrowed from the Italian poets, is that sonorous and massive Latinity, which was once so much in vogue; no man knows better than D'Israeli how to dignify his thought with the discreet use of the grave and stately words of this old Latinity. Finally, blending with all, correcting the excesses of all, and abounding more than any thing else, in his language, is that piquant grace which Pope and Bolingbroke introduced from France: a mode of writing which apes brilliant conversation, deals in short sentences, and affects epigram.*

---

* A striking change took place in the mode of writing our language by its best masters from James I to George I; a change not merely that of expansion and growth, but from the sway of one set of foreign fashions to another and quite the opposite. Compare the swelling and grand periods of the dedicatory preface to the old English Bible, translated under the auspices of James, or even a sentence from Clarendon, some years later (one is enough, for it is generally a page) to the Boileau-like smartness and brief grace of Pope! Since Pope, Johnson has returned to the pomp of the old Latinity, from choice, and his own taste, and not from the taste of his age, which was quite different and did not yield far, except in the case of a few imitative individuals, to even the force of his great example. We think the best writers of the language at the present day, write better than the best masters of either of the old schools—Latin or Gallic. If they have not the full dignity of the ancient Latinity, they have retained as much of it as could be saved after a separation from its excessive magniloquence and *strut*. If they have not the

No living writer equals D'Israeli in the mastery of the strength, dignity, music, and grace, of our language. Macaulay is a magnificent ship-of-the-line, cruising in the seas of history and art, creeds and constitutions, and defending the truth everywhere with terrific force; but the metaphor holds good in this, also, that his style is as monotonous as the thunder of cannon. The style of Lord Brougham is angular, and as rough as a rasp. He writes prose as Coleridge's friend the schoolmaster, who attempted an ode to Sleep, wrote poetry. The remarkable apostrophe with which that ode opened—

"O! thou that smoothed'st the thick-rugged couch of pain"—is a verse hardly more scornful of music and grace than a thousand sentences which dislocate our jaws, or set our teeth on edge, in Lord Brougham's best prose. He has strength—occasional dignity—and no music or grace whatever. Bulwer is full of music—sometimes graceful, but generally too high-toned and ambitious to be so—and is much too fine and mellifluous to be strong. In fact, amongst the thousand, or ten thousand, good living writers of our language, D'Israeli is the only one we can recall who seems to us to possess the perfect mastery of every department of its excellence.

But his greatest power is in his imagination. Style is a result of art—or chiefly so. The high conception springs from nature, and is beyond art. His imagination is rich enough to have made him a rare poet; and what is of most practical account in the field which he has preferred to that of verse, it is always ready at his call. Its gold is not in the ingot, but in current coin, and he plays the spendthrift as safely as Fortunatus, for his purse is self-replenishing. He never speaks of a thing lovely in nature or art—of a beautiful woman, a stately tree, a fair landscape, a painting of his favorite Murillo, a triumph in sculpture or architecture, a storied land, a sweet thought or vision of the better poets—that his own thought does not become flashing or tender. He never seems to weary, or be so damped that he cannot kindle.

The critics of *Vivian Grey* used to characterise his imagination as wild and unbridled. If it was ever meant by this that his imagination would have been better for taming, we oppose ourselves to the opinion. An imagination like the German Werner's may be called wild in the derogatory sense of the term, for it conceives impossible monsters, and nothing clearly. D'Israeli imagines no monsters, and always imagines

---

artificial grace of Pope and Bolingbroke, as so distinct and seen a quality, they have the same grace combined with other merits of style which correct its artificiality.

clearly. He runs riot—flashes—dazzles—seems to exercise no restraint upon himself—but a natural symmetry in his powers guards him at every point, and he can no more commit a homely excess, than a beautiful child can an awkwardness. . . .

*   *   *   *   *

A great merit which D'Israeli possesses, and without which no novelist ever attained to more than a chance success, is in the truth and vigor of his dramatic power. His passion, wit, humor, pathos, and merriment flow from the lips of his characters and color their action as if nature, not a feigning novelist, had made and placed them before us. His dramatic triumphs occur oftenest in his scenes of polished and gay life, but he succeeds every where. . . .

*   *   *   *   *

In offset to the lavish, and perhaps tedious, laudation which we have bestowed upon D'Israeli, we must say something of his faults. First, then, we think that he is too careless in his plots, and apt to be occasionally dull for want of incident. . . .

Again he is a singularly bad *raconteur*, on the large scale which novel-writing requires. In episodes of story, like that wild tale of Hans the Child-Hunter, which Essper George tells to Vivian Grey in their midnight ride through a German forest, he is successful enough. But his books themselves want that adroit linking and sequency which should be present everywhere to secure and conduct the attention, and by which tamer and far inferior authors often make us forgive a thousand faults. D'Israeli is not to be compared to James as a *raconteur*, and for this cause *Contarini Fleming* or *Tancred*, either of which has more beautiful thought and exquisite writing on a single page than such a novel as the *False Heir* has in its three or four hundred, is not near so easily read to the end as that indifferent book.

Furthermore, we are inclined to be a little disgusted with D'Israeli's miraculous boys and high-flown stuff about youth. Vivian Grey, at Chateau Desir, playing the part of Bolingbroke; Contarini Fleming, an ardent lover at nine, and at twelve commanding a banditti of boys, who positively steal cattle, stop travellers on the highways, and indulge in hard drinking in an old tumble-down castle in a desolate neighborhood; Tancred, with his "Asian mystery," etc., etc., are rather too much of a singular fantastic thing. We get tired of it; a plain boy, with dirty hands, would be a relief to us. If "Young England" is the poetic, silken-haired, particularly gloved young gentleman, inflated with pre-mature wisdom, grand aspirations, and all manner of politic rascalities that D'Israeli so frequently and so fondly portrays to us, then we must say that the English senate, army, navy, church, and benches of civil honor and trust, which are to be filled by the rising generation, will sadly fall away. . . .

*   *   *   *   *

We leave D'Israeli, whom we admire for so much, and censure for so little, and hurry on to another niche and its statue. . . .

Cooper is, beyond question, the very head of our American novelists. We have a multitude of them of various merit and kind, but he is isolated far above them. He wears the imperial purple, whilst they crowd below, in all guises and degrees from Paladins to Jesters. We have "heroes who divide the provinces, and for the most part amuse themselves with slight deeds." Kennedy is one of these. We have old crippled field-marshals who are too restless to be quiet, and yet too much spoiled by long inaction for fresh campaigns. Such a worn-out field marshal is Paulding. We have captains of light-horse—active Free Companions—who hire their services . . . and perform some very dashing exploits. Willis is a plumed and burnished specimen of these condottiere. We have partisan leaders, who do fine things on a limited scale and waste their prowess in a multiplicity of small adventures. We rank Simms at the head of these. We have silly drolls, who act Pulcinello and amuse the mob with the humors of a Puffer Hopkins; Professor Ingrahams, who peddle their pinchbeck breastpins and galva-nized pencils amongst the villages, and carry off the savings of servant maids; and, lowest of all, we have pamphleteers, who do up the last murder or seduction in high life into dirty novelettes, and like the little animal that routs its enemies with its execrable odour, make decency and virtue stand aside and hold the nose. We have this extensive variety amongst the subordinates; but we have only one supreme head. Only Cooper occupies the sovereign post. He has won it for himself, and we think him entirely worthy of it.

We gave this highest rank of all to Cooper, because he is the most creative and most dramatic of our novelists—and the only true *poet* amongst them. That his creative power is high and rare, no one who has read his books can for a moment doubt. He is, in fact, a great original genius. His conceptions of character are as vivid, as warm with the flush of life, as ever came from the creative mind of man. We can think of no novelist, save Scott, who has conceived so many characters so well.

In this department—the conception and delineation of character—the term creative is critically applicable, and it is supposed to be strictly applicable in no other. In the making of events or incidents, the creative power is humbled in the critical vocabulary and becomes simply *inventive*. In pictures of natural scenery, which are apt to be considered mere copies from reality but which, nevertheless, oftener spring up purely as visions of the mind and are no more copies than the human figures, we commonly call the producing talent *scenic*. But in both cases we think, as in the conception and production of character, the prouder term *creative* may be rightly applicable.

It is often only the same high faculty operating upon different subjects. . . . in illustration, let us take the scene in Cooper's own Deerslayer, in which the hero shoots his first Indian. The Deerslayer himself, Natty Bumpo, is a triumph of creative genius. No one will gainsay this. But what is he, in the scene, without the incident of the death of the chief? A great conception and most successful delineation of character, he is more winning to us in this scene than in any other in the five novels of which he is the hero. Holding the head of his dying enemy upon his knee, bathing the swarthy brows with water from the lake at his feet, ministering to the spiritual man, meanwhile, the simple, quaint, and touching consolations of his forest religion, blended from the creed of Christians, the superstitions of the tribes, and his own communion with nature, the young pale-face is no where a greater triumph of creative genius than here. He is developed by the incident. He lives and moves in the incident. Who shall separate the figure from its surroundings, strangle the breath in it, and then say, "Here, with this stripped and breathless figure the high creative genius stays behind —with these cast off surroundings, and the stifled breath a meaner power had to do?"

And to us also the natural accompaniments of the scene, the blue lake, the trees silent in a windless air, the far-spreading solitude of wild nature, the whole touched with a beauty which surpasses life, and proves it to have been "all made out of the artist's brain," like the angel in Christabel's chamber, seem quite as inseparable a portion of the creative triumph. The actor, the incident, the scenic surroundings seem to us to make an inseparable *one*, in which the creative power cannot be critically argued to stop anywhere but with the limits of the whole. If we are wrong and the creative power is not exercised in these things, we have only to say that no novelist was ever more inventive in incident than Cooper, or manifested a finer scenic ability. And after all, this is the gist of the matter; the rest is a mere question as to critical terms. . . .

Of Cooper's dramatic power there is no question, and need be no argument. But what may not be so evident to cursory readers, the mind of this great prose author is a highly poetical one. The passage in the *Pathfinder*, in which Natty Bumpo modestly gives the catalogue of his nick-names and descants upon the reasons which won them for him from the poetry of the frontier tribes, is like a page from a poem exquisite in its music, and fresh as the dewy forest itself. . . .

Certain indiscretions, growing perhaps out of vanity, embroiled Cooper many years ago on his return from Europe, with the political press of the North. Since that unlucky beginning, he seems to have been wasting time and temper in rather ridiculous libel suits. One evil effect of this miserable warfare against a power too strong for the strongest, has been seen in the failing American reputation of the greatest American novelist. . . . Whether this unjust state of things will endure for the life of Cooper, depends upon himself. Let him stop with his libel-suits, laugh at the squibs of his persecutors, and write good novels. If he does this, he will once more sleep without nettles on his pillow. . . . Wounded vanity and a faulty temper may prevent this cheerful and reasonable course and obscure his fame amongst us until the man, with his bickerings, is dead and only his books, with their merits, live. That his works will live, is as sure as that the world will continue to have good minds that love good books. . . . The five Leatherstocking novels—five acts of a noble drama—are not books to be forgotten. Nor are the sea tales of perishable stuff. Some heavy books there are—chiefly his European novels—which will doubtless sink like lead, if they have not already done so.

Cooper is known to prefer *The Bravo* to the rest of his novels. This is one of those freaks of parental love, common enough with authors and mothers. *The Bravo* is unquestionably a dull book. We think *The Deerslayer* the best of his novels. It is better in *style* than the others, especially than *The Last of the Mohicans*, which, great as it is in all substantial merit, and most absorbing in interest of all, is yet very meanly written; moreover, it develops more fully than any other of the Leatherstocking novels with which, as one of that series, we more immediately compare it, the author's best and most sustained character; finally, there is more of that sweet and gentle poetry, of which we have spoken as characteristic of Cooper, in this novel than in the others. It is seldom that a book, written after so many, is better than its predecessors, or that the winter of sixty radiates a warmer poetry of thought than the summer of thirty. The phenomenon, in the case of Cooper, leads us to hope that he has many more delightful books in store for us. We bid him adieu with out best courtesies; and at the same time give our readers a respite—if not a perpetual release.

*   *   *   *   *

(*SLM*, December 1847)

EDGAR A. POE

(The following paper is a sequel to Mr. Lowell's memoir, so called, of Mr. Poe, published two or three years since in *Graham's Magazine*. Mr. P. edited the *Messenger* for several years, and the pages of that magazine would seem therefore a proper place for the few hurried observations which I have here made upon his writings and genius.

P. P. C.)

Since the memoir of Mr. Poe, written by James Russell Lowell, appeared, Mr. P. has written some of his best things; amongst them "The Raven," and "Dreamland"—poems—and M. Valdemar's case [*sic*]—a prose narrative.

"The Raven" is a singularly beautiful poem. Many readers who prefer sunshine to the weird lights with which Mr. Poe fills his sky, may be dull to its beauty, but it is none the less a great triumph of imagination and art. Notwithstanding the extended publication of this remarkable poem, I will quote it almost entire—as the best means of justifying the praise I have bestowed upon it.

The opening stanza rapidly and clearly arranges time, place, etc. for the mysteries that follow.

* * * * *

Observe how artistically the poet has arranged the circumstances of this opening—how congruous all are. This congruity extends to the phraseology; every word is admirably selected and placed with reference to the whole. Even the word "napping" is well chosen, as bestowing a touch of the fantastic, which is subsequently introduced as an important component of the poem. . . . We now pass these externals and some words of exquisite melody let us into the secret of the rooted sorrow which has led to the lonely night-watching and fruitless study.

> "Vainly I had sought to borrow
> From my books surcease of sorrow—sorrow for the lost Lenore—
> For the rare and radiant maiden, *whom the angels named Lenore*
> *Nameless here forever more.*"

A death was never more poetically told than in the italicised words.

[Remaining stanzas summarized or quoted verbatim.—Editor.]

The rhythm of this poem is exquisite, its phraseology is in the highest degree musical and apt, the tone of the whole is wonderfully sustained and appropriate to the subject, which, full as it is of a wild and tender melancholy, is admirably well chosen. This is my honest judgment; I am fortified in it by high authority. Mr. Willis says:—"It is the most effective single example of fugitive poetry ever published in this country and unsurpassed in English poetry for subtle conception, masterly ingenuity of versification, and consistent sustaining of imaginative lift. It is one of those dainties which we *feed on*. It will stick to the memory of every one who reads it."

Miss Barrett says:—"This vivid writing!—this power *which is felt!* 'The Raven' has produced a sensation—a 'fit horror' here in England. Some of my friends are taken by the fear of it, and some by the music. I hear of persons *haunted* by the Nevermore, and one acquaintance of mine, who has the misfortune of possessing a 'bust of Pallas,' never can bear to look at it in the twilight. Our great poet, Mr. Browning, author of Parcelsus, etc., is enthusiastic in his admiration of the rhythm. . . . The certain thing in the tale in question is the power of the writer, and the faculty he has of making horrible improbabilities seem near and familiar."

The prose narrative, "M. Valdemar's Case"—the story of which Miss Barrett speaks—is the most truth-like representation of the impossible ever written. M. Valdemar is mesmerized *in articulo mortis*. Months pass away, during which he appears to be in mesmeric sleep; the mesmeric influence is withdrawn, and instantly his body becomes putrid and loathsome—*he has been many months dead*. Will the reader believe that men were found to credit this wild story? and yet some very respectable people believed in its truth firmly. The editor of the Baltimore *Visiter* republished it as a statement of facts, and was at the pains to vouch for Mr. Poe's veracity. . . .

With Mr. Poe's more recent productions I am not at all acquainted —excepting a review of Miss Barrett's works, and an essay on the philosophy of composition. The first of these contains a great deal of noble writing and excellent criticism; the last is an admirable specimen of analysis. I believe Mr. P. has been for some time ill—has recently sustained a heavy domestic bereavement—and is only now returning to his literary labors. The public will doubtless welcome the return of so favorite an author to pursuits in which heretofore he has done so much and so well.

Unnecessary as the labor may be, I will not conclude this postscript to Mr. Lowell's memoir, without making some remarks upon Mr. Poe's genius and writings generally.

Mr. P's most distinguishing power is that which made the extravagant fiction of M. Valdemar's case sound like truth. He has Defoe's peculiar talent for filling up his pictures with minute life-like touches —for giving an air of remarkable naturalness and truth to whatever he paints. Some of his stories, written many years ago, are wonderful in this fidelity and distinctness of portraiture; "Hans Phaal," "A Descent into the Maelstrom," and "MS. Found in a Bottle," show it in an eminent degree. . . .

But in Mr. Poe, the peculiar talent to which we are indebted for Robinson Crusoe, and the memoirs of Captain Monroe, has an addition. Truthlike as Nature itself, his strange fictions show constantly the presence of a singularly adventurous, very wild, and thoroughly poetic imagination. . . .

*   *   *   *   *

This added gift of a daring and wild imagination is the source of much of the difference between our author and Defoe. Defoe loves and deals always with the homely. Mr. Poe is nervously afraid of the homely—has a creed that Beauty is the goddess of the Poet—not Beauty with swelling bust and lascivious carriage, exciting passions of the blood, but Beauty sublimated and cherished by the soul—the beauty of the Uranian, not Dionean Venus. Defoe gives us in the cheerful and delightful story of his colonist of the desert isles, (which has as sure a locality in a million minds as any genuine island has upon the maps) a clear, plain, true-sounding narrative of matters that might occur any day. His love for the real makes him do so. The "real" of such a picture has not strangeness enough in its proportions for Mr. Poe's imagination; and with the same talent for truthlike narrative, to what different results of creation does not this imagination, scornful of the soberly real, lead him! Led by it he loves to adventure into what in one of his poems he calls—

> "a wild weird clime
> Out of space, out of time;—"

deals in mysteries of "life in death," dissects monomanias, exhibits convulsions of soul—in a word, wholly leaves beneath and behind him the wide and happy realm of the common cheerful life of man.

That he would be a greater favorite with the majority of readers if he brought his singular capacity for vivid and truthlike narrative to bear on subjects nearer ordinary life, and of a more cheerful and happy character, does not I think admit of a doubt. But whether with the few he is not all the more appreciable from the difficult nature of the fields which he has principally chosen, is questionable. For what he has done, many of the best minds of America, England, and France, have awarded him praise; labors of a tamer nature might not have won it from such sources. For my individual part . . . I would like to read one cheerful book made by his *invention*, with little or no aid from its twin brother *imagination*—a book in his admirable style of full, minute, never tedious narrative—a book full of homely doings, of successful toils, of ingenious shifts and contrivances, of ruddy firesides—a book healthy and happy throughout, and with no poetry in it at all anywhere, except a good old English "poetic justice" in the end. Such a book, such as Mr. Poe could make it, would be a book for the million, and if it did nothing to exalt him with the few, would yet certainly *endear* him to them.

Mr. Lowell has gone deeply and discriminatingly into Mr. Poe's merits as a poet. Any elaborate remarks of mine on the same subject would be out of place here. I will not, however, lose this opportunity of expressing an admiration which I have long entertained of the singular mastery of certain externals of his art which he everywhere exhibits in his verse. His rhythm, and his vocabulary, or phraseology, are perhaps perfect. . . .

*   *   *   *   *

As regards the Wiley & Putnam publication of Mr. Poe's tales—a volume by which his rare literary claims have been most recently presented to the public—I think the book in some respects does him injustice. It contains twelve tales out of more than seventy; and it is made up almost wholly of what may be called his analytic tales. This is not *representing* the author's mind in its various phases. A reader gathering his knowledge of Mr. Poe from this Wiley & Putnam issue would perceive nothing of the diversity and variety for which his writings are in fact remarkable. Only the publication of all his stories, at one issue, in one book, would show this diversity and variety in their *full* force; but much more might have been done to represent his mind by a judicious and not wholly one-toned selection.

(*SLM*, January 1848)

Letters

Cooke to Poe, Sept. 16, 1839.
Griswold Collection

MY DEAR SIR,—I received your friendly letter a long time ago but have scarcely been at home since its receipt. My wife enticed me off to visit her kins-people in the country, and I saw more of guns & horses and dogs than of pens and paper. Amongst dinner, barbecues, snipe shooting, riding parties &c. I could not gain my brains into the humour for writing to you or to any body else. I reached home two days ago, & now "hasten slowly" to assure you of my undiminished regard & respect for you—and to tell you (as above) the reasons of my neglect in leaving yr. letter so long unanswered.

I do not believe you ingenuous or sincere when you speak in the terms which you use touching the value of my rambling compositions —my contributions to the Messenger &c.—yet it of course cannot be disagreeable to me to find myself considered worth flattering. I will send you occasionally—if possible—such matters as I may consider worth inserting in the Gen⁰⁰· Maga.* with pleasure; I cannot promise anything like the systematic contribution which I was guilty of in White's case, for the "madness of scribbling" which once itched & tickled at my fingers-ends has been considerably cured by a profession & matrimony—money-cares and domestic squabbles—buying beef & mutton, and curing my child's croups, colicks, &c. The fever with which I was afflicted has given way to a chill—or, as romantic young persons say, "The golden dream is broken."

As to *Ligeia*, of which you ask my opinion, (doubtless without any intention of being guided by any person's but your own) I think it very fine. There is nothing *unintelligible* to my mind in the "sequel" (or conclusion) but I am impertinent enough to think that it (the conclusion) might be mended. I of course "took" your "idea" through-out. The whole piece is but a sermon from the text of "Joseph Glanvil" which you cap it with—and your intent is to tell a tale of the "mighty will" contending with & finally vanquishing Death. The struggle is vigorously described—and I appreciated every sentence as I advanced, until the Lady Ligeia takes possession of the deserted *quarters* (I write like a butcher) of the Lady Rowena. There I was shocked by a violation of the ghostly proprieties—so to speak—and wondered how the Lady Ligeia—a wandering essence—could, in quickening *the body of the Lady Rowena* (such is the idea) become suddenly the visible, bodily, Ligeia. If Rowena's bodily form had been retained as a shell or case for the disembodied Lady Ligeia, and you had only become aware *gradually* that the blue Saxon eye of the "Lady Rowena of Tremaine" grew daily darker with the peculiar, intense expression of the "look" which had belonged to Ligeia—that a mind of grander powers, a soul of more glowing fires occupied the quickened body and gave an old familiar expression to its motions—if you had brooded and meditated upon the change until proof accumulated upon proof, making wonder certainty, and then, in the moment of some strangest of all evidence of the transition, broken out into the exclamation which ends the story— the *effect* would not have been lessened, and the "ghostly proprieties" would, I think, have been better observed. You may have some theory of the story, or transition, however, which I have not caught.

As for your compositions of this class, generally, I consider them, as Mr. Crummles would say, "phenomenous." You *write* as I sometimes *dream* when asleep on a heavy supper (not heavy enough for nightmare).—The odd ignorance of the name, lineage, &c. of Ligeia—of the circumstances, place, &c. under which, & where, you first saw her— with which you begin your narrative, is usual, & not at all wondered at, in dreams. Such dimness of recollection does not *whilst we dream* excite any surprise or diminish the *vraisemblable* aspect of the strange matters that we dream of. It is only when we wake that we wonder that so material an omission in the thread of the events should have been unnoticed by the mind at a time when it could dream in other respects so plausibly—with such detailed minuteness—with such self-possession.

But I must come to a conclusion, as I tire myself with this out-of-the-way sort of writing.

I will subscribe to the Gentlemⁿ's Mag. Shortly & also "contribute" to it.

Yrs. sincerely
P. P. COOKE.
Charlestown, Sep. 16, 1839

P. S.—I would not say *"saith Lord Verulam"*—it is out of the way. I am very impertinent.

Poe to Cooke, Sept. 21, 1839.
Griswold Collection

Philadelphia, September 21, 1839.

MY DEAR SIR,—I received your letter this morning—and read it with more pleasure than I can well express. You wrong me, indeed, in supposing that I meant one word of mere flattery in what I said. I have an inveterate habit of speaking the truth—and had I not valued your opinion more highly than that of any man in America I should not have written you as I did.

I say that I read your letter with delight. In fact I am aware of no delight greater than that of feeling one's self appreciated (in such wild matters as "Ligeia") by those in whose judgment one has faith. You read my most intimate spirit "like a book," and with the single exception of D'Israeli, I have had communication with no other person who does. Willis had a glimpse of it—Judge Tucker saw about one half way through—but your ideas are the very echo of my own. I am very far from meaning to flatter—I am flattered and honored. Beside me is now lying a letter from Washington Irving in which he speaks with enthusiasm of a late tale of mine, "The Fall of the House of Usher,"— and in which he promises to make his opinion public, upon the first opportunity,—but from the bottom of my heart I assure you, I regard his best word as but dust in the balance when weighed with those discriminating opinions of your own, which teach me that you feel and perceive.

Touching "Ligeia" you are right—all right—throughout. The *gradual* perception of the fact that Ligeia lives again in the person of Rowena is a far loftier and more thrilling idea than the one I have embodied. It offers in my opinion, the widest possible scope to the imagination—it might be rendered even sublime. And this idea was mine—had I never written before I should have adopted it—but then there is "Morella." Do you remember there the *gradual* conviction on the part of the parent that the spirit of the first Morella tenants the person of the second? It was necessary, since "Morella" was written, to modify "Ligeia." I was forced to be content with a sudden half-consciousness, on the part of the narrator, that Ligeia stood before him. One point I have not fully carried out—I should have intimated that the *will* did not perfect its intention—there should have been a relapse —a final one—and Ligeia (who had only succeeded in so much as to convey an idea of the truth to the narrator) should be at length entombed as Rowena—the bodily alterations having gradually faded away.

But since "Morella" is upon record I will suffer "Ligeia" to remain as it is. Your word that it is "intelligible" suffices—and your commentary sustains your word. As for the mob—let them talk on. I should be grieved if I thought they comprehended me here. The "saith Verulam" shall be put right—your "impertinence" is quite pertinent.

I send the "Gentleman's Magazine" (July, August, September). Do not think of subscribing. The criticisms are not worth your notice. Of course I pay no attention to them—for there are two of us. It is not pleasant to be taxed with the twaddle of other people, or to let other people be taxed with ours. Therefore, for the present, I remain upon my oars—merely penning an occasional paragraph, without care. The critiques, such as they are, are all mine in the August and September, with the exception of the three first in each—which are by Burton. As soon as Fate allows I will have a Magazine of my own—and will endeavor to kick up a dust. Do you ever see the "Pittsburg Examiner" (a new monthly)? I wrote a Review of "Tortesa," at some length in the July number. In the October number of the "Gentleman's Magazine," I will have "William Wilson" from "The Gift" for 1840. This tale I think you will like—it is perhaps the best, although not the last, I have done. During the autumn I will publish all in two volumes —and now I have done with my egotism.

It makes me laugh to hear you speaking about "romantic young persons" as of a race with whom, for the future, you have nothing to do. You need not attempt to shake off or to banter off Romance. It is an evil you will never get rid of to the end of your days. It is a part of yourself—a portion of your soul. Age will only mellow it a little, and give it a holier tone. I will give your contributions a hearty welcome, and the choicest position in the magazine.

Sincerely yours,
EDGAR A. POE.

Cooke to Poe, Dec. 19, 1839.
Griswold Collection

Charlestown
Jefferson Co. Va.
Dec. 19. 1839.

My dear Sir You must not expect me to make you an exception amongst my correspondents, and write to you "punctually on receipt of yours," nor must you suspect the nature of my feeling toward you because I do not.

I have read your "Fall of the House of Usher," your "William Wilson" and your "Conversation of Eiros and Charmion" and I will say something about them, as all authors like praise and compliment.

In the first place I must tell you (what I firmly believe) that your mere style is the very best amongst the first of the living writers; and I must let you know that I regard style as something more than the mere manner of communicating ideas. "Words are used by the wise as counters; by the foolish as coin" is the aphorism of a person who never appreciated Jeremy Taylor or Sir Thomas Browne. You do not, to be sure, use your words as those fine old glowing rhetoricians did, as tints of the pencil—as the colours of a picture—you do not make your sentences pictures—but you mould them into an artful excellence—bestow a care which is pleasantly perceptible, and accomplish an effect which I can only characterize as the visible presentation of your ideas instead of the mere expression of them.

In your "Fall of the House of Usher," unconnected with style, I think you very happy in that part where you prolong the scene with Roderick Usher after the death of his sister; and the glare of the moon thro' the sundering house, and the electric gleam visible around it, I think admirably conceived.

Of "William Wilson" I am not sure that I perceive the true clew. From the "Whispering Voice" I would apprehend that you meant the second William Wilson as an embodying of the *conscience* of the first; but I am inclined to the notion that your intention was to convey the wilder idea that every mortal of us is attended with a shadow of himself—a duplicate of his own peculiar organization—differing from himself only in a certain angelic taint of the compound, derived from heaven, as our own wild humours are derived from Hell (figuratively);

—I cannot make myself understood, as I am not used to the expression of a wild *half thought*. But, although I do not clearly comprehend, I certainly admire the story.

Of "Eiros & Charmion" I will only say that I consider the whole very singular and excellent, and the skill of one small part of it unapproachable.

"Was I much mourned, my Eiros"—is one of the finest touches in the world. I read, the other day, a small piece in an old Messenger entitled "Shadow a Fable" which I take to be yours. Considered apart from some affectation it is very terrible. The Poetry headed "The Haunted Palace" which I read in the Balt. Museum where it first appeared, and which I instantly understood as a picture of an intellect, I consider beautiful but grotesque.

By the way you have selected an excellent title for your volume of Tales. "Tales of the grotesque and the Arabesque" expresses admirably the character of your wild stories—and as Tales of the grotesque & arabesque they were certainly never equalled.

I am writing a Book which I call "Maurice Weterbern"—what it is you will some time or other see. I am bestowing great *care* but little *labour*, upon it.

I send you two pieces of verse (*Poetry* I dare not call them) which I made a year ago; if you think them worth publishing publish them—if not I am too hacknied to consider your decision an affront.

There is not room for more—so farewell.

Yrs. sincerely
P P Cooke

E. A. Poe Esq.
P. S. Write to me.

Cooke to Poe, Aug. 4, 1846.
Griswold Collection

MY DEAR SIR,—Your letter of Apr. 16th is to this day unanswered! I have however the excuse to make that I have been a good deal away from home, and whilst *at* home greatly drawn off from literature and its adjuncts by business, social interruptions, &c. This much of explanation, no doubt, will satisfy one so well assured as you must be of my regard & admiration.

You propose that I shall take up your memoir where Lowell drops it, and carry it on to the present date of your publications. I will do so, if my long delay has not thrown the work into the hands of some other friend, with entire pleasure. I, however, have not Graham's Mag. for February 1845, and if you still wish me to continue the memoir you must send that number to me. I some months ago procured your Tales & Poems, and have read them collectively with great pleasure. That is a wonderful poem ending—

> "Hell rising from a thousand thrones
> Shall do it reverence."

"Lenore," too, is a great poem. The closing stanza of "To One in Paradise" (I remember it as published in "The Visionary") is the perfection of melody. "The Raven" is your *best* poem.

John Kennedy, talking with me about your stories, old & recent, said, "the man's imagination is as truth-like and minutely accurate as De Foe's"—and went on to talk of your "Descent into the Maelstrom," "MS. found in a Bottle," "Gold Bug," &c. I think this last the most ingenious thing I ever read. Those stories of criminal detection, "Murders of the Rue Morgue," &c., a prosecuting attorney in the neighborhood here declares are miraculous. I think your French friend, for the most part, fine in his deductions from over-laid & unnoticed small facts, but sometimes too minute & hair-splitting. The stories are certainly as interesting as any ever written. The "Valdemar Case" I read in a number of your Broadway Journal last winter—as I lay in a Turkey blind, muffled to the eyes in overcoats, &c., and pronounce it without hesitation the most damnable, vraisemblable, horrible, hair-lifting, shocking, ingenious chapter of fiction that any brain ever conceived, or hands traced. That gelatinous, viscous sound of man's voice! there never was such an idea before. That story scared me in broad day, armed with a double-barrel Tryon Turkey gun. What would it have done at midnight in some old ghostly country house?

I have always found some one remarkable thing in your stories to haunt me long after reading them. The *teeth* in Berenice—the changing eyes of Morella—that red & glaring crack in the House of Usher—the pores of the deck in the MS. found in a Bottle—the visible drops falling into the goblet in Ligeia, &c. &c.—there is always something of this sort to stick by the mind—by mine at least.

My wife is about to enter the carriage and as I wish to send this to the P. O. by her, I must wind up rapidly. I *am now* after an interval of months again at work in the preparation of my poems for publication. I am *dragging*, but perhaps the mood will presently come. I bespeak a review of my Book at your hands when I get it out. I have not time now to copy Rosalie Lee. It is in Griswold's last edition. I am grateful to you for the literary prop you afford me; and trust to do something to justify your commendations. I talked recently with a little Lady who has heard a lecture of yours in which you praise my poetry—in New York. She had taken up the notion that I was a great poetic roaring Lion.

Do with my MS. as you choose. What do you design as to the Stylus? Write to me without delay, if you can rob yourself of so much time.

[Philip Pendleton Cooke]
(Signature missing)

Millwood, Clarke Co. Va.
    Aug. 4th, 1846.

Poe to Cooke, Aug. 9, 1846.
[Harrison, James A., *Life and Letters of Edgar Allan Poe*]
New York, August 9, 1846.

MY DEAR SIR,—Never think of excusing yourself (to me) for dilatoriness in answering letters. I know too well the unconquerable procrastination which besets the poet. I will place it all to the account of the turkeys. Were I to be seized by a rambling fit—one of my customary *passions* (nothing less) for vagabonding through the woods for a week or a month together—I would not—in fact I *could* not be put out of my mood, were it even to answer a letter from the Grand Mogul informing me that I had fallen heir to his possessions.

Thank you for the compliment. Were I in a serious humor just now, I would tell you frankly how your words of appreciation make my nerves thrill—not because you praise me (for others have praised me more lavishly) but because I feel that you comprehend and discriminate. You are right about the hair-splitting of my French friend:—that is all done for effect. These tales of ratiocination owe most of their popularity to being something in a new key. I do not mean to say that they are not ingenious—but people think them more ingenious than they are—on account of their method and *air* of method. In the "Murders in the Rue Morgue," for instance, where is the ingenuity of unravelling a web which you yourself (the author) have woven for the express purpose of unravelling? The reader is made to confound the ingenuity of the suppositious Dupin with that of the writer of the story.

Not for the world would I have had any one else to continue Lowell's Memoir until I have heard from you. I wish *you* to do it (if you will be so kind) and nobody else. By the time the book appears you will be famous, (or all my prophecy goes for nothing) and I shall have the *eclat* of your name to aid my sales. But, seriously, I do not think that any one so well enters into the poetical portion of my mind as yourself—and I deduce this idea from my intense appreciation of those points of your own poetry which seem lost upon others.

Should you undertake the work for me, there is one topic—there is one particular in which I have had wrong done me—and it may not be indecorous in me to call your attention to it. The last selection of my Tales was made from about 70, by Wiley and Putnam's reader, Duyckinck. He has what he thinks a taste for ratiocination, and has accordingly made up the book mostly of analytic stories. But this is not *representing* my mind in its various phases—it is not giving me fair play. In writing these Tales one by one, at long intervals, I have kept the book-unity always in mind—that is, each has been composed with reference to its effect as part of *a whole*. In this view, one of my chief aims has been the widest diversity of subject, thought, & especially *tone* and manner of handling. Were all my tales now before me in a large volume and as the composition of another—the merit which would principally arrest my attention would be the wide diversity and variety. You would be surprised to hear me say that (omitting one or two of my first efforts) I do not consider any one of my stories *better* than another. There is a vast variety of kinds and, in degree of value, these kinds vary—but each tale is equally good *of its kind*. The loftiest kind is that of the highest imagination—and, for this reason only, "Ligeia" may be called my *best* tale. I have much improved this last since you saw it and I mail you a copy, as well as a copy of my best specimen of analysis—"The Philosophy of Composition."

Do you ever see the British papers? Martin F. Tupper, author of "Proverbial Philosophy," has been paying me some high compliments —and indeed I have been treated more than well. There is one "British opinion," however, which I value highly—Miss Barrett's. She says:— "This vivid writing!—this power *which is felt!* The Raven has produced a sensation—'a fit horror' here in England. Some of my friends are taken by the fear of it and some by the music. I hear of persons *haunted* by the 'Nevermore,' and one acquaintance of mine who has the misfortune of possessing a 'bust of Pallas' never can bear to look at it in the twilight. . . . Our great poet Mr. Browning, author of Paracelsus, etc., is enthusiastic in his admiration of the rhythm. . . . Then there is a tale of his which I do not find in this volume, but which is going the rounds of the newspapers, about Mesmerism, throwing us all into most admired disorder or dreadful doubts as to whether it can be true, as the children say of ghost stories. The certain thing in the tale in question is the power of the writer & the faculty he has of making horrible improbabilities seem near and familiar." Would it be in bad taste to quote these words of Miss B. in your notice?

Forgive these egotisms (which are rendered in some measure necessary by the topic) and believe me that I will let slip *no* opportunity of reciprocating your kindness.

Griswold's new edition I have not yet seen (is it out?) but I will manage to find "Rosalie Lee." Do not forget to send me a few personal details of yourself—such as I give in "The N. Y. Literati." When your book appears I propose to review it fully in Colton's "American Review." If you ever write to him, please suggest to him that I wish to do so. I hope to get your volume before mine goes to press—so that I may speak more fully.

I will forward the papers to which I refer *in a day or two*—not by to-day's mail. Touching "The Stylus:"—this is the one great purpose of my literary life. Undoubtedly (unless I die) I will accomplish it—but I can afford to lose nothing by precipitancy. I cannot yet say when or how I shall get to work—But when the time comes I will write you. I wish to establish a journal in which the men of genius may fight their battles, upon some terms of equality, with those dunces the men of talent. But, apart from this, I have *magnificent* objects in view —may I but live to accomplish them!

Most cordially your friend,
EDGAR A. POE.

Cooke to Nathaniel Beverley Tucker, March 29, 1847.
Coleman Manuscript Collection. Tucker House, Williamsburg, Va.

Vineyard—Near Millwood—Clarke Co., March 29, 1847.

My dear Sir: Your letter of the 20th I received yesterday and lose no time in answering it. What you say about the modern taste for discords in measure, is doubtless true enough; but I think of some qualifications of your opinion, which I have not time now to write down. . . . The only secret that I know for making poetic measure sound rough without becoming unmusical, is to violate the right placing of an accent here and there, and to terminate the line with a word of two or more syllables where the accent is on the penultimate syllable, leaving the ultimate a metrical superfluity.

* * * * *

I write with your letter before me and take up its topics in the order in which you have put them. I fear very much that you have been disappointed in my book of poems (doubtless you have by this time received it). The criticism you give me on "Tetenoire" is entirely just. I never was satisfied with the *tone* of that poem, and now you let me into the secret reason of my dislike of it. I have told an old ballad tale in the manner of the pretty, thought-diluting, modern school of versifiers. My good wife has many times heard me say that I liked "Tetenoire" less than any poem in the book because of this error of tone. I wrote it under no "ancient ballad" inspiration. I dashed off a prose sentence containing the rapid outline of the story, with some honest old ballad feeling in my blood at the time, but wrote it many months afterwards in the hurry of completing my book for print, and when all feeling of the sort was gone.

Orthone (which my dear wife who is staunch for Geoffrey cannot bear on account of the "sow") is, I think vastly better, because it is *true to the Froissart tone*. Even the homely "devilment" of the straw & the sow, I think would have been badly exchanged for more graceful apparitions of the merry spirit in the shapes of a singing bird, and stag; shapes which I had half an idea of violating Froissart so far as to make him assume. I recollected in time, the difference between the northern & southern genius of Europe, and retained the rude Gothic images of the north, where Froissart had put them. Sir Peter of Bearn is also passable in tone, but wants *point* of event, in the end. . . .

The lines you quote from the ancient ballad are great—greater doubtless than the old bard took them to be.

> "The king looked over his left shoulder—
> A grim look looked he."

The *picture* here, of the fierce old man, is as clear as noonday. I dwarf before that ancient power of words. But is not the world of readers to blame for a great part of the modern incompetency? They would not tolerate that rude brevity of utterance, or would forget to take in the vivid picture because not more ostentatiously "done up."

The Master of Bolton & the miscellaneous poems, will better please you doubtless than the other "Ballads." A word as to the name *Ballads*. My poems were *designed* to be ballads, after the manner of Lockhart's Spanish ones. The proem was printed *as* a "proem to the Froissart Ballads." I was committed in print to the name. I wrote all of them after the proem, and they assumed a shape & look very different from the original design, and are, in fact, only *ballads*, by courtesy of the most liberal interpretation of the word—as Scott's poem of Branksome was a *Lay*.

I sincerely hope you will show me my faults without fear of my proving restive. I feel the want of this friendly office. In your review I wish you to speak out your honest opinions. I leave to yourself to draw the line between the private & public fault-showings.

*   *   *   *   *

By all means send me the sheets of the Play. I will read them with great pleasure, and perform in every respect, as fully & well as I can, every service that you may demand of me. As for my influence and acquaintance, however, with booksellers, and managers of theatres, they are like the women of Valencia—'nada.' This recent book of mine, you know, is my first. Carey & Hart bought it of me, through Griswold & John Kennedy, who spurred me to the task of writing it, with six months' praise, and growling at my idleness. Whatever it may *gain* me in the shape of acquaintance &c with publishers, of course will be at your service.

*   *   *   *   *

Letters—Passages

(The following passages from letters to John R. Cooke are identified only by date. Salutations and signatures are omitted.)

Dec. 29, 1840

I reached here yesterday, got your letter of the thirteenth inst., and lose no time in compensating my long silence by assuring you of my incessant and unalterable love for you and all those about you—my mother, my brothers, my sisters, my Father's sister—my own nearest of kindred in the world. I have shown you in past times my true character—its faults as well as its better traits—and surely you know that indifference or unkindness toward you or them is as foreign to it as can be. If I love any ones in the world they are yourself and those under your roof-tree. I do not know but that you are dearer to me than *my own*—all of you. Old times—ties of prosperity and adversity —remembered scenes—the old hearth-stone common to us all—these can never be displaced in a nature like mine (and rarely can they be equalled in their warm influences) from their hold upon the heart & its affection. I love my wife and my children, God knows, and it is wrong to speak of degrees of love in these cases, but toward you all I cannot help saying that I feel *as much love* softened and enhanced by all the tenderness of thought that the absent win of us. Do not, therefore, my dearest Father, now or in any time to come, entertain any suspicion of my heart. It is in the right place and nothing *can* ever put it into a wrong place. Let this be a sufficient answer to your reproach that I treat you unkindly.

I have been away from this place six weeks. My family were weather-bound in Charlestown on their return from Saratoga—reaching Charlestown early on the first day of the great snow-fall. I got them ten days after as far as the Bower where I remained until yesterday. I have been in the woods daily for three weeks (Sundays excepted) with Stephen Dandridge, turkey-shooting. I have, however, in the same time read a great deal—the second & third vols. of Scott's Life of Napoleon among other things. I read every afternoon about three hours and as many hours after bed-time (8 o'clock) nightly. I think Scott's Napoleon is the grandest book of the 19th century; I had always heard that it was unworthy of him. His mawkish friends (Napoleon's) say the Book is one sided & prejudiced; I am sure, for one, that it gives a nobler view of the giant than any books of eulogy & lavish admiration that I have read, and I have read a good many about him. Scott's talent for Romance writing has helped rather than injured the Book. It has not tainted his narration of facts, but has enriched & made graceful the other duties of his task. Napoleon in Moscow looking from a window of the Kremlin upon the burning city and saying in an undertone "These be Scythians indeed"; and in his flight muttering as he traced the course of the Beresina upon his maps (hunting out a passing place) "Ah! Charles the Swede—Pultowa!" becomes one of Scott's Romance Kings:—We are made familiar not only with the broad views of the man, in this Book, but with his poetic emotions.

I have read a good deal in the old Edinburgh Reviews, and (as the Roundhead preachers used to say) "to my edification and the comely growth of my grace."

I begin reading Blackstone—The English original, not Tucker's—to-day. I will read it with a glance instead of a gaze. I want to get a bird's eye view of the Science (which habit, I trust, will render "Joyeuse," to me, as any); and this I can't do if I loiter too much on parts.

I will certainly go to Missouri in the spring, and, as far as I can now judge, directly to Palmyra. There, if I conclude to cast anchor in that place, I will work out my fortunes yet, and the world shall hear something of me. I am entirely without despondency or fear. My family have a decent living (economy can make a meagre income go very far) in any event. All that I have to do is to *increase their comforts* by adding to the plain necessaries of life its luxuries—the dessert of fair fruits to the dinner of beef & bacon.

The only black dog that haunts my steps is that your death might throw my dear mother and the children upon my shoulders before they are strong enough to support them. To be sure I would take them to my arms and dare all things for them—even batter my brains out against any opposing wall that fortune might raise in my path towards their maintenance; but altho I would sacrifice life itself to keep them from the descent of a step in position, yet what would the sacrifice avail them. It is, my dearest father, a terrible thing to mingle up with the awful idea of a dear & near one's death the painful and miserable reflections that I have, just now, been bold enough to speak out to your ear. Let Providence preserve you, the only present stay of the dear children & my mother, until I can build up my home in the bountiful West, and then with the blessing of the same Providence the honour & unsullied position of our house shall be left *intact* to the generation who in the nature of things will be their next guardians. It is lamentable to see the old families of the land, the first in gentility & *caste, reduced;* to see their descendants gradually sinking by marriage & association into humbler classes; and to see *mine* thus would break my heart. All this tends to what I have before urged on you. Insure your life—no matter for how small a sum. Two, three, five thousand dollars would be a buoy to them in case of your premature death. If you cannot spare the money requisite for effecting the insurance from your income, borrow it. Create a new debt rather than *run the great risque.*

I have thot somewhat on another subject. Get over your repugnance to a West Point Education. Send Henry or John Esten to West Point. Get a situation for one there, and place the other in the Navy. This selection of their destinies for them, so to speak, will make them safe in the first and most important point of view. A *needy* condition can never befall them. The Bar is a lottery. I earnestly entreat that you will not only think of this but consent to do it. The officers of the Army & Navy *are never out-ranked* in American society. The "sailor," besides, will see "many countries" and have fair opportunities of observation, and if he should prove possessed of even my poor modicum of brains will make good literary use of his "chances." The young "Lieutenant" will probably run no worse career than Uncle St. George is running— and *may* do greater things than Uncle has done. I *dream* of fighting my way into position (political) and it may be (stranger things have happened) that I shall be able on some day or other to do something towards their advancement. Sainty can be what time will point out his fitness for.

Anne is well and in good spirits. She is my *comfort.* We love and know each other. My little girls are beautiful children. The youngest, Maria Pendleton, is full of life and merriment, and very much in face like Ma. Lizzy calls her "Pennon" and is devoted to her. Liz. herself is, *I think,* the most perfect child I ever saw. They were greatly admired at the Bower—where, in truth, we (you I & all) have many and genuine friends. Steve and I are confidential & brotherly. I esteem & love him—

I am on *cold* terms with no one; I do not condescend to have *enemies;* I am a *stranger* to every man except those who are my rightful friends. Andrew Kennedy (he told John Kennedy that he loved me better than any male friend, out of the circle of his brothers, that he had in the world) Anthony Kennedy, the Dandridges male & female, the Pendletons, Edmund Hunter & his family, the Strothers & some few out of the family make up my friends. The Colston's have seized on Anne & shewn us both great attentions—urging us to visit Honeywood—even *sending* for Anne, in her absence. &c. &c. Uncle Edward I have not put with the rest because our friendly relations are *of course*. Not a cloud has passed between us since your removal. Altogether I am presently quite as comfortable as a man longing for action can be.

There were several reasons why Anne and I did not visit you this fall. One was the circumstance that Mr. N. Burwell would spend the winter in Richmond. Another that we had but an indifferent nurse. Another that I wish to live the life of a recluse in no city where I know so many people as I do in Richmond—(and my taste would lead me to adopt a recluse life for some years in any city). Another, and the *least* powerful, reason, was the expense about which you have bothered yourself so needlessly. I have a fund in Wheeling which I could have anticipated (125 dols.) or I could have anticipated Anne's income.

I will of course visit you before I go westward. I am impatient for a reunion however temporary. . . . You offer me money. Send me 10 or 15 dols. If you can do so easily. God bless you. Yours ever most affectionately

P. P. C.

P. S. Uncle Phil says the persons who bot. the house here are calling frequently about the deed to them.

Sept. 20, 1842.

* * * * *

I came to Martinsburg and engaged lodgings, and rented an office, on the nineteenth of Aug.; I came to town to *reside*, & to begin work, on the 1st. of Sep.—I have, since the latter date, paid strict attention to the little business I have—been constant in my attendance in my office— and given up the use of spirit, & my gun. . . .

I yesterday wrote a declaration in assumpsit, two pages (foolscap) & better, long. I am so far from dodging my work, that in truth I could hardly endure to remain in my office if it were not for the useful & cheering employment which my few cases afford me. I inherit from you a great many qualities; I have always been as *active* in my disposition as yourself, but my activity has never been upon the right line, like yours; I am not happy, or even in good bodily condition, if I am utterly unoccupied in mind & body, and it is so with you; in fact (altho' with your notion of my love of ease, & my indolence, you will hardly admit it) I am restless when unemployed, active & laborious when employed, utterly unable to endure ennui, and happy when engaged in work that my reason & conscience approve of. No one ever saw me sitting in the sun with my legs cocked up, my eyes half shut, my hands in my pockets or lazily whittling a stick,—which I conceive to be the true description of a lazy man; what some persons have called laziness in me was of a very different complexion. They have called me a lazy man because I would walk twenty miles a day over briars, rocks, brakes, creeks, mountains, swamps, etc., etc., *with a trivial object in view.* I think my good old friend, Mr. Rankin, had the better view of this, when he said, I "was very industrious, but didn't go to work on the right sort of business." I bear in mind, with kindly recollection, the way in which the old gentleman concluded what he had to say—"but I always said you would come right, and work as hard after money, as you ever did after Squirrels." I trust yet to have the reputation of my well-doing reach the good old man, out at his little homestead on the Saline, where on a summer's day, he talked in this cheery way to me.

* * * * *

You will hardly believe it, but it is true, that out of $8.00 that I had left on my arrival from Richmond, I have still about $1.00 left. I am as strictly saving as any man in Berkeley. I have not *received* a dollar from my profession or any other source; and I stand no chance of receiving any for a month or two. I owe (apart from my Bankrupt matters—and by the way I cannot get my certificate from Staunton until I send $10.00 to the clerk of the F. C.) about $15.00. If you *can*, let me have as soon as possible, $15.00. I blush to think that there is no end yet to your working for *me*—who ought surely to be able to make a support without your aid. But all things cannot be accomplished in an hour. I will certainly make $250 before Spring—and that will be riches to me with my habits.

Let me know whether you are getting along with anything like ease under the local debts which when I left Richmond had accumulated rather annoyingly upon you.

I am as happy a man as any hereabout—happier than any of my

friends. Uncle Phil has received but $60. since last winter. The Dandridges are sued & bothered and distressed. As Keats says in Hyperion —(it seems quizzical—but I quote gravely)

> "There is a listening fear in their regard,
> As if calamity had but begun;
> As if the vanward clouds of evil days
> Had spent their malice, and the sullen rear
> Was with its stored thunder laboring up."

They are increasing & multiplying under God's commandment—but the future is getting dark, and they, like Job, execrate the day whenever a child is born; they are clinging more than ever to that hope "of the falling"—the great & bountiful West.

* * * * *

Nov. 28, 1842

* * * * *

I am about to make a sort of Encyclopedia of law for my own use. I take all the branches of law, arrange them in alphabetical order from "Abatement" down to "Waste" and read enough to make a comprehensive note under every title. I have begun it, but made very little progress. It will take me more than a year to get through the task, but as Robinson Crusoe said when *he* spent two years in hacking down a great tree, and three more in hacking it out into a boat, "I waste no time for I have abundant leisure.". . .

* * * * *

My condition here is comfortable enough. I have however to be *extremely* economical. The money you sent me I doled out, in the payment of little debts &c., cent by cent, almost, and now have but twenty-five cents left. When I am to *make* money is a question which I cannot answer although I frequently ask it of myself. I find it as hard a task, and as difficult, as the alchymists did to transmute metals. I have been near making some several times but, as with them, the wonderful secret eluded me at the eleventh hour. I have already assured you, and now assure you again, that my greatest vexation in life is the not being able to do without your assistance in pecuniary matters. There is a striking and offensive impropriety in my taking my support, at twenty-six, from my father. The young of the eagles (of which high breed I persuade myself I am come) feed themselves when their wings are old enough. And so does every other animal, when matured, except that good for nothing creature a "Virginia gentleman.". . .

Feb. 1, 1843.

I received your letter, enclosing one from Ma, on the 24th. ult. The rub you give me about dating my letter two or three days too late—or "writing it the day after you got it." I will endeavour to prevent a repetition by looking into the almanac when I come to date this. But in fact I am so little charged with the business of other people, and my own daily business is so slight & dull & commonplace, that I do not mark the course of time at all. One day is the likeness of another. The sun rises, mounts to noon, declines & sets; I rise, eat, *read, write*, talk, & go to bed. And this is "of human life the story"—that is of my present human life. An earthquake would be preferable to so dead & monotonous a calm. And yet there is the quiet happiness which men call comfort in such a life.

I was more rejoiced than I can well express to hear so favourable an account of Ma's health, and so favorable an account of your business. I have not made up my mind about the trip to Richmond. I will endeavour to make myself a lawyer, as you so frequently call on me to do. But I am a little sick of a calling which heretofore has been so fruitless with me. I will however try to spur myself up with ambitious reflections, & it may very well be that the aspirations I once had, will return, & be realised, as you would have them. At present I look to my establishment in Clarke as the haven of security into which, battered & wreck-beaten, I am entering. With so much of disaster behind me, and with so recent an escape from it operating on me, I am not yet in the humour to devise plans for a return into the surge; I may get into the humour *after while*, when I am a little wearied with the tameness & security of my life. Arguing from my knowledge of my quick & restless nature, the country life I look forward to, *will not long satisfy* me.

I have recent news from Clarke that make me satisfied that Mr. Burwell & myself will shortly be friends again. Anne seems to be convinced of it. Mrs. Burwell is expressing herself strongly against the continued hostilities—and expressing her desire to see me "as in old times." When this reconciliation is effected all will be plain before me.

* * * * *

Anne & the children are well. I get a letter from Anne once a week. I go to see her about once in the month & remain a week. She is looking very pretty, & the children are as fine little girls as any in the world.

I have no more to write—except an expression of my unchangeable love for you & all of your household.

*   *   *   *   *

P. S. You ask if I want money. Not particularly—but, as I have none, you may send me 3 or 4 dols. when you can conveniently—to keep the devil out of my pocket.

April 26, 1843

I received your letter of Apr. 2d. to day—on my return from Clarke . . . I found Anne well, and *my third daughter* large, fat, and as pretty as children so young can be . . . Mr. Burwell did not show himself. I heard in Clarke that he said "Mr Cooke is a man of violent temper and if we made up now, he might break out on me before the fall; we had better be on the present footing until the last moment." I give the language almost word for word as, I believe, he spoke it. What he means by "the last moment" I can only guess. I suppose he means that we had better remain unreconciled until it becomes *necessary*, from my residence in his near neighbourhood, and from my connection with him in various inevitable transactions, to get rid of differences. He said that "he did not mean to give up the management and control of his land" to me—that I "was not well enough acquainted with farming" &c. From which I infer, what I did not before infer, that such a plan has been a matter of self questioning with him, and will be carried into effect when we are on good terms again.

*   *   *   *   *

I have made *up my mind* to adopt the course you have been urging upon me. I will begin forthwith to study law, and cherish, as a scheme to which all others must bend, the design of removing to Richmond & working out my destiny on that theatre. . . . As to the eventual execution of the whole plan of removal, it will depend on contingencies somewhat; but I think I will be able to carry it into effect *after a certain event*—and certainly I will take care not to forfeit any advantage that fortune may place in my reach hereafter, by giving way to my temper, or indulging myself in useless or prejudicial amusements or habits. A quiet, dignified, & exemplary life, I think, will reinstate me where I once stood, or nearly so, as to "expectancies" &c. This and all other forms of prosperity depend on Fortune somewhat, but surely they may be made easier of acquisition by good management—and I will not neglect it.

I am engaged in writing Ballads founded on some of the quaint narratives of "The good knight John Froissart." There will be seven ballads *1. The bridge of Lusac. 2. Orthone. 3. The lists of Betanzos. 4. Lord Marneil. 5. The flying Hart. 6. The death of young Gaston of Foix. 7. Bellperche.*—The whole will form a volume of verse which I mean to give to a publisher. With it will terminate my labours in verse. I have advanced considerably in the work & write with surprising ease.

Times in this region, are not only hard, but perfectly flinty. Boyd can scarcely get money enough to be married on at the lowest rate of *"nuptial expenditure."* Washington Hammond, Tom Baylor, Jos. Crane, Col. Hite &c. &c. are gone by the board in Jefferson; David McGuire in Clarke is at the last pecuniary gasp; Edmund Hunter seems to be in no danger, but Anthony Kennedy is ruined, I think, beyond a doubt. I never see any body with money. George Reynolds & Daniel Snyder have availed themselves of Bc Law.

These times have doubtless affected not only your receipts but your business generally. There is a pressure of distress, so universal, & so crushing, that men I should think would dread or be unable to meet, the smallest expenditure even in the pursuit of their property-rights. . . .

Altho' I am in want of a little money I am not in crying want of it. Make me a small remittance when you best can. Dont trouble yourself in the meanwhile with any notion that I *suffer* for want of it.

* * * * *

My paper is exhausted. Give my warm love to Ma, Aunt, Mary, Sal, & the boys—and Aunt Giddy. Present my regards to Mr. Steger. Some of these days I will write to him. Remember me most affectionately to the Mosbys. God bless you.

Oct. 13, 1843.

I received a short time ago, a letter from you and more recently still one from my dear Mother. Tell her that my next letter to Richmond shall be written to her. . . .

* * * * *

I am writing "Mary Hunter of Cotsworth" and my "Froissart Ballads." By the way the whole of the New World numbers of Froissart cost only $2.00—the next time you buy a book buy that for me,* and also Leibig's two works—"Animal Chemistry" & "Agricultural Chemistry"—you can get them for 12½ cents each. They are not for sale here.

I send you two poems which I have written lately. Give them to Minor to be published in the Messenger. They may as well be published with my name to them as they are good enough for the latitude. But as *you* think.

* * * * *

Tell Ma that she could not have struck my weak point better than in procuring the tomato & pumpkin seed for me. I shall be a notable gardener, and planter of trees & pruner of vines. "The Vineyard" shall, I am determined, be an abundant, nice, country seat. Ask her to keep the seeds dry, & not to *give away any of them.*

Give my love to Aunt, Mary and the boys, and certainly to Aunt Giddy. Tell the boys that I hope great things of them—that is that I hope to see them useful, accomplished, and honourable gentlemen. The better books are the wells for them to draw from. Light, desultory reading, except to relieve the mind when it has been over-worked, is, I think, hurtful. The exact sciences, & history (read with an intelligence that groups facts & puts them away in the mind) and the best poetry of the best Poets, afford matter enough for any youth no matter how he may devour books, and should constitute the great bulk of his study until he enters upon professional reading. The best poetry of men like Milton, Wordsworth &c. is full of great truths, magnificently uttered; and the pomp of numbers sometimes inflames the mind when it would go to sleep over prose.

* * * * *

P. S. Anne & the children are well & happy. The Dandridges & Pendeltons are all well. They constitute my chief society, & I have enough, without hunting farther, to make me comfortable. E. Hunter & I are staunch friends. Uncle Edward seems to be doing well. I saw him 3 weeks ago.

---

* Anne has just written to me that she has bought Froissart at Bell's in Winchester—so don't buy it for me. She had heard me say I meant to get it.

Jan. 8, 1844

*　*　*　*　*

I have just returned from Clarke—that is, I reached here this morning from the Bower where I tarried a day or two on my way back. Anne & my little ones are well and happy. Anne fairly sings at the idea of having so nice a home so soon; and the elder little girls seem to be quite as joyful as she. They are darling little ones—gentle, sweet in their ways, and perfectly devoted to me. It is one of Anne's peculiarities of management to resolve every thing before them into a question of approbation or disapprobation on "Papa's" part—and to keep me in every possible way in their little warm hearts. I promise myself a happiness hereafter all the sweeter for the annoyances I have sustained —*annoyances* is the word, for I have never suffered anything severer.

What you say of your diminished income would probably disturb a person less used than I to such things. There is such a discrepancy in all these latitudes, between income and expenditure that I hear, breathe, see nothing but pecuniary botheration. It is so entirely bad that it has become almost a matter of *desperate fun*. What you say about the continued embarrassments of country people is, so far at least as all hereabout are concerned, entirely true. Wheat is selling here for 65 cts. —corn for 25 cts.—beef-cattle for from 2 to 3 dols per hundred &c. &c. —How then are the farmers to get this money which is accumulated in the cities? Some of them *are* getting it by loan—a desperate resort for a mere *farmer*. The popular mind must shake off the *cowing* effects of the recent wide disasters, before things will be well again. In the mean time let every stout hearted man cure what he can cure & laugh at what he can't cure—or at any rate let him endure with a scornful sort of resignation instead of that calmer fortitude that preys on the heart. I think the better philosophy, however, is the laughing philosophy.

I am very little affected by want of money. I owe 7 or 8 dols. that *ought to be* paid, and which I occasionally blush to think about. But I am scarcely ever dunned and it is after all only annoyance—not serious trouble.

Minor is pestering me with his prospectus underscoring several sentences about *valuable* and *brilliant* contributors, *and* the importance to him of subscribers. He has sent me two. If he means to ask me to write for the Messenger for nothing and, in addition to this, to pay him $5 per an. for the work—he is stupid and a little mean. I do not *want* the Messenger for nothing. I used to accept Mr White's vols. (for he gave it to me by the volume) but always gave them away. If he wishes me to get him subscribers—I only say I am unfitted for such work.

*   *   *   *   *

I have not studied much of late. I will begin *to day* however to do some law work, and will endeavour to get my mind into the better channels. I am temperate, upright, pure in my life, and keep a constant watch over my temper. Thank God I find myself respected and beloved here. I say this to you without hesitating and affecting humility. All of my real sorrow in life is for those outbreaks of temper which used to disturb your happiness. . . .

July 6, 1844.

I received your letter yesterday and as you say you will leave Richmond for Lewisburg in a few days, I have determined to write to you at once. By the way, before I forget it, ask Ma to procure me garden seeds as she did last summer. I am very fond of good dinners, and have a great fancy for raising uncommon vegetables. You forgot to tell me in your letter (see mine just preceding it) what Ma answered to my question about the squash. I want to know whether they are pumpkins or cymblins—to be eaten when young or to be left till ripe. A cymblin you know can't be eaten when ripe;—remember the old joke you used to tell, long ago, about Jerome Bonaparte, or some other Frenchman in this country, who had put in a large crop of cymblins for winter food for his hogs. On the other hand it would be a good joke if I used my pumpkins half grown.

What you say about my poetic vein being exhausted, I feel an inward assurance, is a mistake. I agree with you entirely, however, in believing that poetical composition gains a man neither wealth nor honours in this country. It is in the maturity of countries that the harp is listened to—or rather in the old age of countries, when energy has given way to ease & indulgence, and men have leisure to delight in the arts. The Anglo-Saxon who is pressing towards California with a knapsack on his back, has no leisure for scholarly indulgence; and he is a type of our population. I *know* that six months of continuous composition, such as that at Glengary in my nineteenth year, would develop my "poetical vein"; and that any apparent poverty in its present yield is owing not to exhaustion but to the fact that the shaft has been, in years of disuse, choked with rubbish. . . . What you say about prose is all true. It after all is the weapon for a stout-minded man; it does effective *work* in the world, and I mean to accomplish myself in its use if I can. Poetry shall be only my occasional indulgence. I am little ashamed to have written so much egotism.

* * * * *

Mr F. is more of a man than you ever had reason to believe him. I have heard several speeches from him lately—elaborately prepared (written) addresses—which show mind of a pretty fair order. He is *improving*. He is working for position; and his plan of operations is to make a few speeches, laboriously compiled, revised, recogitated &c., at favorable times and places, and to see that they are not forgotten by the press. He is succeeding very well. A. Hunter is smattering his reputation away by making a great many ill-prepared speeches, & F. is building up his by "being seldom heard" and doing well *when* heard. He has been uniformly attentive, hospitable, &c. to me, and yields singularly to all my notions about literature—as if he felt some deficiency on his part & superiority on mine. He pays me a great many compliments—I am waiting *to find out his object in it*. It will appear some day.

* * * * *

P. S. I have frequently been called on to *speak* since the canvass began. I have always refused—but have consented to speak next week, in the Club house here.

Feb. 4, 1847.

I have intended for some weeks past to write to you, but got into habits of daily shooting in the mountains, and never could bring myself fairly to work with my pen. On the completion of my poems for the Press sometime in December, I shut my port folio for a holiday— which I have thus long taken.

* * * * *

I perceive that Schillers' Hist. of Thirty Years War is out, in an American form. The want of this book was one great reason of my inability to get on with Lutzen. I will send to Alexandria shortly and get it—then write that book which you have urged me to finish, so often. Do you recollect some verses to my little daughter Lizzy— "Lily"—that I sent you for Minor several years ago? You returned them to me, saying you did not like them (in effect) and dissuading me from their publication. You also made some remarks to the effect that most men of genius were apt to write verses under the impulses of youth, but afterwards lost the poetic faculty—hinting that mine was gone. I am very easily persuaded to think lightly of my verses, and threw those to "Lily" to one side. About a year ago, having none better, I resuscitated them & sent them to Griswold, since then they have gone the rounds, and in one instance been pronounced sufficient of themselves to place me "in the front rank of living poets." They were so spoken of in a Northern periodical. What do you think of your poetical judgment after that? Or can you blame me for going against your advice to stick to prose, so long as the world lauds my verse.

* * * * *

With the exception of Liz all are well with us. She is not *seriously* sick—only troublesomely so, having the fag end of a chill & fever spell upon her. The little creature is as meek and gentle as a fawn. Anne is somewhat spicy in her temper, and I am no suckling dove, so where the child gets her gentle beauty of character, and meekness of temper, I cannot imagine.

With strict economy, which after all involves no other inconvenience or self-denial than my inability to visit you (that I can just now think of) we get on comfortably enough—making the two ends meet, indeed improving a little. Besides we are entirely *safe*.

What is doing with the Wheeler & Bennett case? How do you get on? My sole cares of life centre on you and yours—*ours* is a word nearer my true feeling. Courage and patience wear out the longest day. Your great heart is competent to its burthens—I thank God for so much, and look to the future trustfully & courageously.

* * * * *

Nov. 29, 1849.

I received your kind and welcome letter on Saturday evening last, and lost no time in seeing McGuire touching the business part of it. He will collect the money (about 55 dols. after deducting the three portions, his own, Nat's, & Anne's from the 65) perhaps this week. Two of the paying parties live in Winchester—of the rest one or two did not have money (I believe) when he applied for it. If I had the amount I would advance it to you; but I have no money, and will have none until after next harvest, except my dues from Thompson of the Messenger, who is poor and pays badly. Even after harvest I shall be pinched (in the best issue) as poor Mr. Burwell put in only a half crop here the past season in consequence of the drought and the extreme difficulty of breaking up the ground. McGuire *cannot* authorize you to proceed in the case without revival—he has no authority of any sort in the business, to delegate. He has endeavoured to procure authority for you; but no one can give it. Mrs. Burwell . . . renounces all connection with the estate of Col. Burwell, and an adm. *de bones non* must be appointed. In the mean time all here are soldiers whose general is lost & has not been replaced. McGuire will apprise you more distinctly of these things when he writes sending the money.

Anne has written a letter to Ma, whom God bless & make hale & hearty again soon. Kiss her for me. As soon as "I come to my estate"— or that of Anne & the little folks rather—I will pounce down among you if I can beg borrow or steal a hundred dollars.

Tell John I have *not been able* to write to him but will as soon as possible. I had to content myself with 2 instead of the 3 chapters of my serial in the parcel last sent, and am just now engaged *Minerva invita* in preparing a fresh batch which ought in fact to be in Richmond by this time, instead of in my head. Tell him no harm will ensue if he makes up the University delay with *hard study*. He is perhaps learning a pecuniary lesson in your difficulty in getting him started which will amply compensate for the delay, by giving him the temper to economize & to get his money's worth of knowledge &c. &c.

Anne thinks the girls might write to her. Give my affectionate love to them, Henry, & Saint. I am positively sick with writing & chewing before a hot fire. I have done a morning's work at my novel before writing this.

Bibliography

[Materials used in the dissertation *Philip Pendleton Cooke:* A Critical and Biographical Study are listed. Items reprinted by The *Southern Literary Messenger* (abbreviated as *SLM*) or in *Froissart Ballads, and Other Poems* (abbreviated as *FrB*) are so noted.]

I. COOKE'S WRITINGS

1. VERSE

"Song of the Sioux Lovers," *The Knickerbocker Magazine*, II (July, 1833), 60.

"Autumn," *The Knickbocker Magazine*, II (November, 1833), 368.

"The Consumptive," *The Knickerbocker Magazine*, III (February, 1834), 99–100.

"Dhu Nowas," *The Knickerbocker Magazine*, III (April, 1834), 292.

"There's a Season" (untitled), reprinted from *The Winchester* (Va.) *Republican* in *The Gazette*, Martinsburg, W. Va., January 29, 1835.

"The Creation of the Antelope," *SLM*, I (January, 1835), 216.

"A Song of the Seasons," *SLM*, I (January, 1835), 232.

"Young Rosalie Lee," *SLM*, I (March, 1835), 332. *FrB*.

"The Last Indian," *SLM*, I (April, 1835), 402–403.

"Carriers' Address to the Patrons of The Winchester Republican, January 1, 1836." Printed by *The Republican*. Mrs. A. B. Bevan, Millwood, Va.

"Lady Leonore and Her Lover," *SLM*, II (January, 1836), 109–110.

"The Huma," in the essay "A Leaf from My Scrap Book," *SLM*, II (May, 1836), 372.

"Lines," *SLM*, II (August, 1836), 557.

"The Ballad of Count Herman," in the Kennedy Memoir; first known publication in the article "An Unpublished Poem of Philip Pendleton Cooke," by W. J. Hogan, *The Educational Forum*, I (November, 1936), 81–86.

"January 1, 1838," clipping, Dr. R. P. Cooke, Lexington, Va. (Carriers' Address).

"Sonnet—To Mary," *SLM*, IV (August, 1838), 488.

"On Dreaming That I Heard a Lady Engaged in Prayer," *SLM*, IV (August, 1838), 542.

"Lines on the Sudden Death of a Very Dear Friend," *SLM*, VI (September, 1840), 675. Reprinted as "An Old Unpublished Poem. From Philip P. Cooke, of 'Vineyard,' to Lewis Burwell, 'Prospect Hill,' " *The Clarke Courier*, Berryville, Va., May, 1882. (Clipping in the possession of Dr. R. P. Cooke, Lexington, Va.)

"Earl March and His Daughter," *Burton's Gentleman's Magazine* (February, 1840), 92.

"Florence Vane," *Burton's Gentleman's Magazine* (March, 1840), 108. Reprinted in "A Letter about Florence Vane," *SLM*, XVI (June, 1850), 360–370. *FrB*.

"Love and Care," *SLM*, VI (March, 1840), 163.

"Life in the Autumn Woods," *SLM*, IX (December, 1843), 729–730. *FrB*.

"The Power of the Bards," *SLM*, IX (December, 1843), 744. *FrB*.

"Emily, Proem to the 'Froissart Ballads,' " *Graham's Magazine*, XXVIII (January, 1846), 30–32. *FrB*.

"The Mountains," *The Broadway Journal*, II (December 20, 1845). Reprinted in *SLM*, XII (May, 1846), 265–267. *FrB*.

"The Murder of Cornstalk," *SLM*, XII (June, 1846), 337–339. *FrB*.

"Love and Be Kind," *SLM*, XII (July, 1846), 426. *FrB*.

"To My Daughter Lily," *Graham's Magazine*, XXIX (August, 1846), 66. *FrB*.

"Lines," *Graham's Magazine*, XXIX (September, 1846), 143. Reprinted with title "To Edith," in *FrB*.

"Geoffrey Tetenoire," *SLM*, XIII (March, 1847), 145–147. *FrB*.

"The Master of Bolton," *FrB*.

"Orthone," *FrB*.

"Sir Peter of Bearn," *FrB*.

"Our Lady's Dog," *FrB*.

"Imaginary Ills," *FrB*.

"The Famine Tower," in the article "Dante," *SLM* XII (September, 1846), 545–554. Reprinted with the title "The Story of Ugolino," in *FrB*.

"The Death of Arnold Winkelried," *SLM*, XIII (October, 1847), 610–611.

"Pan and Echo," *The Illustrated Monthly Courier*, I (November 1, 1848).

2. ESSAYS

(*Published in* SLM, *unpublished elsewhere.*)

English Poetry, Chap. I, I (April, 1835), 397–401; Chap. II, I (June, 1835), 557–565; Chap. III, II (January, 1836), 101–106.

"Leaves from My Scrap Book," II (April, 1836), 314–316.

"Leaf from My Scrap Book" (including "The Huma"), II (May, 1836), 372.

"Old Books and New Authors," XII (April, 1846), 199–203.

"Dante" (including "The Famine Tower"), XII (September, 1846), 545–554.

Living Novelists, Chap. I, XIII (June, 1847), 367–373; Chap. II, XIII (September, 1847), 529; Chap. III, XIII (December, 1847), 745–752.
"Edgar A. Poe," XIV (January, 1848), 34–38.
"The Feudal Armies of France and England," XIV (June, 1848), 362–365.

3. SKETCHES AND PROSE TALES

(Except where noted, published only in SLM.)
John Carper, the Hunter of Lost River, Chaps. I–II, XIV (February, 1848), 90–94; Chaps. III–V, XIV (March, 1848), 167–175; Chaps. VI–VII, XIV (April, 1848), 222–228.
The Two Country Houses, Chaps. I–III, XIV (May, 1848), 307–318; Chaps. IV–V, XIV (June, 1848), 349–356; Chaps. VI–VIII, XIV (July, 1848), 436–450.
The Gregories of Hackwood, Chaps. I–III, XIV (September, 1848), 537–543; Chaps. IV–VIII, XIV (October, 1848), 612–622.
"Captain Guy; or, The Unpardonable Sin," *The Illustrated Monthly Courier*, I, No. 4 (October 2, 1848).
"Joseph Jenkins' Researchers into Antiquity: Erisicthon," XIV (December, 1848), 721–726.
The Crime of Andrew Blair, Chaps. I–III, XV (January, 1849), 46–54; Chaps. IV–VI, XV (February, 1849), 101–108; Chaps. VII–VIII, XV (March, 1849), 148–154.
The Chevalier Merlin, Chaps. I–III, XV (June, 1849), 326–335; Chaps. IV–VI, XV (July, 1849), 417–426; Chaps. VII–IX, XV (August, 1849), 473–481; Chaps. X–XII, XV (September, 1849), 569–576; Chaps. XIII–XV November, 1849), 641–650; Chaps. XVI–XVII, XV (December, 1849), 727–734; Chaps. XVIII–XX, XVI (January, 1850), 42–50. (Uncompleted).
"A Morning with Cagliostro. From Notes of a Conversation with Mr. Joseph Jenkins," XVI (December, 1850), 743–752.
"The Turkey-hunter in His Closet," XVII (October–November, 1851), 659–662.

II. UNPUBLISHED MATERIALS

1. MANUSCRIPTS

Cooke, John Esten. A Legend of Turkey Buzzard Hollow. Cooke Collection. Duke University Library.
——. Note Books. Dr. R. P. Cooke, Lexington, Va.
——. Personal Recollections of John Esten Cooke, the Younger. Dr. R. P. Cooke, Lexington, Va.
——. Philip Pendleton Cooke. Dr. R. P. Cooke, Lexington, Va.

Cooke, Philip Pendleton. Alumni File of, Princeton University Alumni Office.

——. Manuscript Note to "Florence Vane"; Memorandum of Fruit Trees at the Vineyard. Mrs. A. B. Bevan, Millwood, Va.

——. Hunting Record for Month of October, 1845. Dr. R. P. Cooke, Lexington, Va.

Cooke, Stephen. Alumni File of, Princeton University Alumni Office.

Cooke, Willianne Burwell. "Complaint of the Old Year, 1836." Mrs. A. B. Bevan, Millwood, Va.

Kennedy, John Pendleton. Bound Volumes: Business Memoranda, Journal 1829–39; Notebooks for 1850–1851; Letters to His Wife; Letters to His Mother. Kennedy Collection. Peabody Institute, Baltimore.

Kennedy, Philip Pendleton. Memoir of Philip Pendleton Cooke. Mrs. A. B. Bevan, Millwood, Va. Referred to in text as Kennedy Memoir.

Marriage Records. Berkeley County Courthouse, Martinsburg, W. Va.

Minutes of the Faculty. Princeton University Library.

Sparhawk, Edward Vernon. Entry from His Diary, copied in Note Book of John Esten Cooke. Dr. R. P. Cooke, Lexington, Va.

Thompson, May Alcott. Philip Pendleton Cooke. Columbia University, New York, 1923. (Master's thesis).

Watts, Helen Lucile. The Life and Writings of Henry Beck Hirst. Columbia University, New York, 1925. (Master's thesis).

2. LETTERS OF PHILIP PENDLETON COOKE

(Published where noted. Most important manuscript collections containing letters related to Cooke are the John Esten Cooke Collection, Duke University; the John Pendleton Kennedy Collection, Peabody Institute; and the Rufus W. Griswold Collection, Boston Public Library.)

To John R. Cooke. In Cooke Collection. Duke University Library:
1840 October 5; November 15; December 29; December 31.
1841 February 4; March 2; September 27; December 2.
1842 No date (early in June); September 3; October 14; November 28.
1843 February 1; March 10; April 26; May 2; May 17; August 10.
1844 January 8; July 6; July 10.
1845 April 28.
1846 March 15; August 25; December 8.
1847 September 16.
1848 March 17; April 13.
1849 November 29.
To John R. Cooke:
1832 June 5, Miss Mariah P. Duval, Charlottesville, Va.
1840 February 14, Miss Duval; March 22, John D. Allen, Johnson City, Tenn.

1841 August—, Miss Anne Meade, Baltimore; November 17, Miss Duval.

1842 Undated, Miss Duval; September 20, Miss Meade; October 20, Miss Meade.

1843 June 21, Miss Meade; October 13, Miss Duval; November 30, Mrs. A. B. Bevan, Millwood, Va.

1845 March—, Miss Meade, March 30, Mrs. Bevan; December 5, Miss Duval.

1847 February 4, Miss Meade.

To Mrs. John R. Cooke:

1843 November 30, Mrs. A. B. Bevan, Millwood, Va.

To Rufus W. Griswold. In Griswold Collection, Boston Public Library:

1845 October 15.

1846 November 8; November 26; December 3.

1847 January 20; February 1; February 19.

To John Pendleton Kennedy. In Kennedy Collection. Peabody Institute, Baltimore:

1845 October 3; November 15; December 1; December 19; n.d.

1846 November 8; November 23; November 27.

To Edgar Allan Poe. In Griswold Collection:

1839 September 16, published in Harrison, James A., *Life and Letters of Edgar Allan Poe,* and elsewhere; December 19.

1846 August 4, published in Harrison, James A., *Life and Letters of Edgar Allan Poe,* and elsewhere.

To Nathaniel Beverley Tucker:

1835 October 25; December 23. Coleman Manuscript Collection. Tucker House, Williamsburg, Va.

1847 March 29. Coleman Manuscript Collection. Tucker House, Williamsburg, Va.

Miscellaneous:

1835 March. To *SLM.* Published *ibid.,* I, 388.

1847 April 29. To Carey and Hart, Publishers, Philadelphia. Yale University Library.

1848 July 27. To Carey and Hart, Publishers, Philadelphia. Ford Collection. New York Public Library. May 11. To Henry B. Hirst. Cooke Collection. (Transcript).

3. LETTERS TO PHILIP PENDLETON COOKE

From John Esten Cooke:

1848 December 31. Manuscript Division, Library of Congress.

From John R. Cooke:

1845 March 30. Mrs. A. B. Bevan, Millwood, Va.

From Henry B. Hirst:

1848 June 28. Cooke Collection. (Transcript).

From John Pendleton Kennedy:
  1842 June 17. J. H. Whitty, Richmond, Va.
  1845 December 22. Manuscript Division, New York Public Library. (Transcript).
  1846 June 12. Manuscript Division, New York Public Library. (Transcript).
  1846 November 26. Kennedy Collection.
From Edgar Allan Poe:
  1839 September 21. Griswold Collection. Reprinted in Harrison, James A., *Life and Letters of Edgar Allan Poe*, and elsewhere.
  1846 August 4. Published in Harrison, *Life*.
From John R. Thompson:
  1848 October 17. University of Virginia Library. (Transcript).

4. ADDITIONAL LETTERS

Cooke, Catherine Esten, to John R. Cooke:
  1817 March 22. Miss Mariah P. Duval, Charlottesville, Va.
Cooke, John Esten, to Edward St. George Cooke:
  1858 June 13. Manuscript Division, Library of Congress.
Cooke, John Esten, to John R. Cooke:
  1850 July 21. Yale University Library.
Cooke, John Esten, to Rufus W. Griswold:
  1851 February 3; June 6. Griswold Collection.
  1855 May 28. Griswold Collection.
Cooke, John R., to Dr. Henry Boteler:
  1828 February 6. Cooke Collection.
  1830 August 24. Cooke Collection.
  1832 July 10. Cooke Collection.
Cooke, Maria Pendleton, to Mrs. John R. Cooke:
  1849 March 6. Miss Mariah P. Duval, Charlottesville, Va.
Duval, Mariah Pendleton, to May Alcott Thompson:
  1923 January 26; Manuscript Division, New York Public Library.
Griswold, Rufus W., to John R. Thompson:
  1850 February 19. University of Virginia Library.
Griswold, Rufus W., to John Pendleton Kennedy:
  1845 September 22. Kennedy Collection.
  1846 February 3. Kennedy Collection.
Kennedy, John Pendleton, to Rufus W. Griswold:
  1846 January 6. Griswold Collection.
  1850 March 9. Kennedy Collection.
Kennedy, John Pendleton, to Mrs. John Kennedy:
  1838 December 2. Kennedy Collection.

Kennedy, John Pendleton, to Mrs. John Pendleton Kennedy:
  1838 March 15; March 20; September 15. Kennedy Collection.
  1839 June 4. Kennedy Collection.
Kennedy, John Pendleton, to Philip Pendleton Kennedy:
  1850 March 7; September 28. Kennedy Collection.
  1851 April 19. Kennedy Collection.
Kennedy, John Pendleton, to Philip C. Pendleton:
  1835 November 30. Kennedy Collection.
  1838 December 12. Kennedy Collection.
  1839 April 18. Kennedy Collection.
Kennedy, John Pendleton, to William Gilmore Simms:
  1851 March 8; June 15. Kennedy Collection.
  1852 February 29. Kennedy Collection.
Kennedy, Philip Pendleton, to Rufus W. Griswold:
  1851 March 28. Griswold Collection.
Pendleton, Edmund, to David Holmes McGuire:
  1850 January 23. Mrs. A. B. Bevan, Millwood, Va.
Poe, Edgar Allan, to James Russell Lowell:
  1844 July 2. Harvard University Library.
Simms, William Gilmore, to John Pendleton Kennedy:
  1851 April 12. Kennedy Collection.
  1852 February 17. Kennedy Collection.
Thompson, John R., to Rufus W. Griswold:
  1851 June 28. Griswold Collection.

III. GENERAL

1. BOOKS

Aler, F. Vernon, *History of Martinsburg and Berkeley County, West Virginia*. Hagerstown, Md.: Mail Publishing Company, 1880.
Allen, Hervey, *Israfel, The Life and Times of Edgar Allan Poe*. New York: Doran, 1927.
Beaty, John O., *John Esten Cooke, Virginian*. New York: Columbia University Press, 1922.
Campbell, Killis, *The Mind of Poe and Other Studies*. Cambridge, Mass.: Harvard University Press, 1933.
Chaucer, Geoffrey, *The Canterbury Tales*, in *The Student's Chaucer*. Ed. by W. W. Skeat. Oxford: Oxford University Press, 1929.
Cooke, Philip Pendleton, *Froissart Ballads, and Other Poems*. Philadelphia: Carey and Hart, 1847.
Cotterill, R. S., *The Old South*. Glendale, Calif.: Arthur H. Clark Co., 1936.

Froissart, Sir John, *The Chronicles of Froissart*, tr. by Lord Berners. Ed. by W. E. Henley in *The Tudor Translations*. London: David Nutt, 1902.

Gordon, Armistead C., Jr., *Virginian Writers of Fugitive Verse*. New York: James T. White & Co., 1923.

Griswold, Rufus W., *Passages from the Correspondence and Other Papers of Rufus W. Griswold*. Ed. by W. M. Griswold. Cambridge, Mass.: Privately Published, 1898.

Gwathmey, Edward M., *John Pendleton Kennedy*. New York: Nelson, 1931.

Harrison, James A., *Life and Letters of Edgar Allan Poe*. New York: Crowell, 1903.

Hart, John S., *A Manual of American Literature*. Boston: Eldredge and Brother, 1872.

Hogg, John, *The Raven, by Edgar Allan Poe, with Literary and Historical Commentary*. London: George Redway, 1885.

Howe, Henry, *Historical Collections of Virginia*. Charleston, S.C.: William R. Babcock, 1845.

Hunter, Martha T., *A Memoir of Robert M. T. Hunter*. Washington: Neale Publishing Co., 1903.

Ingram, John H., *Edgar Allan Poe*. London, 1880.

Jackson, David K., *The Contributors and Contributions to The Southern Literary Messenger (1834–1864)*. Charlottesville, Va: Historical Publishing Co., 1936.

——, *Poe and The Southern Literary Messenger*. Richmond, Va.: Dietz, 1934.

Kercheval, Samuel, *A History of the Valley of Virginia*. Strasburg, Va.: Shenandoah Publishing House, 1925. (Reprint of the revised and enlarged edition of 1850; first edition, 1833.)

Meade, Everard Kidder, *Clarke County, 1836–1936*, with a Historical Sketch by Arthur Bowie Chrisman. Berryville, Va.: Clarke Courier Press, 1936.

Minor, Benjamin Blake, *The Southern Literary Messenger, 1834–1864*. Washington: Neale Publishing Co., 1905.

Mott, Frank Luther, *A History of American Magazines, 1741–1850*. New York: Appleton, 1930.

Norris, J. E., *History of the Lower Shenandoah Valley*. Chicago: A. Warner, 1890.

Old Chapel, Clarke County, Virginia. Berryville, Va.: Blue Ridge Press, 1906.

Parks, Edd Winfield, *Southern Poets*. New York: American Book Company, 1936.

Phillips, Mary E., *Edgar Allan Poe the Man*. Foreword by J. H. Whitty. Philadelphia: Winston, 1926.

Poe, Edgar Allan, *Complete Works.* Ed. by James A. Harrison. Virginia Edition. New York: Crowell, 1902.

——, *The Works of Edgar Allan Poe.* Ed. with an Introduction by Hervey Allen. New York: Walter J. Black, 1927.

Princeton University, Untitled Catalogue for the Academic Year 1839–40. *General Catalogue of Princeton University,* 1746–1906. Princeton, N.J.: Princeton University, 1908.

Tanner, H. S., *A New Universal Atlas.* Philadelphia: Published by the Author, 1836.

Traveller's Guide Through the Middle and Northern States and the Provinces of Canada. Saratoga Springs: G. M. Davison, 1833.

Tucker, Nathaniel Beverley, *The Partisan Leader.* Ed. with an Introduction by Carl Bridenbaugh. New York: Knopf, 1933.

Tuckerman, Henry T., *The Life of John Pendleton Kennedy.* New York: Putnam, 1871.

Wade, John Donald, *Augustus Baldwin Longstreet.* New York: Macmillan, 1924.

Woodberry, George E., *Edgar Allan Poe.* Boston: Houghton, Mifflin, 1892.

2. PERIODICALS AND GENERAL REFERENCES

Allen, John D., Communication to the Editor, *The Educational Forum,* I (May, 1937), 506. (Discusses W. J. Hogan's "An Unpublished Poem of Philip Pendleton Cooke.")

Beaty, John O., "Cooke, John Esten," *Dictionary of American Biography.* New York, 1930, pp. 385–386.

Brooke, St. George Tucker, "The Brooke Family," *Virginia Historical Magazine,* XV, 453.

"Burwell. Entries from Family Bible," *Virginia Magazine of History and Biography,* XXXI (October, 1923), 357–359.

Campbell, Killis, "The Kennedy Papers," *Sewanee Review,* XXV, 348–360.

Comment on Poe Lecture, *The Weekly Tribune,* New York, March 8, 1845.

Cook, Clarence Chatham, "The Gazelle," *The New York Mirror,* May 3, 1845.

——, "Ruth," *The New York Mirror,* May 31, 1845.

Cooke, John Esten, "Deliciae Orientis," *SLM,* XVII (March, 1851).

——, "Recollections of Philip Pendleton Cooke," *SLM,* XXVI (June, 1858), 419–432.

"Cooke, Philip Pendleton," *Cyclopaedia of American Literature.* Ed. by Evert H. and George L. Duyckinck. New York: Scribner, 1856.

Correspondence from Shepherdstown, *The State,* Richmond, Va., April 27, 1881.

"The First Generation of the Pendleton Family in Virginia," *William and Mary Quarterly,* XIV, No. 4 (April, 1916), 252–257.

"*Froissart Ballads*, by Philip Pendleton Cooke," *Graham's Magazine*, XXX (May, 1847), 323–324.

"*Froissart Ballads, and Other Poems*, by Philip Pendleton Cooke," *The Literary World*, I (March 27, 1847), 173–175.

"*Froissart Ballads and Other Poems*," *The Knickerbocker Magazine*, XXIX (April, 1847), 366.

"From Shepherdstown, Jefferson County, Va.," *SLM*, I (February, 1835), 324. (Unsigned letter).

Griswold, Rufus W., "Philip Pendleton Cooke," *The International Magazine*, IV (October, 1851), 300–303. (Reprinted in *SLM*, XVII (October–November, 1851), 669–673.)

Hawley, Frances B., "Cook, Clarence Chatham," *Dictionary of American Biography*, New York, 1930, p. 371.

Heath, James E., "Acknowledgements to Contributors," *SLM*, I (November, 1834), 128.

Hirst, Henry B., "Philip Pendleton Cooke," *Illustrated Monthly Courier*, I (October 2, 1848).

——, "Speculations in Autography," *Illustrated Monthly Courier*, I (July 1, 1848).

Hogan, W. J., "An Unpublished Poem of Philip Pendleton Cooke," *The Educational Forum*, I (November, 1936), 81–86.

Hunt, J., Jr., "A Letter About 'Florence Vane,'" *The Daily Cincinnati Gazette*, Cincinnati, Ohio, April 13, 1850. [Reprinted in *SLM*, XVI (June, 1850), 369–370.]

Hunter, Edmund Pendleton, Notice of Partnership, *The Gazette*, Martinsburg, W. Va., May 29, 1834.

——, "The Fourth of July," *The Gazette*, Martinsburg, W. Va., July 6, 1843.

Kennedy, John Pendleton, Excerpt from an Address in Congress, *The Gazette*, Martinsburg, W. Va., August 1, 1838.

Knott, H. W. Howard, "Cooke, John Rogers," *Dictionary of American Biography*, New York, 1930, pp. 386–387.

"Law School of H. St. George Tucker in Winchester," *William and Mary College Quarterly*, X (October, 1930), 310–311.

"Letter from Patrick Henry to General Adam Stephen," *Virginia Magazine of History and Biography*, XI (October, 1903), 216–218.

Lowell, James Russell, "Our Contributors, No. XVII. Edgar Allan Poe," *Graham's Magazine*, XXVII (February, 1845), 49–53.

"The Martinsburg Academy," *The Gazette*, Martinsburg, W. Va., September, 10, 1840. (Advertisement).

Metcalf, John Calvin, "Cooke, Philip Pendleton," *Dictionary of American Biography*, New York, 1930, pp. 388–389.

Morrison, M. Breckinridge, "The Poetry of the Southern United States," *The Westminster Review*, CLXXXVI (July, 1911), 61–72.

Note on Virginia Economy, *Niles' Weekly Register*, June 18, 1831. (Untitled).

"Notes on New Books," *The Daily National Intelligencer*, Washington, D.C., March 18, 1847.

Note to Poem "Love and Care," *Bentley's Miscellany*, X (1841), 462.

Obituary of John R. Cooke. *The Daily Dispatch*, Richmond, Va., December 18, 1854.

Painter, F. V. N., "Philip Pendleton Cooke," *Library of Southern Literature*, Atlanta: The Martin and Hoyt Co., 1908–13, pp. 1063–1064.

"Palmyra, in Missouri," *The Enquirer*, Richmond, Va., July 21, 1835.

Pendleton, N. L. W., "Florence Vane," Newspaper Clipping in File of Philip Pendleton Cooke, Princeton University Alumni Office.

"Philip Pendleton Cooke," *The Knickerbocker Magazine*, LXIV (November, 1864), 424–426.

Poe, Edgar Allan, "A Chapter on Autography," *Graham's Magazine*, XIX (December, 1841), 273–286.

——, Editorial Notes to Correspondents, *The Broadway Journal*, I (March 15, March 22, 1845); II (September 27, December 13, December 27, 1845).

Preble, Edward, "Cooke, John Esten," *Dictionary of American Biography*, New York, 1930, pp. 384–385.

"Resolution from the Minutes of the American Whig Society, Princeton," *SLM*, XVI (March, 1850), 192.

Review of *Barons of the Potomac and Rappahannock*, by Moncure D. Conway, *Virginia Magazine of History and Biography*, I, No. 2 (October, 1893), 217–219.

"Southern Literary Messenger, No. XI," *The Enquirer*, Richmond, Va., August 21, 1835.

"The Southern Lyre," *The Southern Illustrated News*, Richmond, Va., July 4, 1863, p. 5. (Editorial).

Spaulding, Thomas M., "Cooke, Philip St. George," *Dictionary of American Biography*, New York, 1930, p. 389.

Thompson, John R., "Editor's Table," *SLM*, XVI (February, 1850), 125. (Obituary notice of Philip Pendleton Cooke.)

——, "The Late Edgar A. Poe," *SLM*, XV (November, 1849), 383.

Tucker, Nathaniel Beverley, "Poems, by P. Cooke," *SLM*, XIII (July, 1847), 437–441.

Whiting, W. H., Jr., "Philip Pendleton Cooke," *Hampden-Sydney Magazine*, April, 1928, pp. 9–14.

"The Wynne or Winn Family," *Virginia Magazine of History and Biography*, VI (October, 1898), 203.

Appendix *(Unsigned Items, Perhaps by Cooke)*

Thirty-eight poems and eight essays are credited to Cooke in the bibliography, some of them unsigned or signed with initials or pseudonym but identified as his by mention in letters, memoirs, editorial remarks, or the like. Various references, however, make it evident that Cooke wrote more, perhaps many more, than the identified poems and more than the eight essays. Accordingly, a search for prospects was made in the volumes of the *Southern Literary Messenger* for the years 1834–52, and in the few available files of Valley newspapers that had escaped the hazards of civil war.

Among the dozens of closely-examined unsigned titles in the *Messenger*, six poems seemed persuasive; and a newspaper yielded a seventh. Although none can with perfect confidence be attributed to Cooke, each may be tentatively so, on the basis of a combination of three or more sorts of circumstantial evidence: style, manner, versification, predilection, chronology, geography. The titles are:

"Napoleon," April, 1835; "Where Shall the Student Rest," July, 1835; "Ballad," August, 1835; "Banco, or the Tenant of the Spring," August, 1838; "To My Wife—by a Lawyer," May, 1840; "The Gael," September, 1846; "Lines: Written on Seeing a Young Lady with a Fashionable Protuberance," Martinsburg *Gazette*, Sept. 9, 1841.

The first and the third are agreeable juvenilia, similar to early identified contributions by Cooke to the *Messenger;* and the second and the last are amusing light satires—of the law, and of the bustle. The fourth is a sort of dream-vision with a local setting, employing like the fifth Cooke's favorite form for narrative, four-stress rhyming couplets. The fifth, leading through seventy lines of praise to "My life! my Lady Common-Law," publicly celebrates an espousal which economic considerations, one suspects, had prompted Cooke to accept for the moment with smiling countenance. "The Gael," a composition in twelve stanzas of sixteen elaborately arranged and rhyming short and long lines, is initialed "E. P. H." So is the essay "Dante," which immediately precedes "The Gael" and to which is appended Cooke's verse-translation of an episode in *The Inferno*.

Two essays invite identification on grounds similar to those for the poems: "Another Review of 'Homeward Bound'" in the *Messenger* for November, 1838, and "Shelley" in the *Messenger* for December, 1846. In addition to its qualified praise of Cooper, whom Cooke admired, the article quotes several of Cooke's favorite novelists, exhibits certain mannerisms and qualities of his style, and provides in the first third a lecture on the art of writing fiction, a subject which was of serious interest to Cooke at the time. "Shelley," which argues that that poet had "genius" but lacked "talent," also quotes favorite authors (Sir Thomas Browne and Scott) and in style and presence of mannerisms likewise suggests Cooke.

Notes

1. Griswold Collection, Boston Public Library. Letter dated October 15, 1845. Cooke referred to the *Southern Literary Messenger*, founded in Richmond by T. W. White in August, 1834. The *Knickerbocker Magazine* was established in 1833.

2. R. W. Griswold, ed., *Poets and Poetry of America*, pp. 467–470. The poems selected were "Emily," "Life in the Autumn Woods," and "Florence Vane."

3. From an unpublished manuscript memoir of Cooke by Philip Pendleton Kennedy. The manuscript, hereafter referred to as "Memoir," contains few details of biographical or critical value.

4. An announcement of the winter session in the *Martinsburg Gazette* for Sept. 10, 1840, lists the following subjects as taught: reading, writing, arithmetic, geography, grammar, history, composition, elocution, Latin, Greek, mental and natural philosophy, chemistry, French, and the higher branches of mathematics.

5. Arthur Bowie Chrisman, "A History of Clarke County," in Everard Kidder Meade, ed., *Clarke County, 1836–1936*, pp. 5, 8. Clarke was formed from Berkeley in 1836.

6. [John Esten Cooke] "Recollections of Philip Pendleton Cooke," *Southern Literary Messenger*, XXVI (June, 1858), 421. Hereafter referred to as *"Recollections."*

7. The boys were Philip Pendleton, Jr., Stephen Dandridge, and Edmund Pendleton, all three of whom were nephews of Cooke's mother.

8. From the original in the possession of Miss Mariah P. Duval, Charlottesville, Virginia. Dated "Princeton/June 5th/32 (Tuesday morning)." The house to which Cooke alluded was Glengary, the country estate near Winchester to which the Cookes moved in 1833.

9. Minutes of the Faculty. Entry dated July 17, 1834.

10. *The State*, Richmond, Virginia, Wednesday, April 27, 1881. Boteler's memory probably was in error. Cooke himself indicated that "Florence Vane" was written in 1839.

11. Reprinted in the *Southern Literary Messenger*, XVI (March, 1850), 192.

12. "Philip Pendleton Cooke," *Illustrated Monthly Courier*, I, No. 4 (October 2, 1848). Unsigned.

13. John S. Hart, *A Manual of American Literature*, p. 483. Hart, a graduate of Princeton in 1830, served until 1836 as an instructor.

14. "Memoir."

15. "Recollections," p. 420

16. Letter to John R. Cooke, dated October 13, 1843. In the possession of Miss Mariah P. Duval.

17. "I might easily make this [$200 per annum] by my profession, which I have deserted and neglected, but it would be as bad as a treadmill to me. I detest the law. On the other hand, I love the fever fits of composition."— From "Philip Pendleton Cooke" by Rufus W. Griswold, in the *International Magazine* for October, 1851. Evidently quoted from a letter to Griswold late in 1847.

18. Griswold Collection: John Esten Cooke to Rufus W. Griswold, June 6, 1851.

19. Manuscript diary of John Esten Cooke, in the possession of his son, Dr. R. P. Cooke, Lexington, Va.

20. Cooke Collection, Duke University. Dated July 6, 1844.

21. From P. W. Turrentine's copy of the original in the Coleman Manuscript Collection, Tucker House, Williamsburg, Va. Letter dated October 25, 1835.

22. Here, as in other passages, Cooke evidently quoted phrases from Tucker's previous letters, from Tucker's novel *George Balcombe*, or from his criticism to White, which in some way may have come to Cooke's notice. The allusion is to the essay "English Poetry," which, however, is more than a mere compilation.

23. From P. W. Turrentine's copy of the original in the Coleman Manuscript Collection. Letter dated December 23, 1835.

24. The form in which the name appears in "The Cemetery Record," *Old Chapel, Clarke County, Virginia*. On July 22, 1838, her first child, Elizabeth Lewis, was born. The birth of two other daughters—Maria Pendleton, on April 15, 1840, and Nancy Burwell, on April 27, 1843— preceded the birth of a son, Nathaniel Burwell, on April 24, 1845. The last child, Alethea Collins, was born on January 23, 1848, just two years before the death of its father. To all of them Mrs. Cooke was the devoted mother; to Cooke, the devoted wife. Soon after her marriage, her vision became impaired, perhaps as the result of eye-strain during her schooldays following an attack of measles. By the early sixties she could scarcely see. But no one who had not been told of her infirmity could have guessed it from her manner. She lived on after her husband's death at The Vineyard, with her first- and third-born children, who never married. Those who remember her later years pictured her as a rarely beautiful, stately old lady, knitting in an arm-chair while the daughters read to her, or absent-mindedly fingering the great keys in the basket on her lap. She died at The Vineyard on November 23, 1899.

25. From a letter dated Sunday, March 22, 1840, in the possession of the author. The letter was composed in Charlestown, where Cooke was still residing.

26. From the original in the possession of Miss Anne Meade. Undated.

27. *The Two Country Houses,* published in 1848, but begun in 1843 with the title "Mary Hunter of Cotsworth."

28. The Martinsburg *Gazette,* July 6, 13, 1843.

29. Miss Anne Meade. Letter dated "The Vineyard, Near Millwood, March 7, 1845." The outcome of the land venture cannot be determined, though available evidence suggests that for the Cookes the speculation proved unprofitable.

30. Manuscript in the possession of Mrs. A. B. Bevan.

31. Cooke Collection. April 28, 1845.

32. *The Broadway Journal,* II, No. 25 (December 27, 1845), 391. Four years earlier, while Poe was connected with *Graham's Magazine,* he had included Cooke in his second "Chapter on Autography," published in that periodical, XIX, No. 6 (December, 1841). The entry reads: "P. P. Cooke, Esq., of Winchester, Va., is well known, especially in the South, as the author of numerous excellent contributions to the 'Southern Literary Messenger.' He has written some of the finest poetry of which America can boast. A little piece of his, entitled 'Florence Vane,' and contributed to the 'Gentleman's Magazine' of this city, during our editorship of that journal, was remarkable for the high ideality it evinced, and for the great delicacy and melody of its rhythm. It was universally admired and copied, as well here as in England. We saw it not long ago, *as original,* in Bentley's Miscellany! Mr. Cooke has, we believe, nearly ready for the press, a novel called 'Maurice Werterbern,' whose success we predict with confidence. His MS. is clear, forcible, and legible, but disfigured by some little of that affectation which is scarcely a blemish in his literary style."

33. Nothing came of the "treaty," and no other mention of it has been found.

34. Kennedy Collection. Letter dated October 3, 1845.

35. Cooke Collection. November 29, 1849.

36. Information supplied by Mrs. Bevan. Practically no details regarding Cooke's death are given in the various sketches of his career. For example, Dr. W. H. Whiting, Jr., whose ancestral home is almost in sight of The Vineyard, contented himself in his discussion of Cooke with this sentence: "Mr. Cooke died Jan. 20, 1850, not yet thirty-four years of age." ("Philip Pendleton Cooke," *Hampden-Sydney Magazine,* April, 1928, p. 11.) In Cooke's file in the Princeton alumni office is a newspaper clipping which relates that Cooke was "drowned in the Opequan creek near 'The Bower' in Jefferson county, late one fall while hunting." Attached is a letter from N. L. W. Pendleton, dated January 21, 1910. Pendleton doubtless was in some degree related to Cooke; but the clipping hardly deserves to be credited.

Another tradition in the Valley, perhaps a sounder one, is that the practice of blood-letting hastened the course of Cooke's illness, if it did not cause his death.